AN INTRODUCTION TO

THEORETICAL
PHYSICAL CHEMISTRY

This book is in the

ADDISON-WESLEY SERIES IN CHEMISTRY

Francis T. Bonner

Consulting Editor

AN INTRODUCTION TO
THEORETICAL
PHYSICAL CHEMISTRY

by

SIDNEY GOLDEN

Department of Chemistry
Brandeis University

ADDISON-WESLEY PUBLISHING COMPANY, INC.

READING, MASSACHUSETTS, U.S.A.

LONDON, ENGLAND

To my wife

PREFACE

This book has been written to provide students of physical chemistry with a connected exposition of three subjects: thermodynamics, statistical mechanics, and quantum mechanics. Few, if any, of the phenomena with which physical chemists are concerned can be made the objects of theoretical analysis without the concepts and techniques furnished by these subjects. It seems appropriate, therefore, for a book of the present title to be devoted to them. In spite of its title, however, this book deals with subject matter usually regarded as physics. As a result, its contents may prove to be of interest to students of physics as well.

The material is treated here in an order which parallels approximately its historical development: first, thermodynamics; then, statistical mechanics; finally, quantum mechanics. In this manner of presentation, the role of each discipline—its objectives, limitations, and motivation of and by related disciplines—can be best appreciated. However, excessive devotion to historical accuracy has not been attempted. Indeed, each subject is accorded an integrity which can result only from a deliberate neglect of the literal historical development of science. Taste alone would appear to favor an inverse order of presentation. Thereby, the properties of a macroscopic system would be deduced from a knowledge of the appropriate properties of its microscopic constituents. However, the advances in our knowledge of the properties of material systems are clearly marked (frequently, in retrospect) by the emergence of concepts through processes of inductive inference rather than by deduction, as it is usually understood. If students are to acquire something more than an ability to deduce consequences from given sets of assumptions, more than a deductive presentation of a subject is necessary. It is my hope that such has been provided in this book.

While the ultimate interest in theoretical physical chemistry lies in its applications, this book is concerned mainly with its formal aspects. Consequently, a mathematical and analytical viewpoint is emphasized throughout. The emphasis is not directed toward undue mathematical rigor, however. Instead, its aim is to develop in students an ability to: (1) recognize the empirical facts which are basic to each discipline; (2) formulate from the facts, with some degree of mathematical precision, those abstract principles which relate to chemistry; (3) deduce from the principles those consequences which pertain to the behavior of physical chemical systems. Since the role of mathematics in this connection is frequently a semantic one, the language of theoretical physical chemistry, rather than mathematics *per se*, is stressed here. However, wherever possible, advantage has been taken of the opportunity to acquaint students with mathematical applications with which they may be unfamiliar.

vii

Because of the viewpoint which has been adopted here, there is a deliberate de-emphasis of the numerical aspects of the several subjects, both in the text and in the exercises. This is not to be misconstrued, however. Ultimately, the numbers which emerge from experiments are the test of the validity of any theory. As long as physical chemistry is an experimental science, numerical analysis will play a dominant role in the theoretical analysis of its phenomena. Indeed, one may view numerical analysis as the *experimental* part of theoretical analysis. For this reason, it is fitting that proper attention be given to it. Attempts to do so within the limits of the present book could only have proven to be inadequate. Hence, none has been made. This omission is one which, it is to be hoped, the serious student of theoretical physical chemistry will not fail to amend in the course of his training.

The mathematical preparation usually possessed by students of physical chemistry has made it necessary to limit the extent of the accounts of thermodynamics, statistical mechanics, and quantum mechanics. In each treatment, an attempt has been made to provide a compromise between *conceptual generality* and accompanying *mathematical complexity*. As an illustration, the relatively simple mathematics employed in thermodynamics has allowed a more general account of the foundations of this subject to be given than in the case of quantum mechanics. Because of the obviously involved mathematics employed in the latter, the exposition is limited largely to one-dimensional situations; attention is drawn to multidimensional extensions, but it is usually not pursued. The treatment given of statistical mechanics lies in between these two extremes. Within this framework, the difficulties (or, preferably, the lack thereof) experienced by students should be about the same for each of the disciplines treated here. This should facilitate the use of this book either as a text for a single course dealing with all three of the subjects, or for shorter courses devoted to only one or two of them.

Wherever possible, those individuals have been mentioned whose contributions have been instrumental in giving to the subjects treated the form adopted in this book. My indebtedness to them is clear, for without them this book would have had no basis. Nevertheless, I have not always attempted to exhibit their results in literal terms. Rather, I have frequently retained only the basic ideas associated with the results, at least insofar as I understand them. This is especially evident in those sections dealing with the statistical mechanics of Gibbs. The treatment there is expressed in terms more appropriate for quantum-mechanical systems than he could and did employ. Any errors which may have arisen from such adaptations are, of course, my own. I trust that no conceptual misrepresentations are included among them.

S. G.

TABLE OF CONTENTS

CHAPTER 1

INTRODUCTION TO ANALYTICAL THERMODYNAMICS

1.1 The nature of thermodynamic theory. As one of the important tools in modern theoretical investigations, thermodynamics provides a pervasive analytical machinery for describing the equilibria of physical and chemical systems. It manifests an intimate connection between certain properties of systems which can be measured in the laboratory and those quantities which are regarded as essential elements of the abstract physical theory termed thermodynamics. Just what the certain properties are to be is, however, dictated by the theory. As a result, thermodynamics inherently is restricted in the range of physical and chemical phenomena to which it may be applied. Nevertheless, as we shall see, the range of applicability is extensive.

As in any satisfactory physical theory, thermodynamic theory furnishes a set of rules for manipulating the essential elements of the theory. The set of rules relates to the logical structure of the theory. The essential elements of the theory provide the link, so to speak, with reality and make possible the validation of the conclusions which may be reached from the manipulative process. It is necessary, therefore, that the link between the abstract elements of the theory and the physical world be firm and secure. To secure the connection between the abstract and the real requires that attention be devoted to processes of *measurement*. These will be considered presently. However, once we have established this connection, it becomes possible to express the relevant physical quantities and physical processes in mathematical terms so that thermodynamical arguments may be conducted on essentially a mathematical level. Thereupon, the conclusions obtained may readily and simply be transcribed to the physical domain.

By way of anticipation, we may note that the correspondence between the elements of thermodynamic theory and their physical counterparts has a considerable bearing upon the restricted applicability of thermodynamics noted previously. In fact, we shall see that thermodynamics can provide little more than *relations* between the physical quantities which may be measured in the laboratory. Even then, the relations thus provided are restricted: they are expressed most directly in terms of how changes in certain physical quantities will be effected by changes in others, the result being given in terms of still other quantities. Nevertheless, because no detailed assumptions about the structure of matter

1

need to be made in thermodynamic theory, the relations which it provides remain unchanged by our changing knowledge of the detailed structure of matter.

1.2 Measurements of physical properties. It is a matter of experience that the properties of physical systems, as exemplified by their length, mass, color, etc., generally are capable of assuming a variety of values. The means by which the values of the various properties are quantified may be regarded as the essential result of a measurement. Thus, while a particular system may have the property of extension in space, i.e., volume, the specific numerical value which may be ascribed to its volume is the result of certain measurements made on the system. The situation with regard to other properties of the system is entirely similar.

The method by which a measurement of a property may be carried out may be seen to usually involve four distinct features: (1) a standard scale of reference by which the property in question may be given a certain set of values; (2) a theory or procedure which enables one to ascertain values which may be intermediate to those values comprising the standard set; (3) a procedure whereby the relevant property of a given system may be compared with the standard values of the property; and (4) a means by which two values of the property may be ranked as one being greater than the other. These essential features are easily illustrated in terms of measurements of length, force, and temperature.

The measurement of the length of a specific edge of a regular solid may be carried out as follows. A ruler, consisting of a rectangular parallelepiped of steel, has one face etched with a sequence of "lines," each parallel to one of the edges and equidistant from those adjacent to it or the edge. Starting with the edge, the lines are labeled and associated in sequence with the positive integers 0, 1, 2, etc. A point intermediate to two adjacent parallel lines is to be associated with the real number which corresponds to the sum of the lower numerical value of the line and the relative perpendicular distance from the point to the line in question. The way this determination may be carried out is by subdividing the pertinent interval into equally spaced subintervals marked by a subsequence of lines parallel to the original edge. No difficulty of a conceptual sort ensues thereby, for one need only rely on theorems of plane geometry to effect the subdivision. The given point will now, in general, lie between two successive lines corresponding to the subdivision. By again ordering the lines separating the subintervals, we can *estimate* the relative distance desired. Further repetition of the procedure described enables us to determine the number to be ascribed to the intermediate point to any degree of accuracy desired in that number. By this method we achieve a standard set of length values and the means by which intermediate length values are assigned to points on the ruler. The measurement of length of a specific edge of a rectangular solid may now be carried out. The edge is placed on the marked face of the ruler, perpendicular to the parallel lines. Each extreme of the edge is associated with a specific point on the ruler. This association may be made in a variety of ways. However, for definiteness, we may select the procedure of photographing the ruler and the edge to be measured in such a way that the ruler markings and the edge are both discernible in the photograph. The "points" corresponding to the extremes of the edge may then be marked, and the procedure described above may be applied to each such point, to obtain a numerical value of the desired accuracy. The two numerical values will evidently be different, and the larger value of the two is clearly discernible. The difference between the larger value and the smaller value is taken to be the measured value of the length of the edge of the regular solid.

Because of its inherent simplicity, the measurement of length has been considered in some detail. It should be evident that much has been assumed in the foregoing procedure which may be subject to question. These questions, however, are inherent in any measurement procedure and are emphasized especially with regard to the accuracy (i.e., reproducibility) of a measurement. For our purposes, these questions need not be considered. We need to assume, however, that a satisfactorily accurate measurement procedure may be achieved for any physical property which may be quantified. Those physical properties of a system which cannot be measured in this sense must be excluded from our immediate considerations.

While the measurement procedure described for the measurement of length is capable of formal extension to the measurement of a large variety of physical properties, certain measurements make stronger use of the ranking of the measured values, i.e., of feature (4) above. Thus in measuring a force exerted by a system, it is convenient, conceptually, to imagine a device which may be acted on by the force to be measured and by a force presumed known (i.e., one of a set of standard forces). The device may assume a variety of forms which need not be considered here. Nevertheless, an essential feature of the device must be its ability to indicate which of the two forces is the greater. For example, the device may exhibit a pointer and a scale such that the location of the pointer may alter in time when the two forces are compared. We may suppose that the pointer ultimately comes to rest by virtue of the construction of the device. Thereupon, the stationary location of the pointer permits us to discern which of the two forces is greater. (This discrimination is presumed to be incorporated into the device.) The scale regions corresponding to the measured force reckoned as smaller than the standard force are separated from those regions for which the obverse holds by a *null point*. It now becomes a matter of finding one of the standard force values which will result in a null-point reading of the device. Obviously, two different systems which result in a null-point reading with a fixed value of the standard value of the force may be said to exert the same value of the force.

In an elaboration of the measurement of force, it is possible to conceive of a device in which the scale has markings corresponding to certain differences between the force to be measured and that presumed known when the pointer comes to rest. The procedure then employed parallels closely that described in connection with measuring length.

The previous procedure for measuring force is frequently employed for the measurement of temperature. The appropriate device is put into contact with the system, whereupon the scale reading of the pointer will usually change. If, after a stationary value is attained, the device is put into contact with another system, the scale reading of the pointer will, again, usually change. By construction, the differences in the stationary values of the pointer readings are regarded as differences in the temperatures of the respective systems. It is possible, of course, to regard each scale value of the *thermometer* as the measured temperature of a system when the thermometer and the system to be measured are in contact and the pointer reading has assumed a stationary value.

It should be emphasized that the methods described above for measuring length, force, and temperature accomplish little more than to furnish an *operational* definition of these properties. The intrinsic meaning which, it may be felt, should be accorded the properties of a system is not dealt with by such considerations. Nevertheless, from the needs which must be met by a satisfactory definition, the operational viewpoint presents a clear statement of what is meant by a physical property when the latter is amenable to measurements of the kind which have been considered.

To distinguish from the innate physical properties, it will be convenient to refer to *physical variables*, by which will be meant the set of all possible measured values of the corresponding physical properties. If no means can be established for measuring, and thereby quantifying the values of, a certain presumed physical property of a system, we shall be unable to regard it as a physical variable. It is evident that demonstrable properties like taste and odor exhibited by systems do not easily allow reference to them to be made as physical variables.

1.3 Functions of physical variables. It is evident that while the volume of a physical system is capable of being measured directly, it also may be determined in a variety of instances from measurements made of certain lengths manifested by the system. In such cases, the procedure of "measuring the volume of the system" includes a prescription for manipulating, in purely arithmetic fashion, the measured values of the lengths, whatever their values. Such a prescription exemplifies a functional dependence of the physical variable *volume* upon the physical variable *length*. In the example cited, the dependence usually is obtained from geometric considerations.

However, we frequently need to consider physical variables other than those which are functions of one sort of physical variable. To illustrate, we may regard the density of a physical system as a physical variable which is a function of the mass of the system and its volume. It seems clear that any number of physical variables may be combined through a stipulated prescription whereby the sets of their measured values yield a new set of numerical values. Such a prescription is referred to as a function of the pertinent variables. To exhibit the prescription in mathematical terms, we associate the set of values of the first physical variable with x_1, the set of values of the second with x_2, etc. The result of carrying out the prescription gives rise to a set of values which we may represent by f. Then the mathematical statement

$$f = f(x_1, x_2, \ldots) \tag{1.3.1}$$

is taken to mean the following: take one of the values of the set x_1, one of the values of the set x_2, etc., and combine them in a way that is implicit in the symbol $f(x_1, x_2, \ldots)$; the result is a number which is to be regarded as a member of the set of values f. It is evident that the derived physical variable f can be described in detail in terms of the mathematical properties of a function of several variables. It is further apparent that an expression like Eq. (1.3.1) may refer not only to a particular physical system but to all physical systems possessing the pertinent properties. Indeed, this will be our understanding of such expressions.

Frequently the question arises whether some physical property can be regarded as a physical variable which is a function of certain other physical variables. The answer may be obtained from an analysis of the mathematical properties of the function. For the present we shall restrict our attention to physical variables which have continuous sets of values. When we define the various partial derivatives of f as

$$\lim_{\epsilon \to 0} \frac{f(x_1, x_2, \ldots, x_k + \epsilon, \ldots) - f(x_1, x_2, \ldots, x_k, \ldots)}{\epsilon}$$
$$\equiv \frac{\partial f(x_1, x_2, \ldots x_k, \ldots)}{\partial x_k}$$
$$= f_k(x_1, x_2, \ldots), \tag{1.3.2}$$

it is necessary that all the f_k be functions of the variables. It is necessary also that

$$\frac{\partial f_k(x_1, x_2, \ldots)}{\partial x_j} = \frac{\partial f_j(x_1, x_2, \ldots)}{\partial x_k} \tag{1.3.3}$$

for all pairs of k and j. It is possible to show that Eqs. (1.3.2) and (1.3.3) are also sufficient conditions for f to be, in fact, a function of the indicated variables. As a result, whether some alleged physical variable can be regarded as a function of certain others may be established if information about the various derivatives is made available. Such is often the case in thermodynamic theory.

1.4 Physical processes: work and heat. In addition to functional relations between physical variables, there exist relations having their counterpart in certain processes by which the physical variables of a system may be altered. An immediate instance is the so-called work done by or on a physical system. In the simplest situations of a constant force (i.e., fixed magnitude and direction) exerted by a system, the work associated with a displacement in a fixed direction is computed from the relation

$$W = |\mathbf{F}|\,|\mathbf{R}| \cos \alpha, \tag{1.4.1}$$

where $|\mathbf{F}|$ is the magnitude of the force, $|\mathbf{R}|$ is the magnitude of the displacement effected by the force, and α is the angle between the vectors $\mathbf{F}$ and $\mathbf{R}$. In three dimensions, Eq. (1.4.1) is frequently expressed as

$$W = \mathbf{F} \cdot \mathbf{R} = F_x R_x + F_y R_y + F_z R_z, \tag{1.4.2}$$

the subscripts referring to space-fixed cartesian axes. The quantities in Eq. (1.4.2) are the components of the force and the displacement as measured along the axes. It is evident that the work expressed by Eq. (1.4.1) can be regarded in the light of Eq. (1.4.2) as the sum of the work associated with three mutually perpendicular forces.

Now, to determine the work associated with forces and displacements which are not fixed in magnitude and direction, consider a sequence of N small displacements $\Delta \mathbf{r}_j$, $1 \leq j \leq N$, such that the sequence approximates an intended displacement *path*. For each of the individual displacements let there be a force acting which is fixed in magnitude and direction, although the force effecting each small displacement may differ from one displacement to another. Then, in terms of Eq. (1.4.1), clearly

$$W = \sum_{i=1}^{N} \mathbf{F}_j \cdot \Delta \mathbf{r}_j. \tag{1.4.3}$$

In the limit that the number of small displacements becomes indefinitely great, while each of them becomes indefinitely small such that the intended path is more and more accurately approximated by the sequence,

$$W_\Gamma = \lim_{\substack{N \to \infty \\ \Delta \mathbf{r}_j \to 0 \\ \sum_{j=1}^{N} \Delta \mathbf{r}_j = \mathbf{R}}} \sum_{j=1}^{N} \mathbf{F}_j \cdot \Delta \mathbf{r}_j = \int_\Gamma \mathbf{F}(\mathbf{r}) \cdot d\mathbf{r} \tag{1.4.4}$$

the subscript Γ emphasizing that the path must be specified in determining the integral (i.e., line integral). Thus W_Γ depends on how the sequence is stipulated and therefore on the path over which the force may be said to move. Note particularly the dependence of $\mathbf{F}$ on the position $\mathbf{r}$ along the path, and also that the reverse path gives a reversal of the sign in the work,

$$W_{(-\Gamma)} = \int_{(-\Gamma)} \mathbf{F}(\mathbf{r}) \cdot d\mathbf{r} = -\int_\Gamma \mathbf{F}(\mathbf{r}) \cdot d\mathbf{r} = -W_\Gamma. \tag{1.4.5}$$

It frequently is convenient to express

$$W_\Gamma = \int_\Gamma dW \tag{1.4.6}$$

with

$$dW = \mathbf{F}(\mathbf{r}) \cdot d\mathbf{r} \tag{1.4.7}$$

corresponding to a differential element of work, analogous to Eq. (1.4.3) for nonconstant forces and displacements. The only significance to be attributed to Eq. (1.4.7) is that dW is to be employed in Eq. (1.4.6) to compute the work. However, it has a form similar to that of a differential expression of a function of $\mathbf{r}$, so that it is of interest to examine it further. In terms of the previous section, we may consider a function of the three perpendicular coordinates of position which has a differential expression

$$dG(x, y, z) = \frac{\partial G(x, y, z)}{\partial x} dx + \frac{\partial G(x, y, z)}{\partial y} dy + \frac{\partial G(x, y, z)}{\partial z} dz$$
$$= G_x(x, y, z) dx + G_y(x, y, z) dy + G_z(x, y, z) dz. \tag{1.4.8}$$

By comparison,

$$dW = F_x(x, y, z) dx + F_y(x, y, z) dy + F_z(x, y, z) dz, \tag{1.4.9}$$

making use of Eq. (1.4.2).

For dW to be a differential expression of a function of position, it evidently is required that

$$\frac{\partial F_x(x, y, z)}{\partial y} = \frac{\partial F_y(x, y, z)}{\partial x}, \qquad (1.4.10)$$

as well as additional similar relations involving (x, z) and (y, z). Since the components of a force usually may be selected independently, it is obvious that certain choices may be made which will violate Eq. (1.4.10). Hence dW generally is not the differential expression for a function of position. (The notation has been intended to emphasize this possibility.) Furthermore, W_Γ generally is not to be regarded as a function of position in the sense discussed previously.

What about those instances where Eq. (1.4.10) is satisfied as well as the analogous equations in (x, z) and (y, z)? Then dW is the differential expression of a function, and Eq. (1.4.6) can be integrated without reference to Γ. Thus

$$W_\Gamma = W(\mathbf{R} + \mathbf{R}_0) - W(\mathbf{R}_0), \qquad (1.4.11)$$

where $\mathbf{R}$ is the total displacement measured from an origin $\mathbf{R}_0$. It is apparent that the right side is independent of Γ. As a result, we have the relation for circumstances when dW is a differential expression of a function (i.e., a perfect differential):

$$W = \int_{\Gamma_1} dW = \int_{\Gamma_2} dW, \qquad (1.4.12)$$

where Γ_1 and Γ_2 are any different paths corresponding to the same displacement $\mathbf{R}$. In these circumstances, making use of Eq. (1.4.5), we have

$$\int_{\Gamma_1} dW - \int_{\Gamma_2} dW = \int_{\Gamma_1} dW + \int_{(-\Gamma_2)} dW = \oint dW = 0, \qquad (1.4.13)$$

the symbol $\oint$ standing for a cyclic path for which the terminal points coincide. Equation (1.4.13) is necessary, and may be shown also to be sufficient, for W to be a function of the relevant variables in the sense discussed in the previous section. In other words, Eqs. (1.3.3) or (1.4.13) may be employed to ascertain if an alleged function of certain variables is such in fact. That the illustration here is limited to geometrical displacements, of course, does not affect the generality of the statement.

Another important physical process is the one by which heat is added to or abstracted from a physical system. This process can be given meaning in operational terms when it has proved possible to render such meaning to the term *heat*.

When two systems, each manifesting different measurable temperatures, are placed in direct contact (i.e., so-called *thermal contact*) with each other, it usually is observed that the temperature of each will change. (An exception is considered below.) Ultimately, the measured temperature of each system may be observed to differ inappreciably from that of the other system. We simply regard the two systems as attaining the same temperature. The resultant temperature depends on the manner by which the two systems are constrained in their mutual contact.

If, now, a series of experiments is performed with two such systems whose initial temperatures are not greatly different, we find throughout the series of experiments that the changes observed in the temperature of one of the systems are very closely proportional to the changes observed in the temperature of the other system. For the success of such a series of experiments, the two systems must be clearly delineated. Then the same sort of results obtain regardless of the precise nature of the two systems. Hence the results may be described in a picturesque manner by the statement: the heat absorbed by each system is proportional to the increase of temperature experienced by it; a decrease of temperature reflects a loss of heat by the system. In mathematical terms, the heat absorbed

$$q = \overline{C}(t_f - t_i) = \overline{C}\,\Delta t, \tag{1.4.14}$$

where t_f is the final measured temperature attained by the system and t_i is its initial temperature; $\overline{C}$, a factor of proportionality, is referred to as the *heat capacity* of the system. It is found that $\overline{C}$ is, furthermore, proportional to the mass of the system, other things being the same. As a result, one may choose some convenient standard amount of a convenient substance to which $\overline{C}$ may be assigned the value of unity. Then all other systems, as discussed in Section 1.2, may be compared with the selected standard system.

We discover, however, that $\overline{C}$ will depend on t_f and t_i. Consequently, it proves convenient to define

$$C(t) \equiv \lim_{\substack{q \to 0 \\ \Delta t \to 0}} \left(\frac{q}{\Delta t}\right), \tag{1.4.15}$$

in terms of which Eq. (1.4.14) is more accurately (although implicitly) expressed as

$$q = \int_{t_i}^{t_f} C(t)\,dt = \left[\frac{\int_{t_i}^{t_f} C(t)\,dt}{\Delta t}\right]\Delta t. \tag{1.4.16}$$

This expression yields

$$\overline{C} \equiv \frac{\int_{t_i}^{t_f} C(t)\, dt}{\Delta t} \tag{1.4.17}$$

as the temperature-averaged heat capacity of the system. The nature of the temperature dependence of $\overline{C}$ is implicit in Eq. (1.4.17). When $C(t)$ happens to be independent of temperature, so also will $\overline{C}$.

For some systems $C(t)$ has an indefinitely large value at certain temperatures, provided that certain other conditions are met. Thus a mixture of ice and liquid water, for temperatures where they coexist, will experience no change in temperature even when moderate amounts of heat (as discerned by the temperature change in a second system) are added to it. By Eqs. (1.4.14), (1.4.15), and (1.4.17), C, then, evidently is unbounded. Nevertheless, Eq. (1.4.16) is properly behaved in the sense that the integral has a finite value in the limit $t_i \to t_f$. Such processes are termed *isothermal* processes and may be imagined as taking place when the system of interest is placed in thermal contact with a *thermostat*. The latter may be regarded as a system of indefinitely great mass having, as a consequence, an indefinitely great heat capacity and a fixed temperature. As it stands, however, Eq. (1.4.16) requires modification.

The obvious extension of Eq. (1.4.16) to account for various values of $C(t)$ (as they may depend on the specific process) and isothermal processes, is

$$Q_{\mathrm{r}} = \int_{\Gamma} dQ, \tag{1.4.18}$$

in analogy with Eq. (1.4.6). Here

$$dQ = C_{\mathrm{r}}\, dt + \sum_{j=0}^{M} h_j\, dz_j, \tag{1.4.19}$$

where the h_j and z_j are related physical variables that require further elaboration. For the present we may note that the amount of heat absorbed in the example of the ice-water system will be proportional to the amount of ice melted; in this case one of the h's would be the appropriate factor of proportionality, and the associated z could be taken as the mass of ice. Additional elaboration will be deferred for the present. However, in these terms we can apply Eq. (1.4.16) with a restriction to non-isothermal processes. Then, it corresponds to the contribution made by the first term on the right side of Eq. (1.4.19). The remaining terms represent the contributions made by isothermal processes. Thereby, those divergent values of the heat capacity of systems associated with certain isothermal processes are rendered innocuous.

It should be apparent that the considerations pertaining to the differential dW now apply equally well to the differential dQ.

1.5 Characterization of thermodynamic systems. We are now prepared to limit the class of physical systems and physical processes to which thermodynamics applies. By a *thermodynamic system* we mean the most general portion of the material universe. The system generally may contain materials in one form or another capable of interacting with one another as well as with all other materials of the universe. The most general connotations of the term *interaction* are implied: work may be performed, heat may be absorbed, chemical changes may occur. The remainder of the universe will be referred to as the system's *surroundings*. When no interaction is presumed to occur between a system and its surroundings, a system will be said to be *isolated*.

A basic assumption is now introduced: a specification of a certain minimum number of its variables is both necessary and sufficient to characterize a thermodynamic system with regard to *all* its physical properties. In an ultimate sense, the number and kinds of physical variables which may serve in this respect can be determined only by experiment. Thus, if a given thermodynamic system were presumed to be characterized by the physical variables such as volume, composition, temperature, etc., a replica could be constructed in which only these physical variables have precisely the same values as in the original system. If, for corresponding values of the physical variables presumably characterizing the two systems, all other measured properties of the two systems are found to be identical, both the original thermodynamic system and its replica may be said to be characterized by those physical variables which served as the basis for the construction of the replica. To avoid the pitfall of a possible accidental agreement, the characterization must be augmented to require the same conclusion for all possible replicas which may be constructed.

It is evident that to incorporate additional physical variables into a set which already characterizes a thermodynamic system contributes nothing further relevant to its characterization. However, certain sets of physical variables may prove to be more convenient than others, and the actual choice will depend on the use to which the characterization is put.

Each set of values of the set of physical variables characterizing a thermodynamic system is used synonymously with the term *state*. Thermodynamic theory may be said to deal with changes in the thermodynamic states of systems. How this is accomplished is the subject of the succeeding chapters. However, we should emphasize that while the changes in the state of a thermodynamic system may be perfectly meaningful and well defined, the process accompanying these changes may be one of two kinds. In the first kind, the process may consist entirely of a *sequence of states* of the thermodynamic system; in the second kind, it may be impossible to determine, even conceptually, the thermodynamic state of the system at certain stages of the process. By way of a simple illustration, a process whereby the temperature of a system is increased may be carried out in such a manner that certain stages exist for which a "temperature," as measured with a very delicate thermometer, is obtained that varies from region to region throughout the system. It is evident for such stages that the "temperature of the system" is not capable of being specified in the sense which has been described. In such circumstances we can hardly refer to the thermodynamic state of the system in a meaningful way. Analogous behavior with respect to the measured values of other physical properties may be anticipated for these circumstances. As a result, we simply refer to these circumstances as corresponding to no thermodynamic state of the pertinent system or, in other terms, the so-called state of the system is undefined. (Nevertheless, we consider just such circumstances in Section 4.6.)

We conclude the present section with the observation that the processes of measurement discussed in Section 1.2 preclude any rational description of transient phenomena. At the risk of repetition, let us say that the measurement procedures envisaged may yield numerical results which vary with the evolution of time. However, in the sense already indicated, the ultimate result of such a sequence is taken to be the so-called measured value of the physical property being investigated. One may question the wisdom of such a choice, but once it is made, the opportunity for a description of the dynamic behavior of physical systems seems to be precluded. It seems reasonable to expect that thermodynamic theory will, as a consequence of the aforementioned restriction, be confined to a nondynamical description of natural phenomena.

1.6 Summary. In the present chapter we have considered the measured values of the physical properties of material systems.

These are termed physical variables. Properties which depend on more than one kind of physical variable are expressed in mathematical terms as functions of those physical variables. Certain physical processes, notably the performance of work and absorption of heat, are expressed conveniently in mathematical terms as line integrals. It is assumed that the specification of the values of certain of the physical variables characterizes a thermodynamic system. Each set of values is accorded the designation of *thermodynamic state*. Thermodynamics is concerned with changes in the state of thermodynamic systems, particularly those which do not depend upon time.

Exercises

1. Carry through the analysis in the text for the measurement of length with a prescribed "thickness" to the "lines" forming the scale. What difficulties in principle, if any, occur with such a measuring apparatus?

2. Prove Eq. (1.3.3).

3. Construct a two-dimensional planar path for which various specifications of the force-path relation will give a quantity of work along the path which is a perfect differential. Specify other force-path relations for which the work is not a perfect differential.

4. Why is a beaker of water that is being stirred with a spoon not describable as having a thermodynamic state? Is the system then a thermodynamic system?

5. Formulate a mathematical statement from the description in the text of what is meant by a thermodynamic state.

6. Try to devise, in a schematic way, a means for measuring odors so that they may be "quantified."

7. Certain physical variables may correspond to sets of distinct (i.e., not continuous) measured values of the corresponding physical properties. In what way will processes of work involving these variables differ from that discussed in the text?

8. Devise an operational procedure involving explicitly the use of any necessary mechanical devices to construct the ruler described in the text. The problem here is to make an adequate transcription of the pertinent theorems of plane geometry into practical terms.

9. List the assumptions which are implicit in the measurement of length discussed in the text.

10. Illustrate in schematic terms an apparatus for measuring force values and describe the procedure to be followed when it is used.

11. Discuss the errors involved in determining the volume of a regular solid such as a tetrahedron when the primary measurement is that of the length of one of the edges.

CHAPTER 2

THE LAWS OF THERMODYNAMICS

2.1 The zeroth law of thermodynamics. The characterization in Section 1.5 of the state of a thermodynamic system is not uniquely restricted to thermodynamic theory. Each physical theory—and we shall see instances later—makes some analogous statement which effectively defines the various states of the physical system with which it is concerned. In thermodynamics, it is *assumed* that the characteristic physical variables defining the states of a *thermodynamic* system must include temperature, either explicitly or implicitly. This statement is the essence of what may be termed the zeroth law of thermodynamics.

To appreciate the implications of the zeroth law, one may regard a certain set of physical variables as characterizing the states of a thermodynamic system. If temperature is not included among them, it is then determined as a function of their values; if temperature is included, some additional physical variable may be regarded as a function of the characterizing set of variables. In either case, we may expect that a functional relation between a certain minimal set of physical variables *and* the temperature may always be found for thermodynamic systems. It should be evident, of course, that the assumption of the zeroth law is only a reflection of the empirical facts. The relations obtained are to be referred to as *thermal equations of state*. (Referral here, of course, is to the physical variables characterizing the thermodynamic state.)

By way of illustration, consider a simple homogeneous system, termed a *bulk system*, which is found to be completely characterized by values of its pressure P and volume V. In terms of the temperature t, the zeroth law may be expressed mathematically as

$$f(P, V, t) = 0, \qquad (2.1.1)$$

and is referred to as the equation of state of the bulk system. Equation (2.1.1) frequently represents a convenient way of measuring t in terms of P and V. Thus, we may obtain

$$t = t(P, V),$$

and as a result,

$$dt = \left(\frac{\partial t}{\partial P}\right)_V dP + \left(\frac{\partial t}{\partial V}\right)_P dV.$$

14

Hence

$$\left(\frac{\partial t}{\partial P}\right)_V \left(\frac{\partial P}{\partial t}\right)_V = 1, \tag{2.1.2}$$

and

$$\left(\frac{\partial t}{\partial P}\right)_V + \left(\frac{\partial t}{\partial V}\right)_P \left(\frac{\partial V}{\partial P}\right)_t = 0. \tag{2.1.3}$$

The last two equations are particularly useful. They obtain, of course, entirely as a result of the existence of an equation of state in the three variables. Still other relations may be obtained between the physical variables. Thus if Eq. (2.1.1) is expressed as

$$V = V(P, t),$$

$$dV = \left(\frac{\partial V}{\partial t}\right)_P dt + \left(\frac{\partial V}{\partial P}\right)_t dP,$$

whereupon (see Eq. 1.3.3)

$$\frac{\partial^2 V(P, t)}{\partial P \, \partial t} = \left[\frac{\partial}{\partial P}\left(\frac{\partial V}{\partial t}\right)_P\right]_t = \left[\frac{\partial}{\partial t}\left(\frac{\partial V}{\partial P}\right)_t\right]_P = \frac{\partial^2 V(P, t)}{\partial t \, \partial P}. \tag{2.1.4}$$

The utility of Eq. (2.1.4) may be seen from the following. The *coefficient of thermal expansion* of a bulk system may be defined as

$$\alpha = \frac{1}{V}\left(\frac{\partial V}{\partial t}\right)_P, \tag{2.1.5}$$

where the dependence of V and $(\partial V/\partial t)_P$ on P, t is implicit. Similarly the *bulk modulus of compressibility* may be defined as

$$\beta = -\frac{1}{V}\left(\frac{\partial V}{\partial P}\right)_t. \tag{2.1.6}$$

It is possible to employ Eq. (2.1.4) to obtain a relation involving α and β, namely,

$$\left(\frac{\partial \alpha}{\partial P}\right)_t + \left(\frac{\partial \beta}{\partial t}\right)_P = 0,$$

which "connects" the pressure variation of the thermal coefficient of expansion with the temperature variation of the bulk modulus of compressibility.

It should be noted that the explicit evaluation of various derivatives, such as Eqs. (2.1.5) and (2.1.6), requires an explicit form for the equation of state, Eq. (2.1.1). This latter quantity, however, is not given by thermodynamic theory but must be assumed on the basis of either experimental evidence or some other theoretical considerations. Nevertheless, the *relations* which have been obtained remain valid regardless of the explicit equation of state. This situation is often typical of the results of thermodynamics.

2.2 The first law of thermodynamics. The concept of thermodynamic state, as embodied in the zeroth law of thermodynamics, is essential for an analytical statement of the first law of thermodynamics and, in fact, the remaining axioms of the theory.

The experimental basis for the formulation of the first law was established by the work of Rumford and Joule. Both these investigators established the important result that a system could be brought from one certain (initial) state to another certain (final) state by either of two distinct methods: (1) entirely by means of mechanical work performed on the system, or (2) entirely by means exclusive of any mechanical work performed on the system. Stated mathematically, they found processes for which

$$-W_{\text{no heat}}(i \to f) = Q_{\text{no work}}(i \to f), \qquad (2.2.1)$$

where $-W$ represents mechanical work (later extended to include electrical, magnetic, etc.) performed on the system, Q represents heat absorbed by the system, and i and f represent initial and final thermodynamic states, respectively, of the system (that is, i represents, for example, the set of values P_i, V_i, t_i of a bulk system; correspondingly, f represents a different set of values P_f, V_f, t_f). In the restrictive sense of Eq. (2.2.1), Rumford and Joule found that work and heat are "equivalent." (We are introducing here the convention that work done by the system and heat absorbed by the system are reckoned as positive.)

To achieve an analytical expression of the first law, it is convenient to express Eq. (2.2.1) as

$$-\int_{i}^{f} dW = \int_{i}^{f} dQ, \qquad (2.2.2)$$
$$_{\Gamma_1} _{\Gamma_2}$$

where Γ_1 and Γ_2 refer to the processes indicated in that equation. As it stands, the last equation is not entirely satisfactory for our purpose. For it to be so, the experiments must be idealized and extrapolated. Thus, while Eqs. (2.2.1) and (2.2.2) refer to specific pairs of states (i, f) (namely, those actually involved in the experiments), it is necessary to assume that they apply as well to *any* pair of states. Inasmuch as heat readily is abstracted from or added to a system, it is evident that Γ_1 may be stipulated to be any combination of processes which involve both work and heat with the restriction that a final adjustment is made that no *net* heat is involved. In this sense, the right side of Eqs. (2.2.1) and (2.2.2) may be extended to arbitrary pairs of states and arbitrary *adiabatic processes* (i.e., no net heat absorbed or rejected). The specification of Γ_2 does not, however, admit of the same flexibility. As an illustration, the raising of a weight in a gravitational field may be accomplished by performing work on the weight; it is difficult to imagine either the absorption or rejection of heat by the weight as accomplishing the same result. The reverse process, on the other hand, may be carried out by allowing the weight to perform work adiabatically; by a free fall, corresponding to an *isochoric process* (i.e., no work), with an attending rejection of heat, the same final state may be attained. Evidently isochoric processes usually are restricted in the sense of their *direction*.

Nevertheless, for those isochoric processes which may be carried out, it is also apparent that an arbitrary adiabatic process may be assumed such that Eq. (2.2.2) applies. In the sense of Section 1.5, it is possible that Γ_1 and Γ_2 may comprise processes for which the system has no definable thermodynamic state.

Since Γ_1 is adiabatic and Γ_2 is isochoric, it is evident that

$$\int_{i \atop \Gamma_2}^{f} dW = \int_{i \atop \Gamma_1}^{f} dQ = 0,$$

and that

$$\int_{i \atop \Gamma_1}^{f} (dQ - dW) = \int_{i \atop \Gamma_2}^{f} (dQ - dW), \tag{2.2.3}$$

with the result that for any achievable, but otherwise arbitrary, process

$$\oint (dQ - dW) = 0. \tag{2.2.4}$$

Equation (2.2.4) is one analytical statement of the first law of thermodynamics. From Eq. (2.2.3) and the discussion in Section 1.4, we can infer the existence of a certain function of state,

$$E(f, i) = \int_{i \atop \Gamma}^{f} (dQ - dW), \tag{2.2.5}$$

where Γ is an *arbitrary* process. Since (dropping the symbol for the process)

$$\int_{s}^{i} (dQ - dW) + \int_{i}^{f} (dQ - dW) = \int_{s}^{f} (dQ - dW),$$

$$E(i, s) + E(f, i) = E(f, s),$$

or

$$E(f, i) = E(f, s) - E(i, s), \tag{2.2.6}$$

where s is, now, some arbitrary state. Its significance is that of a reference state in Eq. (2.2.6), where it appears as a constant element. Therefore, it may be suppressed for the sake of simplicity. Hence, we shall write

$$E(f, i) = E(f) - E(i). \qquad (2.2.7)$$

The quantity E is referred to as the *internal energy function* for the system, and, in differential form, we have another analytical statement of the first law, namely,

$$dE = dQ - dW. \qquad (2.2.8)$$

Hence, while dQ and dW usually are not differentials of a function (of state), their difference is. The restriction of the last equation to "differential" processes is a formal convenience.

The fact that the internal energy function is a function of the thermodynamic state of a system means that changes in it accompanying various processes need make no reference at all to those processes. More important, a variety of processes may be envisaged for which the same initial and final states pertain, and any one of these may be employed to measure the (same) change in the internal energy function. Thus, to illustrate, we see from Eq. (2.2.5) that an isochoric process,

$$\int_{i \atop \Gamma=\text{no work}}^{f} dW = 0,$$

will give, with the convention expressed in Eq. (2.2.7),

$$E(f) - E(i) = \int_{i \atop \text{isochoric}}^{f} dQ.$$

For the particular isochoric process by which a simple system has only heat added to or abstracted from it, the relevant heat capacity may be taken as

$$C_* = \lim_{q \to 0 \atop \Delta t \to 0 \atop \text{no work}} \left(\frac{q}{\Delta t}\right) \equiv \left(\frac{dQ}{dt}\right)_*, \qquad (2.2.9)$$

in accordance with Eq. (1.4.15), the asterisk being introduced in order to draw attention to the isochoric nature of the heat capacity. Then, evidently,

$$E(f) - E(i) = \int_{*i}^{f} C_* \, dt, \qquad (2.2.10)$$

where C_* is understood to be dependent on the variables of state and the integration is understood to be carried out over a sequence of states consistent with the restriction that no work whatever is involved in any stage of the process. (This last statement may be expressed, in loose terms, as $dW = 0$, which implies that $\int_i^f dW = 0$, but certainly is more restrictive than the latter.) It is convenient to express Eq. (2.2.10) somewhat differently. Thus, from Eqs. (2.2.8) and (2.2.9), we obtain

$$\left(\frac{\partial E}{\partial t}\right)_* = C_*,$$

which, now, establishes that the isochoric heat capacity is a function of state.

The restrictions implicit in Eq. (2.2.10) may be examined in the case of bulk systems. For such systems the only work capable of being done by the system is that attributable to its expansion and may be expressed as

$$dW = P\,dV.$$

For such systems the asterisk in Eqs. (2.2.9) and (2.2.10) is evidently represented by the condition that the volume of the system remains constant. Accordingly,

$$\left(\frac{\partial E}{\partial t}\right)_V = C_V, \tag{2.2.11}$$

and, making use of the equation of state (2.1.1),

$$E(V, t_f) - E(V, t_i) = \int_{V,t_i}^{V,t_f} C_V(V, t)\,dt. \tag{2.2.12}$$

It is evident that the process which has been selected restricts the determination of changes in the internal energy function to states of the same volume.

To remove this restriction a variety of other processes may be exploited to evaluate Eq. (2.2.5). However, a moment of reflection will help us make a judicious choice. Note that the explicit choice made in the illustration considered was that the internal energy function may be regarded as a function of the volume and the temperature of the system (which, of course, it is). Likewise, from the equation of state, the internal energy function may be regarded as a function of the pressure and the temperature of the system. If changes in the internal energy function were determined for processes in which the pressure remained fixed, we would then be in a position to obtain the internal energy function for states of different volumes and temperatures. Examining the differential form of the first law for bulk systems, we see that

$$dE = dQ - P\,dV. \tag{2.2.13}$$

Following a procedure introduced by Legendre, the differential expression $d(PV)$ may be added to both sides of this equation, as a result of which

$$dH \equiv d(E + PV) = dQ + V\,dP, \qquad (2.2.14)$$

where the *enthalpy function* of the bulk system $H = E + PV$ is evidently a function of the thermodynamic state of the system since both E and PV are. The procedure employing isochoric (i.e., constant volume) processes to evaluate changes in E may be duplicated for *isobaric* (i.e., constant pressure) processes, whereupon

$$\left(\frac{\partial H}{\partial t}\right)_P = C_P \equiv \lim_{\substack{q \to 0 \\ \Delta t \to 0 \\ P\ \text{const}}} \left(\frac{q}{\Delta t}\right) = \left(\frac{dQ}{dt}\right)_P, \qquad (2.2.15)$$

and

$$H(P, t_f) - H(P, t_i) = \int_{P, t_i}^{P, t_f} C_P(P, t)\,dt. \qquad (2.2.16)$$

In terms of the internal energy function,

$$E(P, t_f) - E(P, t_i) = \int_{P, t_i}^{P, t_f} C_P(P, t)\,dt - P(V_f - V_i). \qquad (2.2.17)$$

By the equation of state, Eq. (2.2.17) will relate the values of the internal energy function to different values of the volume.

Having, now, two additional although related functions of state implied by the first law, it is of interest to examine certain aspects of their utility. At the outset, one can see from Eqs. (2.2.13) and (2.2.14) that for bulk systems

$$\left(\frac{\partial E}{\partial V}\right)_{\text{adiabatic}} = -P, \qquad (2.2.18)$$

and

$$\left(\frac{\partial H}{\partial P}\right)_{\text{adiabatic}} = V. \qquad (2.2.19)$$

Either of these partial differential equations may serve as the basis of determining (changes in) the values of the internal energy and enthalpy functions. It remains to be seen, however, what the subscript indicated means in terms of a variable which may be constant in value. Indeed, we may anticipate matters by stating that it is not at all obvious that there should be such a variable. Nevertheless, Section 2.3 will deal with just such a variable. For the present, the functions considered may be employed to relate the two heat capacities which have been introduced, C_P and C_V. Evidently

$$\left(\frac{\partial H}{\partial t}\right)_P = \left(\frac{\partial E}{\partial t}\right)_P + P\left(\frac{\partial V}{\partial t}\right)_P,$$

while, since (regarding E as a function of V and t)

$$dE = \left(\frac{\partial E}{\partial t}\right)_V dt + \left(\frac{\partial E}{\partial V}\right)_t dV,$$

$$\left(\frac{\partial E}{\partial t}\right)_P = \left(\frac{\partial E}{\partial t}\right)_V + \left(\frac{\partial E}{\partial V}\right)_t \left(\frac{\partial V}{\partial t}\right)_P.$$

Hence, using Eqs. (2.2.11) and (2.2.15), we obtain

$$C_P - C_V = \left[P + \left(\frac{\partial E}{\partial V}\right)_t\right]\left(\frac{\partial V}{\partial t}\right)_P. \qquad (2.2.20)$$

In an entirely analogous manner, one can show that

$$C_P - C_V = \left[V - \left(\frac{\partial H}{\partial P}\right)_t\right]\left(\frac{\partial P}{\partial t}\right)_V. \qquad (2.2.21)$$

A further reduction of these equations is not possible at present. They may be employed to yield differential equations which may be exploited to determine isothermal changes in the internal energy and enthalpy functions, namely

$$E(V_f, t) - E(V_i, t) = \int_{V_i,t}^{V_f,t} \left[\frac{C_P(V, t) - C_V(V, t)}{(\partial V/\partial t)_P} - P(V, t)\right] dV,$$

and

$$H(P_f, t) - H(P_i, t) = \int_{P_i,t}^{P_f,t} \left[V(P, t) - \frac{C_P(P, t) - C_V(P, t)}{(\partial P/\partial t)_V}\right] dP.$$

The expressions which have been obtained derive entirely from the implication of the first law that there exists a function of state termed the internal energy function and the implication from the zeroth law that there exists an equation of state. For bulk systems, the latter permits the internal energy function to be regarded as dependent on alternative pairs of variables, a feature that facilitates the evaluation of the values of the internal energy function, for all states of the system, in terms of measurable properties of the system. Such a set of values often is referred to as a *caloric equation of state*.

2.3 The second law of thermodynamics. We now take up the question raised earlier in connection with Eqs. (2.2.18) and (2.2.19): is there a variable of a system which may be constant in an adiabatic process? To examine this question we consider, for purposes of simplicity, a bulk system for which the differential expression of the first law may be taken as

$$dQ = dE + P\,dV. \tag{2.3.1}$$

In the succeeding analysis the restriction is implicit that the processes to which this equation applies consist entirely of sequences of completely defined states, since the right side of the equation involves only well-defined variables. Now we ask if it is possible to find a function of state $u(E, V)$ such that

$$u(dE + P\,dV) = u\,dQ = d\phi,$$

where, since ϕ is another function of state, $d\phi$ is a so-called *perfect differential*. Should it be possible to find such a function u, it is both necessary and sufficient (Eq. 1.3.3) that

$$\left(\frac{\partial u}{\partial V}\right)_E = \left[\frac{\partial (uP)}{\partial E}\right]_V = P\left(\frac{\partial u}{\partial E}\right)_V + u\left(\frac{\partial P}{\partial E}\right)_V.$$

As indicated earlier, the previous condition is equivalent to

$$\oint u\,dQ = 0$$

for any path for which $u(E, V)$ is defined. When such a u is found, it is termed an *integrating factor* for dQ (or $dE + P\,dV$). If there exists such a u, then ϕ is determined by integration of Eq. (2.3.1). Then it is evident that $uf'(\phi)$, where $f(\phi)$ is an arbitrary differentiable function of ϕ, also is an integrating factor for dQ. Hence, if one integrating factor exists, any number of integrating factors exist. In these circumstances, clearly, ϕ will be constant during the restricted adiabatic process and our earlier question will have been answered affirmatively.

We noted previously that processes which are adiabatic *in an over-all sense* (that is, $\int_i^f dQ = 0$) may be presumed to occur for arbitrary pairs of initial and final states. We have reason to suppose that an analogous statement may not be made in connection with Eq. (2.3.1), for if dQ is set equal to zero, the resulting equation suggests that a relation may exist between E and V for such processes. In that case it is evident that arbitrary pairs of states may not be connected by means of adiabatic processes. Wherein does the seeming inconsistency lie? It may be seen that the processes under present consideration are those for which a genuine sequence of states is presumed to be involved. In the apparently similar situation of *over-all* adiabatic processes there is no stipulation to that effect. In fact, we usually have to introduce processes which involve "nonexistent thermodynamic states" in order to make possible the connection of arbitrary pairs of states by adiabatic processes. Because the processes under present consideration refer so strongly to a continuous sequence of thermodynamic states, such processes are referred to as *quasi-static reversible*, a term due to Ehrenfest, or, for simplicity, just *reversible*. (The connotation of reversibility here has, of course, to do with the means by which the variables of state are measured. As discussed in Chapter 1, we ordinarily expect that the measured values are stationary in time. The process, then, does not occur in any finite interval of time and represents only a time-independent sequence of states. The reversal of the sequence corresponds to the reversal of the process, which may be contemplated with no conceptual difficulty.)

However, the suggestion that an adiabatic reversible process imposes, for the case under consideration, a relation between E and V is a matter to be decided by experiment. Suppose for the moment that the equation

$$dE + P\,dV = 0, \tag{2.3.2}$$

which is known as a *Pfaff equation*, has a solution relating E and V. Let this relation be

$$\phi(E, V) = C = \text{constant}. \tag{2.3.3}$$

For a prescribed value of C, V evidently is determined as a function of E. For a fixed value of C,

$$
\begin{aligned}
0 = d\phi &= \left(\frac{\partial \phi}{\partial E}\right)_V dE + \left(\frac{\partial \phi}{\partial V}\right)_E dV \\
&= \left(\frac{\partial \phi}{\partial E}\right)_V \left[dE + \left(\frac{\partial \phi}{\partial V}\right)_E \left(\frac{\partial E}{\partial \phi}\right)_V dV\right] \\
&= \left(\frac{\partial \phi}{\partial E}\right)_V \left[dE - \left(\frac{\partial E}{\partial V}\right)_\phi dV\right].
\end{aligned}
\tag{2.3.4}
$$

But for

$$\left(\frac{\partial \phi}{\partial E}\right)_V \neq 0,$$

which we may assume, the bracketed quantity in Eq. (2.3.4) may be compared with Eq. (2.3.2). Hence

$$\left(\frac{\partial E}{\partial V}\right)_\phi = -P.$$

It is evident that $\phi = $ constant corresponds to $dQ = 0$ [see Eq. (2.2.18)].

Now, permitting ϕ to take on values determined by E and V, it follows that

$$dQ = dE + P \, dV = dE - \left(\frac{\partial E}{\partial V}\right)_\phi dV$$

$$= \frac{1}{(\partial\phi/\partial E)_V}\left[\left(\frac{\partial\phi}{\partial E}\right)_V dE - \left(\frac{\partial\phi}{\partial E}\right)_V \left(\frac{\partial E}{\partial V}\right)_\phi dV\right]$$

$$= \frac{1}{(\partial\phi/\partial E)_V}\left[\left(\frac{\partial\phi}{\partial E}\right)_V dE + \left(\frac{\partial\phi}{\partial V}\right)_E dV\right].$$

Therefore

$$\left(\frac{\partial\phi}{\partial E}\right)_V dQ = d\phi, \tag{2.3.5}$$

so that $(\partial\phi/\partial E)_V$ is an integrating factor for dQ. In other words, if and only if a functional relation exists between E and V in a reversible adiabatic process can an integrating factor be found for dQ in the first law of thermodynamics as expressed by Eq. (2.3.1). The functional relation restricts those states which are *accessible* to a given thermodynamic state by an adiabatic reversible path. In fact, the restriction is so stringent that in an arbitrary neighborhood of *any* state there must always be some other states which are not thus accessible. The latter statement, which is equivalent to the functional relation that has been used, is known as Carathéodory's principle and is a general consequence of the solution of Pfaff equations in many variables.

Since we can readily visualize that certain adiabatic reversible processes do not occur in nature (e.g., a weight attached to a spring in a gravitational field and otherwise isolated in a vacuum will not be expected to compress the spring quasi-statically and reversibly and so do work on the spring adiabatically), we assume that natural phenomena are generally thus restricted. In other words, we *assume* that every state of a physical system has always an arbitrary neighborhood of states which are inaccessible to it by means of a reversible adiabatic process. This is Carathéodory's postulatory form of the second law of thermodynamics.

In this form, the second law has no great analytical utility. All that can be said at this point is that there exists an integrating factor for dQ in the first law. Since there are any number of integrating factors if there is one, a variety of analytical expressions may be envisaged which embody Carathéodory's form of the second law. The simplest one, perhaps, arises from the added condition imposed that the ϕ-function for a system of subsystems undergoing reversible processes should be a sum of the ϕ-functions of the separate subsystems. That is, we will select such a set of integrating factors which permit

$$\phi = \sum_{i=1}^{N} \phi_i \tag{2.3.6}$$

for a system having N parts that partake of reversible processes. Then, assuming that the heat absorbed by the entire system in any reversible process is the sum of the heats absorbed by the various parts, we obtain

$$dQ = \frac{d\phi}{u} = \sum_{i=1}^{N} \left(\frac{d\phi_i}{u_i} \right) = \sum_{i=1}^{N} dQ_i. \tag{2.3.7}$$

It is evident that Eqs. (2.3.6) and (2.3.7) can be satisfied if all the u_i's have the same value. To permit the most general process it is necessary to allow all but one of the ϕ_i's to remain fixed, in which case it follows that the u_i's must all have the same value. Under the condition expressed in Eq. (2.3.6), the integrating factors have the same value for systems which can engage in reversible processes with one another. Such a property is possessed by *temperature*. Accordingly, we assume that a suitable integrating factor to dQ may be found which has the same value for all systems at the same temperature, and *define* it to be an *absolute temperature*

$$T \equiv \frac{f(\phi)}{u}, \tag{2.3.8}$$

where u is some integrating factor of Eq. (2.3.1) and ϕ is its integral. Then in Eq. (2.3.5) one obtains

$$\frac{dQ}{T} = \frac{d\phi}{f(\phi)} \equiv dS, \tag{2.3.9}$$

where S is the so-called *entropy function* of the system. In these terms we have the more conventional statement of the second law: for reversible processes

$$dQ = T\,dS. \tag{2.3.10}$$

It remains, of course, to establish how both T and S are measured.

The previously obtained expressions now may be cast into familiar forms expressing the second law. Thus we have for *reversible* processes

$$\oint \frac{dQ}{T} = 0. \tag{2.3.11}$$

Also, for *reversible* processes

$$S_f - S_i = \int_i^f \frac{dQ}{T}. \tag{2.3.12}$$

For *reversible* processes but, in fact, entirely independent of any process since the relation expressed is between the variables of state, we have the differential expression for the first and second laws:

$$T \, dS = dE + P \, dV = dH - V \, dP, \qquad (2.3.13)$$

which is restricted to bulk systems. For other kinds of possible work Eq. (2.3.13) is suitably augmented. Thus, if additional variables of state are necessary to characterize the system, the work associated with such systems generally is of the form

$$dW = P \, dV - \sum_k X_k \, dx_k, \qquad (2.3.14)$$

where the X_k are termed *generalized forces* and the x_k are termed *generalized displacements*; they are assumed to be physical variables that depend on the state of the system. Then we obtain

$$T \, dS = dE + P \, dV - \sum_k X_k \, dx_k. \qquad (2.3.15)$$

Now, it frequently happens for actually occurring processes that additional work is performed *upon* the system by dissipative processes due to friction, viscosity, etc. In such cases in which the states of the system are nevertheless well defined,

$$dE + P \, dV - \sum_k X_k \, dx_k = dQ - dW'',$$

according to the first law, where $dW'' \leq 0$ is the totality of dissipative work. Comparison with Eq. (2.3.15) yields

$$T \, dS = dQ - dW'' \geq dQ,$$

or

$$dS \geq \frac{dQ}{T} \qquad (2.3.16)$$

for a process which may involve dissipative effects. The equality holds, of course, for reversible processes.

With the introduction of the absolute temperature and entropy functions, the analytic utility of the second law can be enhanced through the definition of two other functions of state. Restricting our attention to bulk systems, and applying the method of Legendre to Eq. (2.3.13), we obtain

$$dF \equiv d(E - TS) = -S \, dT - P \, dV, \qquad (2.3.17)$$

and

$$dG \equiv d(H - TS) = -S \, dT + V \, dP, \qquad (2.3.18)$$

which prove to be especially useful functions for describing reversible processes conducted at constant absolute temperature. In these equations, F is known as the *Helmholtz free energy function* and G is known as the *Gibbs free energy function*. In terms of these functions it is evident that

$$S = -\left(\frac{\partial F}{\partial T}\right)_V = -\left(\frac{\partial G}{\partial T}\right)_P, \qquad (2.3.19)$$

while from Eq. (2.3.13)

$$T = \left(\frac{\partial E}{\partial S}\right)_V = \left(\frac{\partial H}{\partial S}\right)_P. \qquad (2.3.20)$$

2.4 Determination of the absolute temperature scale and entropy. To establish the empirical basis by which the second law may be related to physical systems requires, for the version which we have selected, means for measuring values of the absolute temperature and values of the entropy.

In general, to obtain such techniques requires only that an appropriate physical process be described by the second law in which the absolute temperature appears in a natural manner. Almost any process will do, but some will be more convenient experimentally than others. For the purposes of making the procedure explicit, we examine the relationship between the heat capacities at constant pressure and constant volume for a bulk system.

In terms of the second law (Eq. 2.3.13), it follows that

$$P + \left(\frac{\partial E}{\partial V}\right)_T = T\left(\frac{\partial S}{\partial V}\right)_T, \qquad \left(\frac{\partial H}{\partial P}\right)_T - V = T\left(\frac{\partial S}{\partial P}\right)_T,$$

which may be utilized in Eqs. (2.2.20) and (2.2.21). However, before doing so we may utilize the fact that F and G are functions of state. Hence, from Eqs. (2.3.17) and (2.3.18)

$$\left(\frac{\partial S}{\partial V}\right)_T = \left(\frac{\partial P}{\partial T}\right)_V, \qquad (2.4.1)$$

and

$$\left(\frac{\partial S}{\partial P}\right)_T = -\left(\frac{\partial V}{\partial T}\right)_P. \qquad (2.4.2)$$

(Relations like these will be considered systematically in a later section.) Hence,

$$P + \left(\frac{\partial E}{\partial V}\right)_T = T\left(\frac{\partial P}{\partial T}\right)_V \qquad \text{and} \qquad \left(\frac{\partial H}{\partial P}\right)_T - V = -T\left(\frac{\partial V}{\partial T}\right)_P.$$

In terms of the absolute scale of temperature, therefore,

$$C_P - C_V = T\left(\frac{\partial P}{\partial T}\right)_V \left(\frac{\partial V}{\partial T}\right)_P$$

$$= -T\frac{[(\partial V/\partial T)_P]^2}{(\partial V/\partial P)_T}$$

$$= T\frac{V\alpha^2}{\beta}. \qquad (2.4.3)$$

Now to exploit Eq. (2.4.3) we take advantage of the fact that the absolute temperature is a function of any other temperature scale alone:

$$T = T(t). \qquad (2.4.4)$$

Hence,

$$C_P = \left(\frac{dQ}{dT}\right)_P = \left(\frac{dQ}{dt}\right)_P \frac{dt}{dT} = C'_P\left(\frac{dt}{dT}\right),$$

where the prime denotes that the temperature scale is the practical t-scale. Similarly,

$$C_V = C'_V\left(\frac{dt}{dT}\right) \qquad \text{and} \qquad \left(\frac{\partial V}{\partial T}\right)_P = \left(\frac{\partial V}{\partial t}\right)_P \left(\frac{dt}{dT}\right),$$

so that

$$\alpha = \alpha'\left(\frac{dt}{dT}\right).$$

Combining these results with Eq. (2.4.3), we obtain

$$(C'_P - C'_V)\left(\frac{dt}{dT}\right) = T\left(\frac{dt}{dT}\right)^2 \frac{V(\alpha')^2}{\beta},$$

or, rearranging, we get

$$\frac{d\ln T}{dt} = \frac{V(\alpha')^2/\beta}{C'_P - C'_V}.$$

Then, integrating, we have

$$\ln\left(\frac{T_f}{T_i}\right) = \int_{t_i}^{t_f} dt\left[\frac{V(\alpha')^2/\beta}{C'_P - C'_V}\right]. \qquad (2.4.5)$$

Because of Eq. (2.4.4), we can be assured that the integral is a function of t alone. As a result, (T_f/T_i) is determined, if need be, by numerical integration for any t_i and t_f.

In particular, the unit of absolute temperature is not determinable. Hence, and primarily for historical reasons, one may select the *degree* of temperature to be one-hundredth of the temperature interval between the normal freezing point and the normal boiling point of *water*. Then, defining

$$\Phi = \int_{\text{freezing point}}^{\text{boiling point}} dt \left[\frac{V(\alpha')^2/\beta}{C'_P - C'_V} \right],$$

$$T_2 = T \text{ (boiling point)},$$

$$T_1 = T \text{ (freezing point)},$$

we have

$$T_2 - T_1 = 100 \text{ degrees} \quad \text{and} \quad T_2 = T_1 \exp \Phi.$$

Hence

$$T_2 = \frac{100 \text{ degrees}}{1 - \exp(-\Phi)},$$

which determines the absolute scale of temperature. It should be emphasized that while we have proceeded as if T is nonnegative, it is not possible to conclude this at present. Moreover, a different unit of temperature will give different numerical values for what amounts to a different scale of absolute temperature.

Now that we have established a scale of absolute temperature, it is possible to determine the entropy function. In terms of the second law (Eq. 2.3.13), it follows that

$$C_P = \left(\frac{dQ}{dT} \right)_P = T \left(\frac{\partial S}{\partial T} \right)_P, \tag{2.4.6}$$

and

$$C_V = \left(\frac{dQ}{dT} \right)_V = T \left(\frac{\partial S}{\partial T} \right)_V. \tag{2.4.7}$$

As a result,

$$S(P, T_f) - S(P, T_i) = \int_{P,T_i}^{P,T_f} dT \frac{C_P(P, T)}{T}$$

and $\hspace{8cm}$ (2.4.8)

$$S(V, T_f) - S(V, T_i) = \int_{V,T_i}^{V,T_f} dT \frac{C_V(V, T)}{T}$$

enable us to evaluate entropy changes at fixed volumes and pressures in terms of primary measurements of heat capacities. For some purposes, the changes in the entropy function are desired for the same temperature. To establish these values, Eqs. (2.4.1) and (2.4.2) may be used. Thus

$$S(V_f, T) - S(V_i, T) = \int_{V_i,T}^{V_f,T} dV \left(\frac{\partial P}{\partial T}\right)_V$$

and   (2.4.9)

$$S(P_f, T) - S(P_i, T) = -\int_{P_i,T}^{P_f,T} dP \left(\frac{\partial V}{\partial T}\right)_P.$$

These entropy changes require only a knowledge of the equation of state of the system.

It is evident that once the absolute temperature and the entropy function are known, a knowledge of the values of the internal energy function and the enthalpy function permits the two free energy functions to be evaluated. However, note that each of the functions E, H, and S can only be determined to within some arbitrary constant by the methods we have indicated. Indeed, since the first and second laws usually refer to changes of state of a system, such a restriction is to be expected. For differences in the values of these functions no problem arises. However, when a substitution is called for in the free energy functions, it is immediately apparent that differences in the free energy function generally must still involve an arbitrary constant. This problem will be discussed in Section 2.6. For the present we turn to the differential expressions of the thermodynamic functions.

2.5 Derivative relations among thermodynamic functions. Certain useful analytical features of thermodynamics are exhibited by the differential expressions of E, H, F, and G. Recapitulating, for bulk systems, we have

$$dE = T\,dS - P\,dV, \qquad dH = T\,dS + V\,dP,$$
$$dF = -S\,dT - P\,dV, \qquad dG = -S\,dT + V\,dP.$$

(2.5.1)

Since the expressions on the left are perfect differentials, it follows that

$$T = \left(\frac{\partial E}{\partial S}\right)_V = \left(\frac{\partial H}{\partial S}\right)_P, \qquad P = -\left(\frac{\partial E}{\partial V}\right)_S = -\left(\frac{\partial F}{\partial V}\right)_T,$$
$$V = \left(\frac{\partial H}{\partial P}\right)_S = \left(\frac{\partial G}{\partial P}\right)_T, \qquad S = -\left(\frac{\partial F}{\partial T}\right)_V = -\left(\frac{\partial G}{\partial T}\right)_P.$$

(2.5.2)

These relations prove to be useful for evaluating certain changes in the thermodynamic functions. Again, because the quantities on the left side of Eqs. (2.5.1) are perfect differentials, it follows that

$$\left(\frac{\partial T}{\partial V}\right)_S = -\left(\frac{\partial P}{\partial S}\right)_V, \qquad \left(\frac{\partial T}{\partial P}\right)_S = \left(\frac{\partial V}{\partial S}\right)_P,$$

$$\left(\frac{\partial S}{\partial V}\right)_T = \left(\frac{\partial P}{\partial T}\right)_V, \qquad \left(\frac{\partial S}{\partial P}\right)_T = -\left(\frac{\partial V}{\partial T}\right)_P. \qquad (2.5.3)$$

These relations, referred to as *Maxwell's relations*, facilitate the evaluation of certain changes in the thermodynamic functions in terms of quantities readily measured in the laboratory.

By way of illustration (see also Eqs. 2.4.9), let us consider the adiabatic reversible expansion of a bulk system. Clearly we may expect

$$V(S, T_f) - V(S, T_i) = \int_{S,T_i}^{S,T_f} dT \left(\frac{\partial V}{\partial T}\right)_S$$

and confine our attention to the partial derivative

$$\left(\frac{\partial V}{\partial T}\right)_S = -\left(\frac{\partial S}{\partial P}\right)_V$$

by Maxwell's relations. Now

$$\left(\frac{\partial S}{\partial P}\right)_V = \frac{(\partial S/\partial T)_V}{(\partial P/\partial T)_V} = \frac{C_V}{T(\partial P/\partial T)_V},$$

so that

$$\left(\frac{\partial V}{\partial T}\right)_S = -\frac{C_V}{T(\partial P/\partial T)_V},$$

expressing the original partial derivative entirely in terms of quantities directly measureable in the laboratory: heat capacities and equations of state.

For other purposes it is sometimes convenient to be able to render various thermodynamic relations into a form which refers to specific variables as "independent." The procedure for doing this is relatively straightforward when expressed in terms of *Jacobians*. The Jacobian in two variables is

$$J(x, y | u, v) \equiv \frac{\partial(x, y)}{\partial(u, v)} = \begin{vmatrix} \left(\dfrac{\partial x}{\partial u}\right)_v & \left(\dfrac{\partial x}{\partial v}\right)_u \\ \left(\dfrac{\partial y}{\partial u}\right)_v & \left(\dfrac{\partial y}{\partial v}\right)_u \end{vmatrix}$$

$$= \left(\frac{\partial x}{\partial u}\right)_v \left(\frac{\partial y}{\partial v}\right)_u - \left(\frac{\partial x}{\partial v}\right)_u \left(\frac{\partial y}{\partial u}\right)_v. \qquad (2.5.4)$$

Analogous expressions are obtained for more variables. Here u and v are regarded as "independent" variables upon which x and y depend. Clearly,

$$J(y, x|u, v) = J(x, y|v, u) = -J(x, y|u, v), \qquad (2.5.5)$$

$$J(u, v|u, v) = 1, \qquad (2.5.6)$$

$$J(x, x|u, v) = J(y, y|u, v) = 0. \qquad (2.5.7)$$

Moreover,

$$J(x, y|u, v)J(u, v|s, t)$$

$$= \begin{vmatrix} \left(\dfrac{\partial x}{\partial u}\right)_v & \left(\dfrac{\partial x}{\partial v}\right)_u \\ \left(\dfrac{\partial y}{\partial u}\right)_v & \left(\dfrac{\partial y}{\partial v}\right)_u \end{vmatrix} \begin{vmatrix} \left(\dfrac{\partial u}{\partial s}\right)_t & \left(\dfrac{\partial u}{\partial t}\right)_s \\ \left(\dfrac{\partial v}{\partial s}\right)_t & \left(\dfrac{\partial v}{\partial t}\right)_s \end{vmatrix}$$

$$= \begin{vmatrix} \left(\dfrac{\partial x}{\partial u}\right)_v\left(\dfrac{\partial u}{\partial s}\right)_t + \left(\dfrac{\partial x}{\partial v}\right)_u\left(\dfrac{\partial v}{\partial s}\right)_t & \left(\dfrac{\partial x}{\partial u}\right)_v\left(\dfrac{\partial u}{\partial t}\right)_s + \left(\dfrac{\partial x}{\partial v}\right)_u\left(\dfrac{\partial v}{\partial t}\right)_s \\ \left(\dfrac{\partial y}{\partial u}\right)_v\left(\dfrac{\partial u}{\partial s}\right)_t + \left(\dfrac{\partial y}{\partial v}\right)_u\left(\dfrac{\partial v}{\partial s}\right)_t & \left(\dfrac{\partial y}{\partial u}\right)_v\left(\dfrac{\partial u}{\partial t}\right)_s + \left(\dfrac{\partial y}{\partial v}\right)_u\left(\dfrac{\partial v}{\partial t}\right)_s \end{vmatrix}$$

$$= \begin{vmatrix} \left(\dfrac{\partial x}{\partial s}\right)_t & \left(\dfrac{\partial x}{\partial t}\right)_s \\ \left(\dfrac{\partial y}{\partial s}\right)_t & \left(\dfrac{\partial y}{\partial t}\right)_s \end{vmatrix}$$

$$= J(x, y|s, t), \qquad (2.5.8)$$

making use of the laws of matrix multiplication (Section 14.3) and implicit differentiation. This relation is particularly useful. Now, making use of Eq. (2.5.6), we obtain

$$J(x, y|u, v)J(u, v|x, y) = 1. \qquad (2.5.9)$$

It is also readily verified that

$$J(x, v|u, v) = \left(\frac{\partial x}{\partial u}\right)_v, \qquad (2.5.10)$$

which serves as the basis for expressing partial derivatives in terms of Jacobians.

By way of notation, we observe that Eqs. (2.5.2) would be expressed in terms of Jacobians as

$$T = J(E, V|S, V) = J(H, P|S, P),$$
$$P = J(E, S|S, V) = J(F, T|T, V),$$
$$V = J(H, S|P, S) = J(G, T|P, T),$$
$$S = J(F, V|V, T) = J(G, P|P, T).$$

(2.5.11)

Maxwell's relations in this notation become

$$J(T, S|V, S) = J(P, V|V, S),$$
$$J(T, S|P, S) = J(P, V|P, S),$$
$$J(T, S|T, V) = J(P, V|T, V),$$
$$J(T, S|T, P) = J(P, V|T, P).$$

(2.5.12)

The symmetry is to be noted.

Inasmuch as the second pair of variables in the Jacobian represent the so-called independent variables, it becomes a simple matter to express a given Jacobian in terms of those of a specific pair of independent variables. Thus, by Eqs. (2.5.8) and (2.5.9), in terms of r and s, we have

$$J(x, y|u, v) = \frac{J(x, y|r, s)}{J(u, v|r, s)}.$$

The previous problem of reducing $(\partial V/\partial T)_S$, may be used to illustrate the Jacobian procedure. Let us require T and V to be the independent variables. Then

$$\left(\frac{\partial V}{\partial T}\right)_S = J(V, S|T, S) = \frac{J(V, S|T, V)}{J(T, S|T, V)}$$
$$= -\frac{J(S, V|T, V)}{J(T, S|T, V)}$$
$$= -\frac{J(S, V|T, V)}{J(P, V|T, V)},$$

using Maxwell's relations. Hence, expressing the Jacobians in usual terms,

$$\left(\frac{\partial V}{\partial T}\right)_S = -\frac{C_V}{T(\partial P/\partial T)_V},$$

in accord with our earlier results.

The Jacobian procedure lends itself to many ramifications, such as the formation of tables by which the various relations of interest in thermodynamics may readily be constructed. Also, this procedure may be extended to include second derivatives. For our purposes the preceding presentation should suffice.

2.6 The third law of thermodynamics. As we noted earlier, the free energy functions have an arbitrariness, and thus an ambiguity, in their values when they are constructed simply from E, H, T, and S as obtained from measured values of these functions. This may be seen in several ways. For simplicity we may consider that

$$E = \Delta E + E_0,$$

in which ΔE is the value determined by expressions such as Eqs. (2.2.12) or (2.2.17) where the initial state is regarded as a standard of some sort with E_0 as the value of the internal energy function. The quantity ΔE represents the "measured" change in the internal energy functions. In an analogous manner

$$S = \Delta S + S_0,$$

in which ΔS may be determined from expressions such as Eqs. (2.4.8) or (2.4.9), with S_0 the entropy value for the standard state. In these terms it is evident that, since the absolute temperature has no arbitrary constant,

$$F = E - TS = (\Delta E - T\,\Delta S) + (E_0 - TS_0), \qquad (2.6.1)$$

where the first terms in parenthesis may be regarded as the "measured" value of F. It is evident that at the standard state of reference,

$$F_0 = E_0 - T_0 S_0.$$

Therefore

$$\Delta F = F - F_0 = (\Delta E - T\,\Delta S) - (T - T_0)S_0. \qquad (2.6.2)$$

If, now, changes in ΔF (for fixed standard state) are considered, we obtain

$$\begin{aligned} F_2 - F_1 &= (\Delta F)_2 - (\Delta F)_1 \\ &= (\Delta E - T\,\Delta S)_2 - (\Delta E - T\,\Delta S)_1 - (T_2 - T_1)S_0, \quad (2.6.3) \end{aligned}$$

which, clearly, depends on an explicit *knowledge* of the entropy value S_0 of the system in the standard state.

The awkwardness associated with the entropy value S_0 is emphasized when we compute free energy changes that refer to isothermal changes of state. For example, a system may undergo changes in form, chemical constitution, etc., and in each of these instances may have a perfectly well-defined set of states and well-defined thermodynamic functions. In particular, suppose one configuration of the system is designated by α while another is designated by β. Then the free energy change at a fixed temperature and the same reference temperature will be

$$F^\alpha - F^\beta = (\Delta E - T\,\Delta S)^\alpha - (\Delta E - T\,\Delta S)^\beta$$
$$+ (F_0^\alpha - F_0^\beta) - (T - T_0)(S_0^\alpha - S_0^\beta), \qquad (2.6.4)$$

where $T^\alpha = T^\beta = T$. The needed knowledge of S_0^α and S_0^β makes Eq. (2.6.4) even more awkward to use than Eq. (2.6.3).

In these terms the essence of the third law of thermodynamics is the assertion that a certain state may be found such that $(S_0^\alpha - S_0^\beta)$ vanishes whatever α and β may be, as long as the system can be converted from either one to the other. Under these circumstances, a knowledge of the free energy function is not free from the ambiguity we have discussed. However, all manifestations of the system will possess, so to speak, the same ambiguity, so that it is eliminated when differences in free energy are contemplated.

Suppose that there exist some states (T_0, α) and (T_0, β) for which $S_0^\alpha = S_0^\beta$. Then, as a function of temperature

$$S^\alpha = S_0^\beta + \int_{T_0}^{T} \frac{C_\alpha}{T}\,dT \qquad \text{and} \qquad S^\beta = S_0^\beta + \int_{T_0}^{T} \frac{C_\beta}{T}\,dT. \quad (2.6.5)$$

It is assumed that the integrals exist (i.e., are finite for all T, T_0). Furthermore, suppose that by means of an adiabatic process it is possible to go from $(T, \alpha) \to (T', \beta)$ with $T \geq T' \geq T_0$. In that case

$$S^\alpha(T) = S_0^\alpha + \int_{T_0}^{T} \frac{C_\alpha}{T}\,dT \leq S_0^\beta + \int_{T_0}^{T'} \frac{C_\beta}{T}\,dT = S^\beta(T'),$$

or, in terms of the assumed equality of the S_0's,

$$\int_{T_0}^{T} \frac{C_\alpha}{T}\,dT \leq \int_{T_0}^{T'} \frac{C_\beta}{T}\,dT.$$

If now $T' = T_0$, it follows, since C_α and $C_\beta > 0$ empirically, that $T' = T$. Hence if $S_0^\alpha = S_0^\beta$, there cannot be an adiabatic process by which T_0 is reached from above. Because it is assumed that the reversed process can be executed for $T \geq T_0$ (although not necessarily reversibly), a similar conclusion obtains in the process $(T, \beta) \to (T', \alpha)$, $T \geq T' \geq T_0$.

Now suppose that no adiabatic process exists by which the temperature T_0 may be reached from above. Then for $(T, \alpha) \rightarrow (T', \beta)$ it follows that

$$S_0^\alpha - S_0^\beta \leq \int_{T_0}^{T'} \frac{C_\beta}{T} dT - \int_{T_0}^{T} \frac{C_\alpha}{T} dT,$$

which can assure that $T' = T_0$ only if $T = T_0$ when

$$S_0^\alpha - S_0^\beta \geq 0.$$

Because of the assumption that the reversed process can be executed, we also find that

$$S_0^\beta - S_0^\alpha \geq 0$$

or

$$S_0^\alpha = S_0^\beta \tag{2.6.6}$$

under the condition that no adiabatic process capable of reversal will permit T_0 to be reached from above.

We have established the following equivalence. If a temperature T_0 is incapable of being reached from a greater temperature by an adiabatic process involving a change in the state of a system, then at this temperature the entropy of the system is otherwise independent of the state, and vice versa. Stated differently, for any attainable temperature, the entropy of a system is not determined uniquely by the temperature; if it were, this temperature could not be attained from a greater temperature. If, however, this temperature is unattainable, as indicated, then the entropy of the system is uniquely determined at this temperature.

A corollary of this equivalence is that two states of a system which are attainable one from the other, and vice versa, in the limit of the unattainable temperature T_0 have the same value of the entropy.

The third law of thermodynamics assumes, on the basis of experimental attempts (and failures) to reach it, that the zero of temperature on the absolute scale is unattainable. At this temperature the entropy of a system (and all states connected to it by processes capable of reversal at the same temperature) is uniquely determined. Thus

$$\lim_{T \to 0} \Delta S(\alpha \leftrightarrow \beta) = 0, \tag{2.6.7}$$

which is *Nernst's heat theorem*.

A further suggestion due to Planck takes S_0 to be zero. From a thermodynamic point of view, only that S_0 is a constant can be concluded from the third law. By way of anticipation, however, we shall see that the justification of Planck's suggestion is to be found in statistical mechanics.

Two additional features of the third law are noteworthy. First, we need never consider negative values of the absolute temperature for systems which have nonnegative heat capacities. However, this condition has been implicit in the derivation and is not to be regarded as unexpected. In addition, it is necessary (but not sufficient) that

$$\lim_{T \to 0} C_\alpha = 0, \tag{2.6.8}$$

in order that the integrals $\int_0^T (C\alpha/T)\, dT$ will exist.

2.7 Summary. The axiomatic foundations of thermodynamic theory have been discussed in this chapter.

The assumption is introduced that the states of thermodynamic systems require for their characterization the inclusion of temperature among the several characteristic variables. The so-called zeroth law deals with the functional relation between these variables. The thermal equation of state of a simple bulk system is examined to exhibit the kinds of relations to be expected from thermodynamics.

The first law of thermodynamics is formulated on the basis of the experiments of Rumford and Joule. The analytical formulation results in the existence of a function of the state of the system which is called the internal energy function. We consider how the values of this function may be determined from quantities measurable in the laboratory. This is followed by the construction of another useful function of state, the enthalpy function, and additional relations between quantities measurable in the laboratory are obtained to illustrate the use to which these functions may be put.

The differential expression of the first law is examined to determine under what conditions it may be integrated. This examination leads to a formulation of the second law of thermodynamics, due to Carathéodory, but illustrated here only for bulk systems. In a more useful analytical form, the second law establishes the existence of two additional functions of state: the entropy function and the absolute temperature. In turn, the free energy functions of Helmholtz and Gibbs are constructed. The entropy and absolute temperature are related to various partial derivatives of the internal energy, enthalpy, and free energy functions. The empirical basis for utilization of the second law is established by determining the scale of absolute temperatures in terms of quantities measurable in the laboratory. Thereupon, the entropy function can be evaluated from similarly measurable quantities.

With the empirical basis established, the analytical properties of the functions introduced via the first and second laws are examined, especially the derivative relations among them. The procedure of using Jacobians to effect certain transformations in partial derivatives is considered, and Maxwell's relations are obtained.

We need absolute values of the entropy function because it is necessary to evaluate the free energy functions with the least ambiguity. The third law of thermodynamics permits the choice of a standard state of reference such that the least ambiguity in the free energy functions arises from a lack of knowledge of the absolute entropy in this state. Then the entropy of the system in such a state is uniquely determined by the temperature of that state. The third law takes this temperature to be zero on the absolute temperature scale and asserts that it is unattainable by means of an adiabatic process emanating from a greater temperature. This form of the third law leads to Nernst's heat theorem.

Exercises

1. Check Eq. (2.1.3) for a van der Waals gas (Section 3.2) by evaluating each derivative explicitly and substituting.

2. A weight of mass m is reported to have risen in a gravitational field (say, in the earth's field) for a height of one meter. This is reported to have occurred with the mass confined to a vessel, of appropriate size, which was completely evacuated except for the weight. Analyze this supposed process in terms of the first law of thermodynamics.

3. Extend the first law of thermodynamics to include explicitly the energy associated with the motion of the system and the energy that may be associated with the system's location in space (i.e., kinetic and potential energy of its center of mass).

4. A weight of mass m is dropped from a height of one meter at the surface of the earth and ultimately comes to rest on the bottom of a container from which it may be presumed to be completely insulated, thermally speaking. The entire process may be presumed to occur in a vacuum. Apply the first law to this process, and obtain an analytical expression for the final temperature of the mass.

5. Repeat the process in Exercise 4 with the sole modification that it occurs at a fixed pressure P.

6. With what minimum speed would a projectile made of ice have to be traveling so that it would melt completely upon adiabatic impact with an impenetrable object?

7. Two given liquids, each at the same temperature and pressure, are placed in a vessel at the same temperature and pressure. They are allowed to mix under conditions that isolate the vessel and its contents thermally from each other and the surroundings. When measured, the temperature of the resulting solution

differs from the original temperature. The pressure is unaltered. Express the enthalpy change which would occur at the original temperature and pressure in terms of the relevant heat capacities of the two liquids, assuming that the solution has a specific heat which is a mass-weighted mean of the specific heats of the two liquids. Compare with the actual enthalpy change.

8. The illustration of Carathéodory's principle for a Pfaff expression in two independent variables is essentially trivial because

$$M(x, y) \, dx + N(x, y) \, dy = 0$$

usually has a solution for suitably restricted M and N. The reader may examine a text on differential equations for this purpose. However, the real import of Carathéodory's principle usually relates to differential equations with more than two variables. Examine the following differential equations and find integrating factors for them:

$$zx \, dy - yz \, dx + x^2 \, dz = 0,$$

$$(2x^2 + 2xy + 2xz^2 + 1) \, dx + dy + 2z \, dz = 0.$$

Compare them with the following, which do not have integrating factors

$$y \, dx + x \, dy - (x + y + z) \, dx = 0,$$

$$y \, dx + dx + dz = 0.$$

9. In terms of a formulation of the second law of thermodynamics which asserts the existence of an entropy function such that

$$S_b - S_a = \int_{a}^{b} \frac{dQ}{T},$$
$$\text{reversible}$$

show in general that no *cyclic* process can be constructed in which the *net* result is a transfer of heat from surroundings at *lower* temperature to surroundings at a higher temperature.

10. Using the same formulation of the second law as in Exercise 9, show in general that no cyclic process may be constructed in which heat only is absorbed and thereby converted to work.

11. Suppose that in the immediate region (small, but nonzero) of a given state every state is adiabatically accessible to every other state within this region. Show why Eq. (2.3.2) could not be true under these circumstances.

12. Show that the entropy function can never decrease for any adiabatic process.

13. Using the thermal and caloric equations of state of an ideal gas (Chapter 3), show that the ideal gas temperature and the absolute scale of temperature are identical.

14. Derive Maxwell's relations for a system consisting of an extensible spring of length L and tension $\mathfrak{F}$. The sense of $\mathfrak{F}$ is opposite to the sense of extension in L.

15. Express, for bulk systems, in terms of heat capacities at constant volume or pressure, the variables of state (P, V, T), or appropriate derivatives thereof:

$$\left(\frac{\partial S}{\partial T}\right)_G, \quad \left(\frac{\partial P}{\partial T}\right)_F, \quad \left(\frac{\partial G}{\partial T}\right)_F, \quad \left(\frac{\partial F}{\partial S}\right)_T, \quad \left(\frac{\partial T}{\partial P}\right)_H, \quad \left(\frac{\partial V}{\partial T}\right)_E, \quad \left(\frac{\partial G}{\partial F}\right)_S.$$

16. Express the heat capacity of a bulk system at constant pressure in terms of the "independent" variables G and H.

17. Assume that for sufficiently large pressures, the isobaric coefficient of thermal expansion of a simple system remains nonnegative. In such a case show that if a certain value of the pressure of the system may not be exceeded, the entropy at that pressure acquires a value independent of all other parameters of state.

18. Consider an adiabatic process which is incapable of producing a temperature equal to the absolute zero of temperature, but which is incapable of being reversed in the sense discussed in the text. Determine the consequence of such a situation.

19. Prove, on the basis of the third law, that the coefficient of thermal expansion of a system must be vanishingly small in the vicinity of the zero of absolute temperature.

20. Assume the second law of thermodynamics as expressed in Eq. (2.3.10). Show then that the assumption that there are always states in the arbitrary neighborhood of *any* state which are not accessible to it by means of isochoric processes implies the existence of an integrating factor for $dW = T\,dS - dE$.

21. Distinguish clearly between a *thermal* equation of state and a *caloric* equation of state.

CHAPTER 3

THERMODYNAMICS OF DILUTE GASES

3.1 The ideal gas. Although the reader may be familiar with ideal gases, it is perhaps advisable that a digression be introduced here to discuss those properties of ideal gases that lend themselves to a thermodynamic description. Thereby, certain aspects of the formal development which has been presented may be clarified; likewise, it is hoped, the subsequent formal developments may be made less formidable than might be the case in an absence of any model system to which they may be applied.

The ideal gas is a convenient conceptual idealization based on certain properties of real gases. However, no such system actually exists. Nevertheless, because of the difficulties one experiences with real physical systems, the feeling is soon acquired that ideal gases would have to be invented if for no other reason than to provide a test system for thermodynamic results!

The properties of real gases which are embodied in the ideal gas have to do with (1) the thermal equation of state and (2) the caloric equation of state.

The thermal equation of state of an ideal gas is an expression of the law of Charles and Boyle, embellished with Avogadro's hypothesis: for a pure gas

$$PV = \frac{m}{\overline{W}} R\theta, \tag{3.1.1}$$

where P is the pressure exerted by the gas, V is its volume, m is its mass, $\overline{W}$ is its so-called molecular weight, R is a universal constant, and θ is the so-called *ideal gas temperature*. It is evident that Eq. (3.1.1) *defines* θ in terms of measured values of the remaining quantities. For a mixture of N ideal gases, we have

$$PV = \sum_{i=1}^{N} \left(\frac{m_i}{\overline{W}_i}\right) R\theta. \tag{3.1.2}$$

With the definition of the *partial pressure* of a gas as

$$P_i = \frac{m_i/\overline{W}_i}{\sum_{i=1}^{N} (m_i/\overline{W}_i)} P,$$

we have *Dalton's law of partial pressures*

$$P = \sum_{i=1}^{N} P_i, \tag{3.1.3}$$

with

$$P_i V = \frac{m_i}{\overline{W}_i} R\theta, \tag{3.1.4}$$

V here being the total volume of the gas mixture.

For the ideal gas, one readily verifies that

$$\alpha = \frac{1}{V} \left(\frac{\partial V}{\partial \theta}\right)_P = \frac{1}{\theta} \tag{3.1.5}$$

and

$$\beta = \frac{1}{P}, \tag{3.1.6}$$

independent of constitution. In anticipation of subsequent developments, we note that β is positive, a result which must be satisfied generally.

The caloric equation of state does not arise so simply. However, there is an important experimental result that leads to a limitation of what this relation should be. In the experiment, a gas at low pressure is permitted to expand from one vessel into another which previously had been evacuated. One observes that the final temperature of the gas differs negligibly from its initial temperature. In such an experiment, every means is taken to be certain that the process is adiabatic and, because the entire system is mechanically isolated from its surroundings (immovable walls of the containing vessel), isochoric as well. From the first law we may conclude that the internal energy function of the gas is essentially unaltered as a result of the experiment. Because of the constancy of the temperature, we take as characteristic of ideal gases,

$$\left(\frac{\partial E}{\partial V}\right)_\theta = -\left(\frac{\partial E}{\partial \theta}\right)_V \left(\frac{\partial \theta}{\partial V}\right)_E = 0, \tag{3.1.7}$$

or that the internal energy function for an ideal gas may be regarded as depending on the temperature alone. In these terms we are in a position to evaluate Eq. (2.2.20) for ideal gases. We obtain (temperatures measured in terms of θ)

$$C_P - C_V = P\left(\frac{\partial V}{\partial \theta}\right)_P = \sum_{i=1}^{N} \left(\frac{m_i}{\overline{W}_i}\right) R, \tag{3.1.8}$$

which provides us with a check on the first law of thermodynamics since each of the quantities may be determined independently. The relation is not unexpected, since an evaluation of Eqs. (2.2.12) and (2.2.16) would yield the equation of state. This result appears to be as far as one can go using thermodynamic analysis alone.

However, for monatomic gases (as we shall see in Chapter 8) one can derive on the basis of nonthermodynamic results that

$$C_V \text{ (monatomic, per mole)} = \frac{3R}{2}, \tag{3.1.9}$$

and for such gases (per mole)

$$E = \frac{3R\theta}{2}, \tag{3.1.10}$$

where the constant of integration has been set equal to zero. In the case of polyatomic gases, the heat capacity is generally a complicated function of temperature so that no simple expression obtains for the caloric equation of state.

With the thermal and caloric equations of state available for ideal gases, all the remaining thermodynamic functions are easily evaluated. To illustrate, we may evaluate the free energy function of Gibbs. From its definition, we see that

$$G = H + T \left(\frac{\partial G}{\partial T}\right)_P, \tag{3.1.11}$$

the celebrated Gibbs-Helmholtz equation, from which it follows that

$$\left[\frac{\partial (G/T)}{\partial T}\right]_P = -\frac{H}{T^2}. \tag{3.1.12}$$

Hence (identifying θ with T for the present, the definition of the free energy function having no meaning otherwise), since $H = (5RT/2)$, we obtain

$$\frac{G(T, P)}{T} = \frac{G(T_0, P)}{T_0} - \frac{5R}{2} \ln \frac{T}{T_0},$$

or

$$G(T, P) = \frac{G(T_0, P)}{T_0} T - \frac{5RT}{2} \ln \left(\frac{T}{T_0}\right).$$

From Eq. (2.5.1),

$$G(T_0, P) = G(T_0, P_0) + \int_{P_0}^{P} V(T_0, P) \, dP$$

$$= G(T_0, P_0) + RT_0 \ln \frac{P}{P_0}$$

for ideal gases. Hence, writing the value of the Gibbs function in the reference state as

$$G(T_0, P_0) = \frac{5RT_0}{2} - T_0 S(T_0, P_0),$$

we have

$$G(T, P) = \frac{5}{2} RT + RT \ln P - \frac{5}{2} RT \ln T$$
$$-T\left[R \ln P_0 - \frac{5R}{2} \ln T_0 + S(T_0, P_0) \right]. \qquad (3.1.13)$$

Note that the group of terms in brackets corresponds to the entropy value for the reference state, as discussed previously and indicated in Eq. (2.6.1). It is evident that it simply may not be set equal to zero at the absolute zero of temperature. This is impossible because the condition expressed in Eq. (2.6.8) is clearly inapplicable to ideal gases. (The value will, however, be determined in Section 8.1.) However, this behavior does not contradict the third law, since in the sense we have discussed it the entropy constant for T_0 will be independent of P_0.

3.2 The van der Waals gas. Another equation of state which we shall consider is that due to van der Waals. For one mole of gas,

$$\left(P + \frac{a}{V^2} \right) (V - b) = R\theta, \qquad (3.2.1)$$

where a and b are constants independent of P, V, and θ. This expression provides an equation of state which is more faithful in terms of the behavior of real gases.

Again we have the problem of establishing the caloric equation of state. We can establish, first of all, that Eq. (3.1.7) no longer applies. However, a more desirable piece of information will be associated with the volume-dependence of the heat capacity at constant volume. If this dependence is sufficiently simple, we may be able to evaluate Eq. (2.2.12). Now (assuming the equality of θ and T),

$$C_V = T \left(\frac{\partial S}{\partial T} \right)_V.$$

Hence

$$\left(\frac{\partial C_V}{\partial V} \right)_T = T \left[\frac{\partial}{\partial V} \left(\frac{\partial S}{\partial T} \right)_V \right]_T = T \left[\frac{\partial}{\partial T} \left(\frac{\partial S}{\partial V} \right)_T \right]_V.$$

By one of Maxwell's relations, namely Eq. (2.5.3),

$$\left(\frac{\partial C_V}{\partial V}\right)_T = T\left(\frac{\partial^2 P}{\partial T^2}\right)_V.$$

Clearly, from Eq. (3.2.1), with $\theta \equiv T$, this quantity vanishes for a van der Waals gas. As a result, the value of the heat capacity at constant volume will be the same for all volumes and thus have the value for an indefinitely large volume. But under these conditions, the van der Waals gas becomes an ideal gas. Hence for a monatomic van der Waals gas

$$C_V = \frac{3R}{2}.$$

The remarks following Eq. (3.1.10) apply here also. The result of this analysis is that a van der Waals gas has the internal energy function

$$E = \frac{3RT}{2} + f(V), \tag{3.2.2}$$

where $f(V)$ remains to be determined.

Since, by Eqs. (2.5.1) and (2.5.3),

$$\left(\frac{\partial E}{\partial V}\right)_T = T\left(\frac{\partial S}{\partial V}\right)_T - P = T\left(\frac{\partial P}{\partial T}\right)_V - P,$$

we have for a van der Waals gas

$$\left(\frac{\partial E}{\partial V}\right)_T = \frac{a}{V^2},$$

which can be integrated immediately. We obtain for the monatomic van der Waals gas the caloric equation of state (reverting to the ideal gas temperature for comparison)

$$E = \frac{3R\theta}{2} - \frac{a}{V}, \tag{3.2.3}$$

which reduces to Eq. (3.1.10), as expected, for indefinitely large volumes.

We now may determine the Helmholtz free energy function rather simply. For a given temperature,

$$F(T, V) = F(T, V_0) + \int_{T,V_0}^{T,V} dV \left(\frac{\partial F}{\partial V}\right)_T$$

$$= F(T, V_0) - \int_{T,V_0}^{T,V} P \, dV.$$

With Eq. (3.2.1),

$$F(T, V) = F(T, V_0) - RT \ln \left(\frac{V - b}{V_0 - b} \right) - a \left(\frac{1}{V} - \frac{1}{V_0} \right)$$

$$= \left[F(T, V_0) + RT \ln (V_0 - b) + \frac{a}{V_0} \right] - RT \ln (V - b) - \frac{a}{V} \cdot$$

Now we can certainly take V_0 to be indefinitely large, in which case the quantity in brackets must be the volume-independent part of the Helmholtz function of an ideal gas. From Eq. (3.1.13) the latter may easily be determined. The net result is that

$$F_{vdW}(T, V) = F_{\text{ideal}}(T, V) + RT \ln \left(\frac{V}{V - b} \right) - \frac{a}{V} \cdot \qquad (3.2.4)$$

An important property of any gas is its bulk modulus, Eq. (2.1.6). For a van der Waals gas it is simpler to compute

$$\left(\frac{\partial P}{\partial V} \right)_\theta = - \frac{R\theta}{(V - b)^2} + \frac{2a}{V^3} \cdot$$

For sufficiently large and small values of V, it is apparent that the last term is negligible as compared with the second term. Under these circumstances, $(\partial P / \partial V)_\theta$ is negative. For other values of V, and depending upon the value of θ, it is possible for $(\partial P / \partial V)_\theta$ to have positive values. However, as discussed in the following chapter, this is impossible for stable thermodynamic systems. As a result, the van der Waals equation of state is not entirely applicable over all values of P, V, and θ. This is a well-known characteristic of this equation of state, which duplicates the phenomenon of *condensation* of real gases. Anticipating the aforementioned results, we may inquire for what value of θ, say, is $(\partial P / \partial V)_\theta$ always nonpositive. That situation can occur only when θ has a value exceeding that for which

$$\left(\frac{\partial P}{\partial V} \right)_\theta = 0, \qquad (3.2.5)$$

and for which this value may not be increased by changing the volume, i.e.,

$$\left(\frac{\partial^2 P}{\partial V^2} \right)_\theta = 0. \qquad (3.2.6)$$

This occurs when

$$V = 3b$$

and

$$\theta \geq \frac{8a}{27b} \cdot$$

These values are referred to as *critical* values. For the inequality holding, the van der Waals gas is stable for all states. We shall not consider the conditions where this is not the case.

3.3 The virial expansion. In more general terms, the behavior of real gases requires for an accurate representation an even more complicated equation of state than that of van der Waals. Especially convenient for further theoretical investigations is the *virial expansion:*

$$P = \sum_{n=1}^{\infty} \frac{B_n}{V^n}. \tag{3.3.1}$$

The B_n are referred to as *virial coefficients.* For one mole of gas, clearly, $B_1 = RT$. For a van der Waals gas the second virial coefficient $B_2 = (RTb - a)$. However, this will usually be different for an equation of state which differs from that of van der Waals.

We do not propose to deal at all with the virial expansion. However, we note that simplification of the sort observed with the van der Waals equation will be obtained only if all the virial coefficients have a temperature dependence which is linear.

3.4 Summary. To provide model systems which may be used to test thermodynamic results and to illustrate by analytical means what otherwise must be carried out numerically for real physical systems, we have considered two idealized systems: the ideal gas and the van der Waals gas.

Various thermodynamic expressions are evaluated for these two systems, and certain of the thermodynamic functions are constructed. From the latter, others may be derived. The relative simplicity of the results stems from the observation that the thermal equation of state expresses the pressure as a linear function of the temperature.

EXERCISES

1. Develop the consequences of $(\partial H/\partial P)_\theta = 0$ as an alternative criterion for perfect gases.

2. Compute the final temperature in the isentropic expansion of a perfect gas with an initial temperature T_i and initial volume V_i to a final volume V_f.

3. A Carnot cycle is a process consisting of the following reversible stages (for a gas): (1) from an initial temperature and volume, expand isothermally; (2) at the conclusion of this stage, expand adiabatically; (3) at the conclusion of this stage, compress isothermally; (4) finally, at the conclusion of this stage, compress adiabatically. The four stages are so related that the initial temperature and volume are reached at the conclusion of the fourth stage. Calculate the ratio of the net work done during the cycle to the net heat absorbed during the cycle. This is the "Carnot efficiency" of the process.

4. Calculate the entropy change when an ideal gas expands adiabatically into an evacuated vessel of equal volume.

5. Calculate the change in temperature when a van der Waals gas expands adiabatically into an evacuated vessel of equal volume.

6. When a gas is forced through a porous plug at a steady rate under adiabatic conditions, we have an *isenthalpic* process. Show this. Also, calculate the change in temperature experienced as a result of this process for an ideal gas.

7. Calculate the Joule-Thomson coefficient $(\partial T/\partial P)_H$ for a van der Waals gas.

8. In the "condensation" region of a van der Waals gas, we limit the applicability of this equation to those states for which $(\partial P/\partial V)_\theta$ is negative. Also in the condensation region, the cubic nature of the equation is manifested, and there may be found for each temperature two different states that have the same pressure and the same values of the Gibbs free energy function. Thus the previous criterion is satisfied. The states, at a given temperature, that have volumes greater than the larger of the two volumes and less than the smaller are physically realizable states. Determine the limiting states that have been described.

CHAPTER 4

CONDITIONS OF THERMODYNAMIC EQUILIBRIUM

4.1 Real processes, equilibrium criterion, and constraints. Although equilibrium has been referred to in the course of the present development, no attempt has been made to define what is meant by it. This is a task to which we now turn our attention. First, however, we shall examine what may be termed *real processes*. We have seen that in the presence of dissipative processes, the various thermodynamic functions which have been obtained are conveniently related in terms of differential inequalities. Thus, for a dissipative process of any sort whatever, the work associated with friction, viscosity, etc.,

$$dW'' < 0.$$

Note, in contrast to the treatment of Section 2.3, the absence of the equality; in the present treatment only those processes involving dissipative effects are considered. Therefore, from Eq. (2.3.15),

$$T \, dS > dE + P \, dV - \sum_k X_k \, dx_k + dW'' = dE + dW,$$

or the total work done by the system,

$$dW < T \, dS - dE. \tag{4.1.1}$$

This applies to all dissipative processes for which the states are defined. Nevertheless, Eq. (4.1.1) will be applied generally, and when certain stages of a physical process have no definable thermodynamic states, Eq. (4.1.1) must be replaced by an equivalent expression involving line integrals. With this understanding, Eq. (4.1.1) may be adopted as characterizing real processes.

When Eq. (4.1.1) is not applicable to a possible process, it can only mean that such a process is unreal and cannot occur. Hence we may take the negation of Eq. (4.1.1) for all conceivable processes to be the criterion of thermodynamic equilibrium. In other words, a system will be said to be in a state of thermodynamic equilibrium if any conceivable process by which it could change that state, or have it changed, cannot correspond to a real process. In mathematical terms, the condition for thermodynamic equilibrium becomes

$$\delta W \geq T \, \delta S - \delta E, \tag{4.1.2}$$

where δx (read "variation in x") corresponds to any arbitrary small (not necessarily zero) change in the quantity x which may or may not be an actual change. Since the quantity x may depend by the nature of the system on certain other quantities, the differential of x, dx, is constrained in a manner that is related to the differential changes in the so-called independent variables. By contrast, the variation in x, δx, includes all conceivable changes in x, not only those limited by the functional dependence of x on the independent variables. (However, we shall occasionally represent the variation in a particular variable in terms of the variations in the independent variable.) As a consequence, it is usually necessary to specify explicitly the constraints that are to be imposed. This will be made clear in subsequent applications.

An interesting consequence of Eq. (4.1.2) is, for $\delta S = \delta E = 0$,

$$(\delta W)_{S,E} \geq 0, \tag{4.1.3}$$

which is the thermodynamic analog of the principle of virtual work (displacements) in mechanics. It is not so convenient to apply to thermodynamic systems because of the difficulty in knowing just what the constraints imply. Nevertheless, one can conclude immediately that equilibrium demands that no dissipative work be performed on the system. This can be related to the observation that a stirred liquid under conditions of constant temperature and pressure hardly corresponds to our notion of an equilibrium system. By contrast, a liquid rotating in and with a containing vessel may be envisaged as reaching a state of constant entropy and energy *and* equilibrium as well, provided that the container is suspended in a manner which eliminates frictional losses.

In a more useful manner, Gibbs has formulated the equilibrium conditions for *isolated* systems. Since for isolated systems clearly no work is possible, we have

$$(\delta S)_E \leq 0, \qquad (\delta E)_S \geq 0, \tag{4.1.4}$$

as equivalent conditions to be satisfied for thermodynamic equilibrium. The first of these statements simply characterizes the equilibrium states as those which, for a fixed value of their internal energy function, have the greatest possible value of the entropy for isolated systems. The second statement refers to the least possible value of the energy function of the isolated system when the entropy function is regarded as fixed in value.

When the dissipative work is set equal to zero, in accord with Eq. (4.1.2), one obtains as the condition for thermodynamic equilibrium

$$\delta E + P\,\delta V - T\,\delta S - \sum_k X_k\,\delta x_k \geq 0, \tag{4.1.5}$$

the equality corresponding to reversible processes and representing a necessary but not sufficient condition for thermodynamic equilibrium.

4.2 Equilibrium conditions for simple systems. Consider Eq. (4.1.5) in which the X_k's are set equal to zero. Then we have for a bulk system

$$\delta E + P\, \delta V - T\, \delta S \geq 0. \tag{4.2.1}$$

Now suppose that the changes in the energy function are to be determined by the changes from the equilibrium values of the volume and the entropy function of the system. Then, developing δE in a Taylor series and retaining second order terms,

$$\delta E = \left(\frac{\partial E}{\partial S}\right)_V \delta S + \left(\frac{\partial E}{\partial V}\right)_S \delta V$$

$$+ \frac{1}{2}\left[\left(\frac{\partial^2 E}{\partial V^2}\right)(\delta V)^2 + 2\left(\frac{\partial^2 E}{\partial S\, \partial V}\right)(\delta V)(\delta S) + \left(\frac{\partial^2 E}{\partial S^2}\right)(\delta S)^2\right].$$

Substitution of this expression into Eq. (4.3.1) yields, making use of Eq. (2.5.2),

$$\left(\frac{\partial^2 E}{\partial V^2}\right)(\delta V)^2 + 2\left(\frac{\partial^2 E}{\partial S\, \partial V}\right)(\delta V)(\delta S) + \left(\frac{\partial^2 E}{\partial S^2}\right)(\delta S)^2 \geq 0. \tag{4.2.2}$$

Under what conditions can this last equation be satisfied? Immediately it can be seen that only if

$$\left(\frac{\partial^2 E}{\partial S^2}\right) \geq 0 \tag{4.2.3}$$

and

$$\left(\frac{\partial^2 E}{\partial V^2}\right) \geq 0 \tag{4.2.4}$$

can Eq. (4.2.2) be satisfied (for either δV or δS vanishing). There is actually another condition that must be satisfied. To obtain this, we determine the minimum value of the quadratic form, Eq. (4.2.2), which then must be nonnegative. The result is that

$$\left(\frac{\partial^2 E}{\partial V^2}\right)\left(\frac{\partial^2 E}{\partial S^2}\right) - \left(\frac{\partial^2 E}{\partial S\, \partial V}\right)^2 \geq 0. \tag{4.2.5}$$

Making use, now, of the thermodynamic relation Eq. (2.5.2), Eq. (4.2.3) becomes

$$\left(\frac{\partial^2 E}{\partial S^2}\right) = \left(\frac{\partial T}{\partial S}\right) = \frac{T}{C_V} \geq 0$$

or since $T > 0$,

$$C_V \geq 0. \tag{4.2.6}$$

Equation (4.2.4) becomes

$$\left(\frac{\partial^2 E}{\partial V^2}\right) = -\left(\frac{\partial P}{\partial V}\right)_S = \left(\frac{\partial P}{\partial S}\right)_V \left(\frac{\partial S}{\partial V}\right)_P$$

$$= \frac{(\partial P/\partial T)_V \, (\partial S/\partial T)_P}{(\partial S/\partial T)_V \, (\partial V/\partial T)_P} = -\frac{C_P}{C_V}\left(\frac{\partial P}{\partial V}\right)_T \geq 0$$

or

$$\frac{C_P}{C_V}\left(\frac{\partial P}{\partial V}\right)_T \leq 0. \tag{4.2.7}$$

Equation (4.2.5), after some manipulation, becomes

$$\frac{T}{C_V^2}\left(\frac{\partial P}{\partial V}\right)_T \left[T\left(\frac{\partial P}{\partial T}\right)_V \left(\frac{\partial V}{\partial T}\right)_P - C_P\right] \geq 0. \tag{4.2.8}$$

But with Eq. (2.4.3), this yields

$$\left(\frac{\partial P}{\partial V}\right)_T \leq 0. \tag{4.2.9}$$

Moreover,

$$C_P - C_V \geq 0. \tag{4.2.10}$$

Therefore

$$\left(\frac{\partial P}{\partial V}\right)_S \leq \left(\frac{\partial P}{\partial V}\right)_T \leq 0. \tag{4.2.11}$$

The foregoing inequalities are necessary properties of bulk systems in a state of thermodynamic equilibrium. We can anticipate that they arise in a more general thermodynamic system when the x_k's in Eq. (4.1.5) are kept fixed. Moreover, it will be simple to obtain other relations when the volume is kept fixed and only one of the x_k is free to vary. The more complicated situations will not be considered here.

4.3 Open systems. While the previous treatment is capable of a considerable extension of a simple sort, whereby additional work terms may be included, there is another sort of change which has been excluded from our considerations. We have tacitly regarded thermodynamic systems as ones for which no changes occur in the mass of the systems. The laws of thermodynamics that have been considered have this restriction as a consequence. Moreover, such a restriction, which we shall proceed to eliminate, will prevent our using thermodynamics for describing systems and processes (even though they are equilibrium processes) in which changes of mass occur in various parts of the system. It is appropriate to examine the thermodynamic functions which have been introduced from the aspect of their dependence on the mass of the system.

In equilibrium, a portion of a thermodynamical system has certain thermodynamic functions or variables whose values depend generally on the extent of that portion. Such functions of variables are referred to as *extensive*. Primitive illustrations are *volume* and *mass*. Similarly, the internal energy function and the entropy function are extensive. However, there are other variables pertaining to the same thermodynamic system whose values generally do not depend on the size of the portion. These variables have the same value in any arbitrary portion of a homogeneous thermodynamic system in equilibrium and are referred to as *intensive*. Primitive illustrations are *temperature* and *pressure*.

Clearly, the functions E, F, G, and H are extensive if E and S are and if T and P are intensive. Moreover, the ratio of two extensive quantities evidently does not depend on the size of the system to which the properties refer; such ratios are, thus, intensive. Accordingly, any extensive property may be expressed in terms of mass of the system and the property of a *unit mass of the system* (to be referred to as a *specific property*). Thus,

$$E = M\overline{E}, \qquad V = M\overline{V}, \qquad S = M\overline{S}, \qquad (4.3.1)$$

where the barred quantities are specific properties and M is the mass of the system. Equation (4.3.1) constitutes, of course, a definition of the specific properties. However, it is evident that the specific properties may be regarded as a function of intensive variables alone, namely, by way of illustration,

$$\overline{E} = \overline{E}(\overline{S}, \overline{V}), \qquad \overline{S} = \overline{S}(T, \overline{V}), \qquad \text{etc.}$$

Thus all the expressions obtained previously may be regarded as referring directly to the specific properties. A simple multiplication of the equations by the mass of the system under consideration will yield the previous results. But in regarding the equations in this manner, we have emphasized that the changes of the thermodynamic systems are those for which no changes occur in their mass (i.e., specific properties are reckoned per unit of mass). In contrast with Eq. (2.5.1), we write

$$d\overline{E} = T\, d\overline{S} - P\, d\overline{V}.$$

Now, making use of Eq. (4.3.1), evidently

$$dE = T\, dS - P\, dV + (\overline{E} + P\overline{V} - T\overline{S})\, dM, \qquad (4.3.2)$$

which reduces to our earlier result when M is constant. From the point of simplicity of the differential expression, the "natural variables" in which to express the internal energy function appear to be S, V, and M. That is, $E = E(S, V, M)$ contrasted with $\overline{E} = \overline{E}(\overline{S}, \overline{V})$. In these terms, clearly

$$T = \left(\frac{\partial E}{\partial S}\right)_{V,M}, \qquad -P = \left(\frac{\partial E}{\partial V}\right)_{S,M},$$

which may be compared with Eq. (2.5.2), and

$$(\overline{E} + P\overline{V} - T\overline{S}) \equiv \overline{G} = \left(\frac{\partial E}{\partial M}\right)_{S,V}, \qquad (4.3.3)$$

which is new.

We can now obtain

$$
\begin{aligned}
dH &= \quad T\,dS + V\,dP + \overline{G}\,dM, \\
dF &= -S\,dT - P\,dV + \overline{G}\,dM, \\
dG &= -S\,dT + V\,dP + \overline{G}\,dM,
\end{aligned}
\qquad (4.3.4)
$$

as extensions of Eq. (2.5.1). As a result, we have

$$\overline{G} = \frac{G}{M} = \left(\frac{\partial E}{\partial M}\right)_{S,V} = \left(\frac{\partial H}{\partial M}\right)_{S,P} = \left(\frac{\partial F}{\partial M}\right)_{T,V} = \left(\frac{\partial G}{\partial M}\right)_{T,P}.$$

Equations (4.3.2) and (4.3.4) represent generalizations of the first and second laws for simple bulk systems open to the transfer of mass. The extension to somewhat more complex systems may be effected in a similar manner. To do so it is required that, in Eq. (2.3.15), X_k be an intensive variable (corresponding to a generalized force) and x_k be an extensive variable (corresponding to a generalized displacement or extension).

With the foregoing equations it becomes possible to consider a more elaborate equilibrium situation than heretofore. To illustrate, suppose that a system consists of simple homogeneous substances which are invariable in composition. It is evident that we may readily adapt our previous equilibrium condition, Eq. (4.2.1) to

$$\delta E + P\,\delta V - T\,\delta S - \overline{G}\,\delta M \geq 0 \qquad (4.3.5)$$

for each homogeneous subsystem (termed *phase*) and obtain for the entire system consisting of N phases

$$\sum_{i=1}^{N} (\delta E_i + P_i\,\delta V_i - T_i\,\delta S_i - \overline{G}_i\,\delta M_i) \geq 0, \qquad (4.3.6)$$

the subscript here referring to each phase. Now we may inquire into the implications of Eq. (4.3.6) under the constraint that the system is isolated mechanically and thermally from its surroundings. This will correspond, in fact, to the conditions for which the *total* volume is fixed as well as the *total* entropy. That is, we require that

$$\delta V = \sum_{i=1}^{N} \delta V_i = 0, \qquad (4.3.7)$$

$$\delta S = \sum_{i=1}^{N} \delta S_i = 0, \qquad (4.3.8)$$

as well as that

$$\delta M = \sum_{i=1}^{N} \delta M_i - 0. \qquad (4.3.9)$$

But then, for an isolated system of fixed mass [taking the equality in Eq. (4.1.4)],

$$\delta E = \sum_{i=1}^{N} \delta E_i = 0. \qquad (4.3.10)$$

The last five equations define our equilibrium problem.

It may be well to digress for a moment to see what these equations amount to. Basically, we have expressed the notion discussed earlier that an isolated system *ought* to come to equilibrium after a sufficiently long time. The last four equations make certain that the system we have described is indeed isolated. But more than that, we have stated that although the total mass is fixed, the masses of each phase may be variable. This can come about only by a conversion, so to speak, of one phase into another, maintaining simultaneously a fixed composition. Such a process clearly implies an equality of the composition of each of the phases. We shall deal presently with a more general exposition in which this restriction is relaxed. For the moment we emphasize the limitation of our treatment. The remaining equation represents a testing of the system to determine if it has reached equilibrium. The parallel between the equations and what may be regarded as occurring in the laboratory can, perhaps, be imagined.

It is apparent that the equations defining our equilibrium problem permit certain of the variations to be eliminated. The result of such a procedure will be to exhibit a single equation in which the variational quantities displayed will be truly independent. The same result may be achieved in a systematic manner by using Lagrange's method of undetermined multipliers. Each of the last four equations may be multiplied by an arbitrary constant and added to the first. (We consider here only the necessary conditions and hence use the equality.) Then we obtain

$$\sum_{i=1}^{N} [(P_i + a)\,\delta V_i - (T_i + b)\,\delta S_i - (\overline{G}_i + c)\,\delta M_i] = 0. \quad (4.3.11)$$

(Note that the $\delta E = \sum_{i=1}^{N} \delta E_i$ can be, and has been, eliminated directly.) A choice of

$$a = -P_j, \qquad b = -T_k, \qquad c = -\overline{G}_l,$$

will render Eq. (4.3.11) into the form whereby the coefficients of δV_j, δS_k, and δM_l will be zero, with the remaining variational quantities capable of taking on any values whatever. That is,

$$\sum_{i\neq j}^{N} (P_i + a)\,\delta V_i - \sum_{i\neq k}^{N} (T_i + b)\,\delta S_i - \sum_{i\neq l}^{N} (\overline{G}_i + c)\,\delta M_i = 0. \quad (4.3.12)$$

But now all but one variation may be set equal to zero with the assurance that the conditions of constraint are satisfied. It then follows that the coefficient of the residual nonzero variation must itself vanish. Repeating this procedure for each variation in turn, it emerges that

$$P_i = -a, \qquad T_i = -b, \qquad \overline{G}_i = -c \qquad (1 \leq i \leq N), \quad (4.3.13)$$

or that the pressures, temperatures, and specific Gibbs function have the same values for all phases of the system. The latter are evidently functionally distinct, although they must have the same numerical values under the circumstances.

It remains to establish whether Eqs. (4.3.13) generally can be satisfied. Since the temperatures and pressures are to be the same in all phases of the system, we have, evidently,

$$\overline{G}_1(T, P) = \overline{G}_2(T, P) = \cdots = \overline{G}_N(T, P). \quad (4.3.14)$$

As a result, any pair of specific Gibbs functions restricts the pressure to be determined as a function of temperature, and vice versa. No difficulty ensues, therefore, in satisfying Eqs. (4.3.13) for a *pair* of phases. When a third phase is included, an additional restriction is imposed which limits the equilibrium situations to isolated pairs of values of pressure and temperature. At these values, three phases may coexist. Whether more than three phases may coexist in equilibrium is a matter of the coincident values of the specific Gibbs functions having the same value. All that can be said with certainty is that three phases may coexist at isolated values of temperature and pressure. This result is related to the celebrated *phase rule* of Gibbs, which will be considered in full generality in Section 4.6.

For the present, the implications of Eq. (4.3.14) will be examined. For a binary equilibrium (i.e., two coexistent phases) the temperature and pressure are related, as mentioned previously. To express one in terms of the other requires an explicit statement of the values of the Gibbs functions at all temperatures and pressures. An equivalent relationship is to be found in the differential equation relating the two quantities. For all values of the temperature and the pressure for which Eq. (4.3.14) holds, evidently,

$$d\overline{G}_1 = -\overline{S}_1 \, dT + \overline{V}_1 \, dP = -\overline{S}_2 \, dT + \overline{V}_2 \, dP = d\overline{G}_2.$$

Thus

$$\left(\frac{dP}{dT}\right)_{G_1=G_2} = \frac{\overline{S}_2 - \overline{S}_1}{\overline{V}_2 - \overline{V}_1} \qquad (4.3.15)$$

$$= \frac{\overline{H}_2 - \overline{H}_1}{T(\overline{V}_2 - \overline{V}_1)}, \qquad (4.3.16)$$

since for $\overline{G}_1 = \overline{G}_2$, $\overline{H}_2 - \overline{H}_1 = T(\overline{S}_2 - \overline{S}_1)$. Equation (4.3.16) is known as the Clapeyron equation.

It is important to note that, apart from the restrictions having to do with the number of phases, the *amount* of each phase is nowhere alluded to in the equilibrium conditions. As a result, we must recognize that the equilibrium of phases of invariable chemical composition is only *incompletely* characterized by a stipulation of the intensive variables of the system. The relative amounts of each of the coexistent phases will require a specification of certain of the extensive properties of the equilibrium system.

4.4 Equilibrium of homogeneous chemical systems. We examine, now, any one of the phases of the system which was treated previously. However, the previous restriction of invariable composition of the phases is not now imposed. As a result, the characterization of each phase will depend on more than the mass and the usual thermodynamic variables; it will depend on the several masses of which the phase may be constituted.

Equations (4.3.1) are simple examples of *homogeneous functions* of the *first degree* in the variable M. An extension to more than one such variable is made simply. Suppose that an extensive property depends on the masses $m_1, \ldots, m_N$. Such a quantity evidently will have a magnitude which will depend generally in a complicated manner on the total mass of the phase. However, if each of the masses comprising the phase is altered in a fixed proportion to the original amount, then the relative composition of the phase is unaltered and the extensive properties will have their magnitudes altered in the same fixed proportion. Thus, to illustrate, consider the mass dependence of the volume of one of the phases,

$$V = V(m_1, \ldots, m_N). \tag{4.4.1}$$

Here the volume will certainly depend on other intensive variables that we regard as fixed in value for the present. In these terms we have

$$V(\alpha m_1, \ldots, \alpha m_N) = \alpha V(m_1, \ldots, m_N). \tag{4.4.2}$$

Usually a function for which

$$L(\alpha x_1, \ldots, \alpha x_N) = \alpha^p L(x_1, \ldots, x_N) \tag{4.4.3}$$

is referred to as an homogeneous function of the pth degree in the x's. For our purposes, the extensive properties are homogeneous functions of the first degree in the masses, while intensive properties are homogeneous functions of the zeroth degree in the masses. Differentiation of Eq. (4.4.3) with respect to α for fixed x's yields

$$p\alpha^{p-1}L(x_1, \ldots, x_N) = \frac{\partial L}{\partial \alpha}(\alpha x_1, \ldots, \alpha x_N)$$

$$= \sum_{i=1}^{N} \left[\frac{\partial L(\alpha x_1, \ldots, \alpha x_N)}{\partial(\alpha x_i)} \cdot \frac{\partial(\alpha x_i)}{\partial \alpha} \right]$$

$$= \sum_{i=1}^{N} x_i \frac{\partial L(\alpha x_1, \ldots, \alpha x_N)}{\partial(\alpha x_i)}, \tag{4.4.4}$$

making use of the rules for implicit differentiation. Now, letting $\alpha \to 1$,

$$pL(x_1, \ldots, x_N) = \sum_{i=1}^{N} x_i \frac{\partial L(x_1, \ldots, x_N)}{\partial x_i}. \tag{4.4.5}$$

The partial derivatives $\partial L/\partial x_i$ evidently are homogeneous functions of $(p-1)$st degree in the x's if L is homogeneous of pth degree. A second differentiation will give

$$p(p-1)L(x_1, \ldots, x_N) = x_1^2 \frac{\partial^2 L(x_1, \ldots, x_N)}{\partial x_1^2}$$

$$+ 2x_1 x_2 \frac{\partial^2 L(x_1, \ldots, x_N)}{\partial x_1 \partial x_2} + \cdots$$

$$= \sum_{i=1}^{N} \sum_{j=1}^{N} x_i x_j \frac{\partial^2 L(x_1, \ldots, x_N)}{\partial x_i \partial x_j}. \tag{4.4.6}$$

Additional relations may be obtained by further differentiation of Eq. (4.4.3). These relations are due to Euler.

A relationship needed for subsequent purposes is the differential of an homogeneous function. Inasmuch as the function to be considered will depend on variables other than those in which it is homogeneous, we must make certain that changes due to them are not neglected. Then for $p = 1$

$$dL(x_1, \ldots, x_N) = [dL(x_1, \ldots, x_N)]_{x_1,\ldots,x_N} + \sum_{i=1}^{N} \frac{\partial L(x_1, \ldots, x_N)}{\partial x_i} \, dx_i$$

$$= \sum_{i=1}^{N} x_i \, d\left[\frac{\partial L(x_1, \ldots, x_N)}{\partial x_i}\right] + \sum_{i=1}^{N} \frac{\partial L(x_1, \ldots, x_N)}{\partial x_i} \, dx_i,$$

by Eq. (4.4.5). Evidently the changes at constant composition and mass,

$$(dL)_{x_1,\ldots,x_N} = \sum_{i=1}^{N} x_i \, d\left[\frac{\partial L(x_1, \ldots, x_N)}{\partial x_i}\right]. \tag{4.4.7}$$

This last relation can be established explicitly. Since

$$d\left(\frac{\partial L}{\partial x_i}\right) = \left[d\left(\frac{\partial L}{\partial x_i}\right)\right]_{x_1,\ldots,x_N} + \sum_{j=1}^{N} \frac{\partial^2 L}{\partial x_i \partial x_j} \, dx_j,$$

$$\sum_{i=1}^{N} x_i \, d\left(\frac{\partial L}{\partial x_i}\right) = \sum_{i=1}^{N} x_i \left[d\left(\frac{\partial L}{\partial x_i}\right)\right]_{x_1,\ldots,x_N} + \sum_{j=1}^{N} dx_j \left[\sum_{i=1}^{N} x_i \frac{\partial}{\partial x_i}\left(\frac{\partial L}{\partial x_j}\right)\right]. \tag{4.4.8}$$

The last sum vanishes by Eq. (4.4.5), and we obtain Eq. (4.4.7).

We can now write

$$E = \sum_{i=1}^{N} m_i \left(\frac{\partial E}{\partial m_i}\right)_{m \neq m_i; T, P} = M \sum_{i=1}^{N} y_i \left(\frac{\partial E}{\partial m_i}\right)_{m \neq m_i; T, P} = M\bar{E},$$

$$V = \sum_{i=1}^{N} m_i \left(\frac{\partial V}{\partial m_i}\right)_{m \neq m_i; T, P} = M \sum_{i=1}^{N} y_i \left(\frac{\partial V}{\partial m_i}\right)_{m \neq m_i; T, P} = M\bar{V}, \tag{4.4.9}$$

$$S = \sum_{i=1}^{N} m_i \left(\frac{\partial S}{\partial m_i}\right)_{m \neq m_i; T, P} = M \sum_{i=1}^{N} y_i \left(\frac{\partial S}{\partial m_i}\right)_{m \neq m_i; T, P} = M\bar{S},$$

where $y_i = (m_i/M)$ and $M = \sum_{i=1}^{N} m_i$. The comparison with Eqs. (4.3.1) should be noted. The partial derivatives in Eq. (4.4.9) are homogeneous functions of zeroth degree in the masses. We are now in a position to construct the expression for the first and second laws for systems capable of undergoing changes in composition and total mass.

From Eq. (4.4.9)

$$dE = \sum_{i=1}^{N} dm_i \left(\frac{\partial E}{\partial m_i}\right)_{m \neq m_i; T,P} + \sum_{i=1}^{N} m_i \, d\left(\frac{\partial E}{\partial m_i}\right)_{m \neq m_i; T,P}$$

$$= [dE]_{\substack{\text{const. comp.} \\ \text{const. mass}}} + \sum_{i=1}^{N} \overline{E}_i \, dm_i, \tag{4.4.10}$$

where we have written

$$\overline{E}_i \equiv \left(\frac{\partial E(m_1, \ldots, m_N)}{\partial m_i}\right)_{T,P} \equiv \left(\frac{\partial E}{\partial m_i}\right)_{m \neq m_i; T,P}.$$

It is evident that the same procedure may be employed to obtain expressions for the volume and the entropy function. Then if we recall that the differential equation for the first and second law, Eq. (2.5.1), applies to systems of invariable mass and composition, we ultimately obtain for bulk systems

$$dE = T \, dS - P \, dV + \sum_{i=1}^{N} \mu_i \, dm_i, \tag{4.4.11}$$

with

$$\mu_i = \overline{E}_i + P\overline{V}_i - T\overline{S}_i, \tag{4.4.12}$$

an equation first introduced by Gibbs for the purposes at hand. From its derivation, the equation pertains to *independently variable* masses. As previously, one can obtain

$$dH = \quad T \, dS + V \, dP + \sum_{i=1}^{N} \mu_i \, dm_i,$$

$$dF = -S \, dT - P \, dV + \sum_{i=1}^{N} \mu_i \, dm_i, \tag{4.4.13}$$

$$dG = -S \, dT + V \, dP + \sum_{i=1}^{N} \mu_i \, dm_i.$$

As a result, the *chemical potentials*

$$\mu_i = \left(\frac{\partial E}{\partial m_i}\right)_{m \neq m_i; S, V} = \left(\frac{\partial H}{\partial m_i}\right)_{m \neq m_i; S, P}$$

$$= \left(\frac{\partial F}{\partial m_i}\right)_{m \neq m_i; T, V} = \left(\frac{\partial G}{\partial m_i}\right)_{m \neq m_i; T, P}. \qquad (4.4.14)$$

Moreover, from Eq. (4.4.12)

$$G(m_1, \ldots, m_N; T, P) = \sum_{i=1}^{N} m_i \mu_i, \qquad (4.4.15)$$

and hence

$$-S \, dT + V \, dP = \sum_{i=1}^{N} m_i \, d\mu_i, \qquad (4.4.16)$$

which is the so-called Gibbs-Duhem relation. The chemical potentials evidently are homogeneous functions in the masses of zeroth degree.

Consider, now, the conditions for thermodynamic equilibrium of a single phase. As previously, Eq. (4.2.1) may be augmented along the lines leading to Eq. (4.4.11) to yield

$$\delta E + P \, \delta V - T \, \delta S - \sum_{i=1}^{N} \mu_i \, \delta m_i \geq 0 \qquad (4.4.17)$$

as the condition for the equilibrium for bulk homogeneous systems of alterable composition. It is readily apparent that the conditions obtained previously for bulk systems obtain when the m's are kept fixed. We shall consider only some additional conditions ascribable to changes in composition. Because of the definition of the Gibbs function, it is evident that

$$\left(\delta G - \sum_{i=1}^{N} \mu_i \, \delta m_i\right)_{T, P} \geq 0.$$

Developing $\delta G_{T,P}$ in a Taylor series in the variations from the equilibrium composition, and retaining second order terms, we have

$$\sum_{i=1}^{N} \sum_{j=1}^{N} \left(\frac{\partial \mu_i}{\partial m_j}\right)_{m \neq m_j; T, P} (\delta m_i)_{T,P} (\delta m_j)_{T,P} \geq 0. \qquad (4.4.18)$$

Since the variations are arbitrary,

$$\left(\frac{\partial \mu_i}{\partial m_i}\right)_{m \neq m_i; T, P} \geq 0, \qquad \text{all } i, \qquad (4.4.19)$$

while for any pair of independently variable masses, one can obtain

$$\left(\frac{\partial \mu_i}{\partial m_i}\right)_{m \neq m_i; T, P} \left(\frac{\partial \mu_j}{\partial m_j}\right)_{m \neq m_j; T, P} \geq \left(\frac{\partial \mu_i}{\partial m_j}\right)^2_{m \neq m_j; T, P} = \left(\frac{\partial \mu_j}{\partial m_i}\right)^2_{m \neq m_i; T, P}.$$

(4.4.20)

The preceding discussion of equilibrium has not taken into account any constraints imposed by virtue of chemical action. We shall consider only the necessary conditions for homogeneous *chemical equilibrium* and the constraint imposed thereby. To simplify matters, we may suppose that the system is isolated but is capable of changing its composition. In the latter case, while the total mass of the system is fixed, the individual masses may vary. In a chemical reaction, however, the variation is restricted by the *law of definite proportions*. To formulate this restriction we consider a system consisting of N variable masses, and *each* of the possible chemical reactions in which the system may engage is represented schematically as

$$\sum_{i=1}^{N} \nu_i A_i = 0,$$

(4.4.21)

where A_i refers to a distinct chemical species, either reactant or product, and i refers to reactant species when $\nu_i > 0$ and to product species when $\nu_i < 0$. In terms of *moles* or *molecules* the stoichiometric coefficients ν_i may be taken as integers. In terms of the stoichiometric coefficients, the law of definite proportions may be expressed as

$$\frac{1}{\nu_i} \frac{\delta m_i}{\overline{W}_i} = \frac{1}{\nu_j} \frac{\delta m_j}{\overline{W}_j} = \cdots = \delta \xi,$$

(4.4.22)

where the $\overline{W}$'s are constants characteristic of the indicated chemical species. (They are, of course, the molecular weights.) Equation (4.4.22) is due to de Donder.

Now we examine the solution of Eq. (4.4.17) with the constraints imposed in Eq. (4.4.22) and

$$\delta S = 0, \qquad \delta V = 0,$$

corresponding to isolation, whereupon it follows that (considering only the necessary condition)

$$\delta E = 0.$$

The net result of these constraints is the equation

$$\left(\sum_{i=1}^{N} \nu_i \overline{W}_i \mu_i\right) \delta \xi = 0,$$

or since $\delta \xi$ is arbitrary,

$$\sum_{i=1}^{N} \nu_i \overline{W}_i \mu_i = 0. \tag{4.4.23}$$

The quantity $\overline{W}_i \mu_i$ is the chemical potential per mole of the ith species. It evidently is necessary to have an explicit knowledge of the compositional dependence of the μ_i to exploit Eq. (4.4.23). However, as we can anticipate, the condition of chemical equilibrium will imply a relation among the several masses of which the phase is composed, one such relation for each possible chemical reaction. As a consequence, the number of independently variable masses comprising the phase cannot exceed the number of distinct chemical species constituting the phase. The latter will be termed *constituents* while the former will be termed *components*. Evidently if there are N constituents in equilibrium which are interconvertible through R independent chemical reactions, there will be $(N - R)$ components.

4.5 Equilibrium of heterogeneous chemical systems. We turn now to the most general equilibrium situation involving bulk systems: heterogeneous equilibrium. The system under consideration will be presumed to consist of N constituents, in M phases capable of reacting chemically in any one (or all) of R independent reactions. Since Eq. (4.4.17) holds for each phase, the entire system at equilibrium must satisfy

$$\sum_{\alpha=1}^{M} \left[\delta E^{(\alpha)} + P^{(\alpha)} \, \delta V^{(\alpha)} - T^{(\alpha)} \, \delta S^{(\alpha)} - \sum_{i=1}^{N} \mu_i^{(\alpha)} \, \delta m_i^{(\alpha)} \right] \geq 0. \tag{4.5.1}$$

The superscript refers to a particular phase, while the subscript refers to a particular constituent. Restricting our attention to the necessary conditions, the following constraints are introduced:

$$\delta V = \sum_{\alpha=1}^{M} \delta V^{(\alpha)} = 0,$$

$$\delta S = \sum_{\alpha=1}^{M} \delta S^{(\alpha)} = 0,$$

$$\sum_{\alpha=1}^{M} \sum_{i=1}^{N} \delta m_i^{(\alpha)} = 0,$$

whereupon it follows that

$$\delta E = \sum_{\alpha=1}^{M} \delta E^{(\alpha)} = 0.$$

The constraints related to chemical equilibrium are now introduced. They are arrived at by recognizing that Eq. (4.4.22) applies for each reaction in each phase. Thus we have the variation in the ith constituent throughout the system,

$$\delta m_i = \sum_{\alpha=1}^{M} \delta m_i^{(\alpha)} = \sum_{r=1}^{R} \nu_i^{(r)} \overline{W}_i \, \delta \xi^{(r)},$$

corresponding to the net transformation of this constituent by R chemical reactions. The superscript on the right side of this equation refers to a particular chemical reaction. To employ this constraint, we set

$$\sum_{i=1}^{N} \gamma_i \sum_{\alpha=1}^{M} \delta m_i^{(\alpha)} - \sum_{i=1}^{N} \gamma_i \sum_{r=1}^{R} \nu_i^{(r)} \overline{W}_i \, \delta \xi^{(r)} = 0. \qquad (4.5.2)$$

The method of Lagrange may be applied, yielding

$$\sum_{\alpha=1}^{M} \left[(P^{(\alpha)} - \lambda_1) \, \delta V^{(\alpha)} - (T^{(\alpha)} - \lambda_2) \, \delta S^{(\alpha)} - \sum_{i=1}^{N} (\mu_i^{(\alpha)} - \gamma_i) \, \delta m_i^{(\alpha)} \right]$$
$$- \sum_{i=1}^{N} \sum_{r=1}^{R} (\gamma_i \nu_i^{(r)} \overline{W}_i) \, \delta \xi^{(r)} = 0. \quad (4.5.3)$$

The λ's and γ's are adjusted to eliminate the appropriate number of dependent variations (as determined by the constraints). Then one obtains

$$
\begin{aligned}
P^{(\alpha)} &= \lambda_1, && \text{all } \alpha, \\
T^{(\alpha)} &= \lambda_2, && \text{all } \alpha, \\
\mu_i^{(\alpha)} &= \gamma_i, && \text{all } \alpha, \\
\sum_{i=1}^{N} \gamma_i \nu_i^{(r)} \overline{W}_i &= 0, && \text{all } r.
\end{aligned}
\qquad (4.5.4)
$$

Thus the pressure, temperature, and the chemical potential of each constituent is the same in each phase; the condition of chemical equilibrium is satisfied for each independent reaction. Again, a knowledge of the chemical potentials is needed to give a detailed description of the equilibrium.

As with simple equilibrium (Section 4.3), we inquire into the limitations of finding solutions for Eqs. (4.5.4). Because the chemical potentials are homogeneous functions of zeroth degree in the mass variables, they depend on $(N - 1)$ composition variables and on the temperature and pressure of the phase, or a total of $(N + 1)$ phase variables. For M phases, one has $M(N + 1)$ variables for the heterogeneous system. In terms of Eqs. (4.5.4), there are $(M - 1)$ independent relations among the pressures of each phase, with a similar number for their temperatures. For each constituent there are $(M - 1)$ relations among the chemical potentials, making a total of $N(M - 1)$. Finally, there are R additional relations among the chemical potentials arising from chemical equilibrium. The variance,

$$F = \text{no. of variables} - \text{no. of relations}$$
$$= M(N + 1) - 2(M - 1) - N(M - 1) - R$$
$$= (N - R) - M + 2, \qquad (4.5.5)$$

which is the celebrated *phase rule* of Gibbs, here expressed in terms of the number of constituents, independent chemical equilibria, and the number of phases.

4.6 Equilibrium of nonuniform chemical systems. As a further illustration of the utility of the conditions of equilibrium, we consider a non-heterogeneous nonuniform chemical system. For this purpose we consider the inclusion of work terms in addition to those of bulk expansion. In such a case, the equilibrium conditions for a uniform homogeneous system become

$$\delta E + P\,\delta V - T\,\delta S - \sum_k X_k\,\delta x_k - \sum_{i=1}^{N} \mu_i\,\delta m_i \geq 0, \quad (4.6.1)$$

involving the generalized forces X_k and displacements x_k. To adapt this to a nonuniform system, we may suppose that a sufficiently small region within the system is substantially uniform. Taking, then, a fixed small uniform region $d\tau$, Eq. (4.6.1) becomes for that region

$$d\tau\left(\delta\epsilon - T\,\delta\sigma - \sum_k X_k\,\delta x_k - \sum_{i=1}^{N} \mu_i\,\delta\rho_i\right) \geq 0,$$

where ϵ, σ, and ρ_i are the internal energy density, entropy density, and mass density, respectively, and $\sum_k X_k x_k$ refers to a unit volume. For a region of space which confines the system, evidently

$$\int d\tau\left(\delta\epsilon - T\,\delta\sigma - \sum_k X_k\,\delta x_k - \sum_{i=1}^{N} \mu_i\,\delta\rho_i\right) \geq 0 \quad (4.6.2)$$

represents the equilibrium condition for the entire system; the various quantities are generally dependent on spatial coordinates.

We consider the following constraints:

$$\delta\int d\tau\rho_i = 0, \qquad \text{each } i, \qquad (4.6.3)$$

by which we consider no chemical reaction to occur, for simplicity, and

$$\delta \int d\tau \sigma = 0. \tag{4.6.4}$$

In the present case the internal energy need not be fixed as a consequence, since work other than that of bulk expansion may be done. However, we may conclude that the quantity

$$\delta \left[\int d\tau \left(\epsilon - \sum_k X_k x_k \right) \right] = 0. \tag{4.6.5}$$

The last expression will be understood when $(-\sum_k X_k x_k)$ is taken to be the potential energy density of the system in some external field of force. To illustrate, in any external field we associate

$$\sum_k X_k x_k = - \sum_{i=1}^{N} \rho_i U_i(\mathbf{r}), \tag{4.6.6}$$

where ρ_i is the mass density, U_i is the potential energy associated with a unit mass of the ith constituent, and $\mathbf{r}$ is the position vector of the region. The generalized force, in this notation, is

$$\mathbf{X}_k = \sum_i \rho_i \nabla U_i$$

and

$$\sum_k X_k \, dx_k = \sum_i \rho_i \nabla U_i \cdot d\mathbf{r}.$$

(Note that the sign is to be taken so that $-\sum X_k \, dx_k$ is work done by the system.)

Then, multiplying each of Eqs. (4.6.3) through (4.6.5) by an appropriate constant and combining with Eq. (4.6.2), we ultimately obtain the necessary condition

$$\int d\tau \left[-(T - \lambda) \, \delta\sigma_i - \sum_i (U_i(\mathbf{r}) + \mu_i - \gamma_i) \, \delta\rho_i \right] = 0, \tag{4.6.7}$$

or

$$T = \lambda, \qquad \text{constant independent of position}, \tag{4.6.8}$$

and

$$\mu_i + U_i(\mathbf{r}) = \gamma_i, \qquad \text{constant independent of position}. \tag{4.6.9}$$

Here again we note that specification of the chemical potentials is necessary for a detailed description of the equilibrium.

4.7 Summary. In the present chapter we have applied the first and second laws of thermodynamics to formulate a criterion of thermodynamic equilibrium.

The first and second laws, when applied to dissipative processes, give an inequality among differential quantities of work, internal energy, and entropy. This inequality is taken to characterize all real processes and thereby permits equilibrium to be defined as a situation from which no real process may proceed. Characteristic expressions that pertain to equilibrium are then constructed.

The conditions for the equilibrium of simple bulk systems lead to certain consequences for the stability of simple thermodynamic systems, such as nonnegative heat capacities and nonnegative bulk moduli of compressibility.

To extend the applicability of this chapter to chemical systems requires a consideration of their dependence on chemical composition. First, the simple dependence of systems of unalterable composition on their mass is examined and applied to simple heterogeneous equilibria of such systems. The equilibrium conditions impose restrictions on the thermodynamic variables, and these restrictions depend on the number of phases of unalterable composition which may coexist.

The use of homogeneous functions in the mass variables is exploited to establish the expression for the first and second laws of thermodynamics for homogeneous systems capable of having their composition altered. The procedure employed naturally leads to the introduction of the chemical potentials.

Various examples are given of homogeneous chemical equilibrium, heterogeneous chemical equilibrium, and nonuniform, nonreactive chemical systems. In each case the equilibrium conditions are derived, and they find expression in terms of the chemical potentials of the various constituents. Further explicit consequences of the equilibrium conditions require explicit expressions for the chemical potentials.

Exercises

1. Determine that Eq. (4.2.2) implies Eq. (4.2.5).

2. Derive Eq. (4.2.8).

3. Give an argument based on the first and second laws to show that the internal energy function and entropy function are extensive functions for a bulk system.

4. In contrast to Exercise 3, consider those situations for an apparently bulk system where the internal energy function and the entropy function are not extensive functions.

5. Derive the consequences of the equilibrium conditions for a system which is isolated from the surroundings and in which each phase is constrained to a fixed volume (by being enclosed by a permeable membrane).

6. Derive the barometric formula for a pure ideal gas in equilibrium in a uniform gravitational field.

7. Consider a simple two-phase system of a pure substance in equilibrium. In addition to the usual variables of state for each phase, there need to be two more: A and σ, which are associated with the surface separating the two phases. If A is the area of this surface, then the work attributable entirely to changes in the area is $\left(-\int \sigma \, dA \right)$. From this added information, determine the consequences of the condition of equilibrium for this system. (The problem here involves a correct formulation of the constraints.) Determine how the pressures in both phases are related to the *surface tension* σ.

8. In terms of Exercise 8 of Chapter 3, determine the enthalpy of vaporization of a van der Waals gas.

9. Formulate the differential expression of the first and second laws for open systems consisting of N *constituents* connected by R conditions of chemical equilibrium. In these terms there are $(N - R)$ *components* or independently variable masses. The expression desired displays only the dependence on independent variables. The relation between the chemical potential of the constituents and the components should be given explicitly.

10. Formulate the conditions of equilibrium for a system which is capable of performing work in addition to being capable of expansion. Apply these conditions and determine their consequences for a system capable of doing electrical work at constant temperature and pressure.

11. Establish Eq. (4.4.18) and therefore Eqs. (4.4.19) and (4.4.20).

12. Derive the relations analogous to Eq. (4.4.20) for triples of components.

13. Obtain a "stability" condition for chemical equilibrium from Eq. (4.4.18) and Eq. (4.4.22).

14. Assuming that a two-phase equilibrium of a pure substance has one of the phases an ideal gas and that the specific volume of the other phase is negligible in comparison, obtain an expression for the equilibrium pressure of the two-phase system as a function of temperature. Do not assume $\overline{H}_2 - \overline{H}_1$ to be constant, but its value at one temperature and pressure may be presumed known.

15. The Clapeyron equation may be derived directly from the fact that the equilibrium state is defined by

$$\Delta G(T, P) = 0.$$

Do so, using Eqs. (2.1.2) and (2.1.3).

16. Prove in general that increasing the temperature of an homogeneous system in chemical equilibrium under conditions of either constant pressure or volume will displace the equilibrium composition in a direction which is accompanied by an increased absorption of heat.

17. Prove in general that increasing the pressure of an homogeneous system in chemical equilibrium under isothermal conditions will displace the equilibrium in a direction accompanied by a decrease in volume.

18. Calculate an expression for the heat capacity at constant pressure for an homogeneous system in chemical equilibrium.

19. Calculate an expression for the heat capacity of a two-phase system of a pure substance under conditions that the heterogeneous equilibrium is maintained.

20. Show for a heterogeneous system consisting of two components that any two-phase equilibrium which is unaltered by slight changes in composition (i.e., the corresponding equilibrium temperature and pressure are unchanged) must have the two phases of identical composition.

CHAPTER 5

SOLUTION THEORY

5.1 Ideal solutions. Having seen that the chemical potential assumes an important role in the description of equilibria involving the transfer and chemical transformation of substances, we now inquire into its dependence on composition as well as temperature and pressure.

It is clear at the outset that a determination of the values of the chemical potential certainly will involve making measurements on the system. One might suppose that the final result would be a quantity free from ambiguity or indefiniteness. Indeed, we recall that a convenient definition of the chemical potential is

$$\mu_i = \frac{\partial G(m_1, \ldots, m_N; T, P)}{\partial m_i},$$

so that presuming $G(m_1, \ldots, m_N; T, P)$ to be known precisely from experiment, it would appear that μ_i could be determined precisely. However, as discussed in Section 2.6, the free energy functions involve the values of the internal energy function and the entropy function for some standard state of the system. Moreover, these standard values generally may be expected to vary with composition in a manner that we are not precisely aware of at present. Thus it is apparent that absolute values of the chemical potential cannot be achieved by our present development.

We shall find, however, that differences in the values of the chemical potential are usually entirely satisfactory for thermodynamic purposes. Therefore we need only assure ourselves of the feasibility of determining such changes *and* that the value of the chemical potential is known for some standard state of reference. The latter, it will develop, can be selected with great arbitrariness without introducing any lack of precision into the thermodynamic results. However, with the possibility of a wide choice, the standard state should be chosen to be convenient, at least conceptually. While the practice may vary, frequently the choice of the standard state for the chemical potential of a given species is that of the pure substance under the appropriate conditions of temperature and pressure. For this standard state, the reference chemical potential is known with a minimum of arbitrariness, since the chemical potential is then simply the Gibbs function of the pure substance (see Eq. 4.4.15).

To begin, we examine a process which starts with a system consisting of pure substances (i.e., substances in their standard states of reference).

Thus, consider a system of $m_1, \ldots, m_N$ masses of the relevant substances, each of which is a homogeneous phase at the same temperature and pressure as the others. In these circumstances, the Gibbs function for the system is, apparently,

$$G^0 = \sum_{i=1}^{N} m_i \mu_i^0, \qquad (5.1.1)$$

where the zero superscript refers to the pure substance (i.e., standard state). The pure substances are now permitted to mix at the same temperature and pressure, and presuming that an homogeneous phase results, the Gibbs function for the same temperature and pressure is

$$G = \sum_{i=1}^{N} m_i \mu_i. \qquad (5.1.2)$$

The change in the Gibbs function for this process is

$$\Delta G = G - G^0 = \sum_{i=1}^{N} m_i(\mu_i - \mu_i^0), \qquad (5.1.3)$$

which corresponds to the process of mixing.

Usually the process of mixing the constituents at a fixed temperature and pressure will involve the transfer of heat and changes in the volume of the system. Since the initial and final states of our illustrative system have fixed compositions and masses (and thus may be regarded as simple systems), we readily establish that

$$\Delta V \equiv V - V^0 = \left(\frac{\partial \Delta G}{\partial P}\right)_{m;T}, \qquad (5.1.4)$$

$$-\frac{\Delta H}{T^2} \equiv -\frac{(H - H^0)}{T^2} = \left[\frac{\partial(\Delta G/T)}{\partial T}\right]_{m;P}. \qquad (5.1.5)$$

Knowledge of the volume and enthalpy changes on mixing will make possible an evaluation of the pressure and temperature variation of the coefficients in Eq. (5.1.3).

For the present we may emphasize the fact that a large number of systems manifest relatively small changes in their volume and enthalpy on mixing by *assuming* such changes to be negligibly small for *ideal* solutions. Thus, stated mathematically, ideal solutions are defined by

$$\Delta H_{T,P} \text{ (mixing)} = 0, \qquad \Delta V_{T,P} \text{ (mixing)} = 0,$$

as a result of which $\qquad\qquad\qquad\qquad\qquad\qquad\qquad\qquad$ (5.1.6)

$$\Delta E_{T,P} \text{ (mixing)} = 0.$$

As a consequence of these relations, it follows that ideal solutions have

$$\Delta G_{T,P} \text{ (mixing)} = -T \, \Delta S_{T,P} \text{ (mixing)}. \tag{5.1.7}$$

In connection with the chemical potentials, Eqs. (5.1.3) through (5.1.6) give

$$\left[\frac{\partial(\mu_i - \mu_i^0)}{\partial P}\right]_{m;T} = 0 \tag{5.1.8}$$

and

$$\left\{\frac{\partial[(\mu_i - \mu_i^0)/T]}{\partial T}\right\}_{m;P} = 0. \tag{5.1.9}$$

These equations may be integrated immediately to yield

$$\mu_i = \mu_i^0 + Tf_i(m_1, \ldots, m_N), \tag{5.1.10}$$

where f_i is a function of composition *alone*.

In these terms, the entropy of mixing for an ideal solution is, by Eqs. (5.1.3), (5.1.7), and (5.1.10),

$$\Delta S_{T,P} \text{ (mixing)} = -\sum_{i=1}^{N} m_i f_i(m_1, \ldots, m_N), \tag{5.1.11}$$

which clearly depends only on the composition for ideal solutions. Inasmuch as the process envisaged in forming an ideal solution is an adiabatic one, evidently

$$\Delta S_{T,P} \text{ (mixing)} \geq 0,$$

which then requires that not all f_i can be positive. Since the addition of any single constituent can never decrease the entropy,

$$0 \leq \frac{\partial \Delta S_{T,P} \text{ (mixing)}}{\partial m_i} = -f_i(m_i, \ldots, m_N) - \sum_{j=1}^{N} m_j \frac{\partial f_j}{\partial m_i}.$$

Now, because of Eq. (5.1.10),

$$\frac{\partial f_i}{\partial m_j} = \frac{\partial f_j}{\partial m_i}, \tag{5.1.12}$$

and we have

$$\sum_{j=1}^{N} m_j \frac{\partial f_j}{\partial m_i} = \sum_{j=1}^{N} m_j \frac{\partial f_i}{\partial m_j} = 0$$

in view of the fact that the f_i are homogeneous functions of zeroth degree. Hence

$$f_i(m_1, \ldots, m_N) \leq 0, \qquad \text{all } i. \tag{5.1.13}$$

By Eq. (5.1.10) the equality obtains when all $m \neq m_i$ vanish. Because the f's are intensive functions, the same result may be achieved by fixing all $m \neq m_i$ in amount and letting m_i increase indefinitely. As a consequence, we can see that

$$\lim_{\substack{m_i \to \infty \\ m \neq m_i \text{ fixed}}} f_i(m_1, \ldots, m_N) = 0 \qquad (5.1.14)$$

and

$$\lim_{\substack{m_i \to \infty \\ m \neq m_i \text{ fixed}}} \frac{\partial f_i(m_1, \ldots, m_N)}{\partial m_i} = 0. \qquad (5.1.15)$$

Now it is apparent that the term *ideal solution* certainly does not completely characterize the f's of Eq. (5.1.10). Accordingly, further assumptions must be introduced. Motivated by the feature of indistinguishability between the constituents of an ideal solution with regard to their energies and their volumes, we shall examine the consequence of *assuming* that all f's have the same *form*. That is, we shall *assume* that

$$f_i(m_1, \ldots, m_N) \equiv f(\xi_i), \qquad 1 \leq i \leq N, \qquad (5.1.16)$$

where

$$0 \leq \xi_i = \frac{C_i m_i}{\sum_{i=1}^{N} C_i m_i} \leq 1,$$

the C's being constants characteristic of the species. But

$$\frac{\partial f_i}{\partial m_j} = f'(\xi_i) \frac{\partial \xi_i}{\partial m_j} = -f'(\xi_i) \frac{\xi_i \xi_j}{m_j} \qquad (i \neq j),$$

and

$$\frac{\partial f_j}{\partial m_i} = f'(\xi_j) \frac{\partial \xi_j}{\partial m_i} = -f'(\xi_j) \frac{\xi_i \xi_j}{m_i} \qquad (i \neq j).$$

Therefore, by Eq. (5.1.12),

$$m_j f'(\xi_j) = m_i f'(\xi_i)$$

or

$$\frac{\xi_j f'(\xi_j)}{C_j} = \frac{\xi_i f'(\xi_i)}{C_i}. \qquad (5.1.17)$$

It is clear that Eq. (5.1.17) holds for any pair of substances of the mixture; hence the indicated ratios must be a constant independent of substance, say, A. As a consequence, it must follow that

$$f(\xi_i) = A C_i \ln \xi_i, \qquad (5.1.18)$$

which clearly satisfies Eqs. (5.1.14) and (5.1.15). To assure that Eq. (5.1.13) is satisfied, the C's may, with no undue loss of generality, be taken all with the same sign. Then each AC_i may be taken as positive.

The form of Eq. (5.1.18) is, as we shall see, quite useful. It arises from the stipulation that the chemical potentials of the constituents of an ideal solution must be identical in *form*. However, the variable on which these symmetrical chemical potentials must depend is a fraction of some sort. There does not appear to be any *a priori* means for settling the question of what sort. But if we could ascertain that substances which form ideal solutions are also "indistinguishable" on a molar basis, we would be inclined to identify the C's with the reciprocal of the molecular weight of the substance. Just such a situation appears to prevail with regard to *dilute gases*. Equal numbers of moles of dilute gases have a striking number of thermodynamic properties which are similar enough to preclude our making any distinction of the gases' constituents on the basis of these properties. (It is evident, however, that *volume fractions*, or the fraction of volume that the unmixed gases would each occupy at the same temperature and pressure as the mixture, will also correlate in the same way as the *mole fraction;* in the case of ideal gases, the two fractions are identical.)

To determine A, one must resort to experiment, although we shall employ a conceptual experiment involving ideal gases. An ideal mixture of ideal gases may be presumed to be in equilibrium with each of its pure constituents. To achieve this result it is necessary to suppose that semipermeable membranes exist which will discriminate among the various constituent gases. The equilibrium conditions will conform to

$$T_i^0 = T \text{ (mixture)}, \qquad \text{all } i,$$

$$P_i^0 = x_i P \text{ (mixture)}, \qquad \text{all } i, \qquad (5.1.19)$$

$$\mu_i^0(T, P_i^0) = \mu_i(T, P, x_i), \qquad \text{all } i,$$

where the superscript refers to the pure substance of indicated subscript, x_i is the mole fraction of the indicated substance; Dalton's law of partial pressures [Eqs. (3.1.3) and (3.1.4)] is assumed. Now, making use of Eqs. (5.1.10) and (5.1.18) and using $C_i = 1/\overline{W}_i$, we have

$$\mu_i^0(T, x_i P) = \mu_i^0(T, P) + \frac{AT}{\overline{W}_i} \ln x_i.$$

Differentiation with respect to x_i at fixed T and P yields

$$P \left[\frac{\partial \mu_i^0(T, x_i P)}{\partial(x_i P)} \right]_T = \frac{AT}{\overline{W}_i x_i}. \qquad (5.1.20)$$

From the definition of μ_i^0 (it is the specific Gibbs function of the pure substance), the indicated partial derivative is simply the specific volume at T and x_iP. Hence, rearranging,

$$(x_iP)(\overline{W}_i\overline{V}_i) = AT,$$

which can be recognized as the equation of an ideal gas, x_iP being the partial pressure and $\overline{W}_i\overline{V}_i$ being the molar volume of the ith constituent. Since T is identical with the ideal gas temperature, we must set

$$A = R. \tag{5.1.21}$$

Hence we have for the chemical potential of a substance in an ideal solution,

$$\mu_i(T, P, x_i) = \mu_i^0(T, P) + \frac{RT}{\overline{W}_i}\ln x_i. \tag{5.1.22}$$

This expression is one of many forms which will satisfy the thermodynamic conditions for ideal solutions. It is one based on the required similarity of form for the chemical potentials, and exploits mole fractions as composition variables. It gives the correct partial-pressure expression for a mixture of ideal gases. The most important aspect of ideal solution theory is its relation to the properties of the pure constituents. This is emphasized by the μ_i^0 originally in Eq. (5.1.10) and carried through to the present expression.

As a final result of this section, we obtain the entropy of mixing for ideal solutions, per mole of mixture:

$$\Delta \overline{S} \text{ (mixing)} = -R \sum_{i=1}^{N} x_i \ln x_i. \tag{5.1.23}$$

This expression may be obtained directly for ideal gases and serves as a starting point for the description of ideal solutions. We have taken the approach of establishing the form of the chemical potentials and confirming that the entropy of mixing of ideal gases results.

5.2 Colligative properties of ideal solutions. Because of the form of the ideal chemical potentials which has been adopted, many properties of ideal solutions may be expressed in terms that depend entirely on the *amount* of each constituent but not on the *kind*. Such properties are called colligative properties.

A particularly important equilibrium situation is a simple heterogeneous equilibrium involving a gaseous or vapor phase. We have already found the general equilibrium conditions to be

$$T_c = T_g, \qquad P_c = P_g, \qquad \mu_{i,c} = \mu_{i,g}, \tag{5.2.1}$$

the subscripts g and c referring to the gaseous and condensed (i.e., solid or liquid) phases respectively. With Eq. (5.1.22) we obtain

$$\mu_{i,c}^0(T,\ P) + \frac{RT}{\overline{W}_{i,c}} \ln x_{i,c} = \mu_{i,g}^0(T,\ P) + \frac{RT}{\overline{W}_{i,g}} \ln x_{i,g}. \quad (5.2.2)$$

Now for each substance we may suppose that there is a "vapor" pressure, $P_i^*(T)$, which each pure substance would exhibit. In fact, it is that value of the pressure which, for fixed T, will satisfy Eq. (5.2.2) when the mole fraction of the indicated substance is unity. We now can express the chemical potentials of the pure substances in terms of the value of the vapor pressure, as follows. Evidently

$$\mu_i^0(T,\ P) = \mu_i^0(T,\ P_i^*) + \int_{P_i^*}^P \left(\frac{\partial \mu_i^0}{\partial P}\right)_T dP.$$
$$T \text{ const}$$

Since the chemical potential of a pure substance is the specific Gibbs function of that substance, its derivative with respect to pressure is simply the specific volume of that substance. Hence

$$\mu_i^0(T,\ P) = \mu_i^0(T,\ P_i^*) + \int_{P_i^*}^P \overline{V}_i^0(T,\ P)\ dP. \quad (5.2.3)$$
$$T \text{ const}$$

Substitution of this result into Eq. (5.2.2) yields (the isothermal path of the integrations being understood)

$$\int_{P_i^*}^P \overline{V}_{i,c}^0(T,\ P)\ dP + \frac{RT}{\overline{W}_{i,c}} \ln x_{i,c} = \int_{P_i^*}^P \overline{V}_{i,g}^0(T,\ P)\ dP + \frac{RT}{\overline{W}_{i,g}} \ln x_{i,g}$$

or

$$\ln\left[\frac{x_{i,g}}{x_{i,c}^{(\overline{W}i,g/\overline{W}i,c)}}\right] = \frac{-\overline{W}_{i,g} \int_{P_i^*}^P [\overline{V}_{i,g}^0(T,\ P) - \overline{V}_{i,c}^0(T,\ P)]\ dP}{RT}. \quad (5.2.4)$$

Now the vapor may be approximated by an ideal gas, whereupon, since

$$\overline{W}_{i,g} \overline{V}_{i,g}^0 = \frac{RT}{P},$$

one obtains

$$\left[\frac{P x_{i,g}}{P_i^* x_{i,c}^{(\overline{W}i,g/\overline{W}i,c)}}\right] = \exp\left[\frac{\overline{W}_{i,g} \int_{P_i^*}^P \overline{V}_{i,c}^0(T,\ P)\ dP}{RT}\right]. \quad (5.2.5)$$

For the conditions

$$\overline{W}_{i,g} = \overline{W}_{i,c} \quad \text{and} \quad \frac{\overline{W}_{i,g} \int_{P_i^*}^P \overline{V}_{i,c}^0(T,P)\,dP}{RT} \ll 1,$$

we obtain

$$Px_{i,g} \doteq P_i^* x_{i,c}, \tag{5.2.6}$$

which is the celebrated *Raoult's law*. Stated in words: the partial pressure of a component of an ideal solution is proportional to the mole fraction of that component in the solution, becoming identical with the vapor pressure when the solution is the pure component. Clearly all reference to the actual substance is contained in P_i^*.

Since many solutions appear to exhibit the required behavior, Raoult's law is frequently employed as a starting point for constructing the ideal chemical potentials. However, from Eq. (5.2.5) we discover that Raoult's law appears to be only an *approximation* derived from the assumption of ideal solutions. We can effect some improvement by referring, not to the normal vapor pressure, but rather to the vapor pressure which the pure substance will have when the condensed phase is at the total pressure of the vapor phase. One readily verifies that for a vapor that satisfies the equation of state of an ideal gas, the vapor pressure of the pure substance is

$$P_i \text{ (vapor)} = P_i^* \exp\left[\frac{\overline{W}_{i,g} \int_{P_i^*}^P \overline{V}_{i,c}^0(T,P)\,dP}{RT}\right]. \tag{5.2.7}$$

It is this value which must be used instead of the so-called normal vapor pressure. Thereupon, Raoult's law is exactly obtained.

A particularly useful form for the equilibrium condition (Eq. 5.2.2) occurs when the mole fraction in the vapor phase is unity. Then

$$\mu_{i,g}^0(T,P) = \mu_{i,c}^0(T,P) + \frac{RT}{\overline{W}_{i,c}} \ln x_{i,c}.$$

There is no difficulty in employing Eq. (5.2.5) to determine the vapor pressure of the solution. Frequently, however, the experimental situation is one for which the total pressure P is held fixed and the corresponding equilibrium temperature is determined as a function of $x_{i,c}$. The procedure used previously may be modified as follows. For a given P there evidently is a temperature T^* for which

$$\mu_{i,g}^0(T^*,P) = \mu_{i,c}^0(T^*,P).$$

Since

$$\frac{\mu_i^0(T, P)}{T} = \frac{\mu_i^0(T^*, P)}{T^*} + \int_{T^*}^{T} \left[\frac{\partial(\mu_i^0/T)}{\partial T} \right]_P dT,$$
$$\scriptsize P \; \text{const}$$

and since

$$\left[\frac{\partial(\mu_i^0/T)}{\partial T} \right]_P = - \frac{\overline{H}_i^0}{T^2},$$

one obtains

$$\ln x_{i,c} = - \frac{\overline{W}_{i,c}}{R} \int_{T^*}^{T} \left(\frac{\overline{H}_{i,g}^0 - \overline{H}_{i\,c}^0}{T^2} \right) dT. \qquad (5.2.8)$$
$$\scriptsize P \; \text{const}$$

A knowledge of the specific enthalpy of vaporization $(\overline{H}_{i,g}^0 - \overline{H}_{i,c}^0)$ is needed in order to evaluate this expression. Frequently the solutions are so dilute $(x_{i,c} \to 1)$ that one can use the limiting slope

$$\lim_{x_{i,c} \to 1} \left(\frac{\partial x_{i,c}}{\partial T} \right)_P = - \frac{\overline{W}_{i,c} \, \Delta \overline{H}_{\text{vap}}}{R(T^*)^2}, \qquad (5.2.9)$$

rather than the integrated form, with no undue loss of accuracy. Equation (5.2.9) is the so-called "boiling-point elevation" expression. Inasmuch as the mole fraction of the completely volatile component $(x_{i,g} = 1)$ is related simply to the mole fraction of the nonvolatile solutes, Eq. (5.2.9) again makes no reference whatever to the nature of the solute, but only to its amount.

Still another illustration of the equilibrium properties of ideal solutions is found in the osmotic pressure of such solutions. Usually a semipermeable membrane is employed to separate one phase from another, thereby allowing the second of Eqs. (5.2.1) to be relaxed. Each of the phases may have a different pressure. In particular, one of the phases is taken to be a pure component. Contrasted with the previous illustration, the phases are both taken to be condensed phases (usually liquid, but the present treatment makes no general distinction between condensed phases). The pressure exerted on the solution will be designated by π. Then one readily obtains, instead of Eq. (5.2.2), for the *permeable constituent*

$$\mu_i^0(T, P) = \mu_i^0(T, \pi) + \frac{RT}{\overline{W}_i} \ln x_i, \qquad (5.2.10)$$

where the subscripts have been dropped for the sake of simplicity since the condensed phases are quite similar.

Clearly [see Eq. (5.2.3)]

$$\mu_i^0(T, \pi) = \mu_i^0(T, P) + \int_P^\pi \overline{V}_i^0(T, P)\, dP,$$

so that

$$\ln x_i = - \frac{\overline{W}_i}{RT} \int_P^\pi \overline{V}_i^0(T, P)\, dP. \qquad (5.2.11)$$

For dilute solutions, again as $x_i \to 1$,

$$\lim_{x_i \to 1} \left(\frac{\partial x_i}{\partial \pi} \right)_T = - \frac{\overline{W}_i \overline{V}_i^0}{RT}. \qquad (5.2.12)$$

It is useful to represent Eq. (5.2.12) somewhat differently. For dilute solutions, π is relatively small, permitting the approximate integration to

$$(1 - x_i) \doteq \frac{\overline{W}_i \overline{V}_i^0}{RT} (\pi - P)$$

or

$$(\pi - P) \doteq \frac{(1 - x_i) RT}{\overline{W}_i \overline{V}_i^0}, \qquad (5.2.13)$$

an expression formally analogous to the equation of state of an ideal gas for the nonpermeable solute. Again we note that reference is made only to the amount of such substances.

5.3 Chemical equilibrium in ideal solutions. While the essence of ideal solutions appears as a sort of indifference of one constituent for another, the case of chemical reaction would seem to suggest quite a different state of affairs. Here, surely, the reactants are not indifferent to one another. Yet, the effect of chemical reaction can be regarded as entirely distinct from ideality of solutions or lack thereof. The ideality of the solutions with which we are concerned may be realized by mixing the pure substances in amounts that prior experiments have shown to be the equilibrium composition. Upon mixing, the composition will be unaltered, by construction. Thus the effect of chemical reaction will have been suppressed entirely. The effects of nonideality of the resulting solution may now be examined in the light of Eqs. (5.1.6).

For those solutions which are ideal in the sense stipulated, we shall assume the chemical potentials to be of the form Eq. (5.1.22). For chemical equilibrium we have, according to Eq. (4.4.23),

$$\sum_{i=1}^N \nu_i \overline{W}_i \mu_i^0(T, P) + RT \sum_{i=1}^N \nu_i \ln x_i = 0. \qquad (5.3.1)$$

Hence

$$\prod_{i=1}^{N} x_i^{\nu_i} = \exp\left[-\frac{\sum_{i=1}^{N} \nu_i \overline{W}_i \mu_i^0(T, P)}{RT}\right]. \qquad (5.3.2)$$

Now the stoichiometric coefficients are, by convention, positive for reactants and negative for products. Hence,

$$-\sum_{i=1}^{N} \nu_i \overline{W}_i \mu_i^0(T, P) = G_{\text{products}}^0(T, P) - G_{\text{reactants}}^0(T, P),$$
$$= \Delta G^0(T, P)$$

for the reaction described in Eq. (4.4.21). In these terms one obtains

$$\frac{\prod_{\text{products}} x_i^{|\nu_i|}}{\prod_{\text{reactants}} x_i^{|\nu_i|}} = \exp\left[-\frac{\Delta G^0(T, P)}{RT}\right] \equiv K_e(T, P), \qquad (5.3.3)$$

the so-called equilibrium constant which is independent of composition. Its relation to the change in the Gibbs function for the standard state is noteworthy. It should be emphasized here that in terms of our formulation, the equilibrium constant is a function of both temperature and pressure.

5.4 The standard state. Whereas ideal solutions have been characterized by no changes in volume and enthalpy upon mixing at constant pressure and temperature, the fact is that real solutions will hardly conform precisely to these conditions. However, from the observation that both ΔV and ΔH frequently are small in the formation of real solutions, it is possible to define a *standard state* for the constituents such that at *some particular composition* the conditions for ideality are satisfied precisely. In the range of the standard composition, the solutions are described reasonably adequately by the formalism already employed.

We begin by considering the following extensive properties of a solution:

$$V = \sum_{i=1}^{N} m_i \left(\frac{\partial V}{\partial m_i}\right)_{m \neq m_i; T, P}, \qquad H = \sum_{i=1}^{N} m_i \left(\frac{\partial H}{\partial m_i}\right)_{m \neq m_i; T, P}. \qquad (5.4.1)$$

Suppose now that at some composition $(m_1^* \ldots, m_N^*)$ each substance is *assigned* specific properties, in accordance with those just listed,

$$\overline{V}_i^* \equiv \left(\frac{\partial V}{\partial m_i}\right)_{m \neq m_i; T, P}, \qquad \overline{H}_i^* \equiv \left(\frac{\partial H}{\partial m_i}\right)_{m \neq m_i; T, P}, \qquad (5.4.2)$$

the quantities to be evaluated at the composition $(m_1^*, \ldots, m_N^*)$. For each of these quantities it is possible to evaluate the chemical potential in the standard state. Thus, since

$$\left(\frac{\partial \mu_i^*}{\partial P}\right)_{T,m^*} = \overline{V}_i^* \qquad (5.4.3)$$

and

$$\left[\frac{\partial(\mu_i^*/T)}{\partial T}\right]_{P,m^*} = -\frac{\overline{H}_i^*}{T^2}, \qquad (5.4.4)$$

the relevant chemical potential may be found by a suitable integration of these equations. It should be evident that the $\mu_i^*(T, P)$ thus found (apart from constants of integration which we may presume to be evaluated as in the case of pure substances) is entirely determined in terms of measurable quantities. Once the standard composition is specified, the chemical potential depends only on the temperature and pressure. It is, in fact, the chemical potential of a *fictitious* pure substance or, rather, the chemical potential of that substance in a standard state which has just been defined.

By this means we may refer to the fictitious mixing process for which

$$\Delta V = \sum_{i=1}^{N} m_i \left[\left(\frac{\partial V}{\partial m_i}\right)_{m \neq m_i; T, P} - \overline{V}_i^*\right],$$

and   (5.4.5)

$$\Delta H = \sum_{i=1}^{N} m_i \left[\left(\frac{\partial H}{\partial m_i}\right)_{m \neq m_i; T, P} - \overline{V}_i^*\right],$$

which, by construction, vanish at the standard composition $(m_1^*, \ldots, m_N^*)$. As a result, one may anticipate that the changes in volume and enthalpy thus computed will be indeed small in the vicinity of the standard composition.

A specific example of a standard state which differs from that of the pure components is the one referred to as "the state of infinite dilution." For the pertinent composition we have all but one of the masses negligibly small in amount. Thus, choosing that one as m_k, we have

$$(m_1^*, \ldots, m_k^*, \ldots, m_N^*) \to (0, \ldots, m_k, \ldots, 0),$$

$$\overline{V}_i^* = \lim_{(m_1, \cdots, m_{k-1}, m_{k+1}, \cdots, m_N) \to 0} \left(\frac{\partial V}{\partial m_i}\right)_{m \neq m_i; T, P},$$

and

$$\overline{H}_i^* = \lim_{(m_1, \cdots, m_{k-1}, m_{k+1}, \cdots, m_N) \to 0} \left(\frac{\partial H}{\partial m_i}\right)_{m \neq m_i; T, P}.$$

By way of contrast, another standard state of reference that may be employed to advantage is the "state of saturated solution." The fact

that there may be an upper limit to the mutual solubility of substances
strongly points up the nonideality of their solutions. Nevertheless, the
use of ideal solution theory as an approximation for nearly saturated
solutions is also justified here. The definitions of the reference chemical
potentials which have just been considered may be applied with no
difficulty. However, it is possible to circumvent this procedure by taking
advantage of the equality of the chemical potentials (for the constituent
with respect to which the solution is saturated) in the solution and the
pure substance. For such a substance, clearly.

$$\mu_j \text{ (saturated solution)} = \mu_j \text{ (pure substance)}. \qquad (5.4.6)$$

By defining the chemical potential in solution to have the form considered for ideal solution, we see that the standard chemical potential
may then be determined. We shall return to this determination shortly.

With a variability of choice imposed on the standard state of reference,
it is possible to *approximate* any small range of solution compositions by
ideal solution theory. Clearly, the smaller the range is, the better the
approximation may be expected to be. In this respect, ideal solution theory
plays the role of a "differential" theory of solutions. Having decided to
use ideal solution theory in such an extended sense we find that the
theory of Sections 5.1 through 5.3 is immediately applicable. Thereby,
the chemical potentials are given the form

$$\mu_i(T, P, x_i) = \mu_i^*(T, P) + \frac{RT}{W_i} \ln x_i, \qquad (5.4.7)$$

where, in contrast to Eq. (5.1.22), the asterisk is used to distinguish from
the standard state of pure substance. The burden thus falls on the evaluation of μ_i^*. For the infinitely dilute standard state, nothing remains to
be added to what has been said. For the saturated solution state, we note
that in terms of Eq. (5.4.7), Eq. (5.4.6) assumes the form

$$\mu_j^*(T, P) + \frac{RT}{W_i} \ln (x_j)_{\text{sat}} = \mu_j^0(T, P).$$

Thus the standard chemical potential in this case is

$$\mu_j^*(T, P) = \mu_j^0(T, P) - \frac{RT}{W_i} \ln (x_i)_{\text{sat}}. \qquad (5.4.8)$$

Since $(x_i)_{\text{sat}}$ varies with temperature and pressure, this dependence must
be taken into account in expressions like Eq. (5.4.4). Furthermore, since
the saturated solution may be affected by other materials in solution, the
use of this particular standard state may be severely circumscribed in
general applications.

5.5 Nonideal solutions. It should be noted that the technique we have described for treating solutions is quite the same for ideal, dilute, and saturated solutions. In fact, in each of these cases a suitably chosen standard state of reference for the "pure substances" permits the use of *ideal solution* theory. The essential feature incorporated thereby has been to approximate the volume and the enthalpy function for the solution by ones which vary in the masses of the constituents in a *linear manner*. The suitable choice of a standard state has only to do with the adequacy of such an approximation to the real state of affairs prevailing. In the present section we consider a modification of the ideal solution theory that goes beyond the linear approximation and permits us to give an accurate description of real solutions. As is customary, the chemical potential of any component will be represented by an augmentation of the chemical potential which it *would have* were it in an ideal solution, namely,

$$\mu_i \equiv \mu_i^*(T, P) + \frac{RT}{W_i} \ln x_i + \frac{RT}{W_i} \ln \gamma_i, \qquad (5.5.1)$$

where γ_i, referred to as an *activity coefficient*, suitably corrects the ideal chemical potential. Clearly, the ideal solution approximation obtains when each activity coefficient is unity. The activity coefficients generally are to be regarded as functions of temperature, pressure, and composition. The expression of the chemical potential by Eq. (5.5.1) is a purely formal one; if we are to give it any physical significance, the activity coefficients must be capable of being found in terms of experimentally determinable quantities.

To accomplish this objective we take note of certain relations that must be satisfied by the activity coefficients. From the Gibbs-Duhem relation (Eq. 4.4.16) we have

$$\sum_{i=1}^{N} m_i \, (d\mu_i)_{T,P} = 0$$

or

$$\sum_{i=1}^{N} m_i \, (d\mu_i)_{\text{ideal},T,P} + RT \sum_{i=1}^{N} \left(\frac{m_i}{W_i}\right) (d \ln \gamma_i)_{T,P} = 0.$$

However, since the ideal chemical potentials have already been constructed to satisfy the Gibbs-Duhem relation, evidently

$$\sum_{i=1}^{N} \left(\frac{m_i}{W_i}\right) (d \ln \gamma_i)_{T,P} = 0, \qquad (5.5.2)$$

a result which may already have been anticipated from the form of Eq.

(5.5.1). Because of the definition of the standard state of reference, we can see that

$$(G - G^*) = \sum_{i=1}^{N} m_i(\mu_i - \mu_i^*) = RT \sum_{i=1}^{N} \left(\frac{m_i}{\overline{W}_i}\right) \ln x_i$$

$$+ RT \sum_{i=1}^{N} \left(\frac{m_i}{\overline{W}_i}\right) \ln \gamma_i. \quad (5.5.3)$$

Now we can express the (fictitious) free energy of mixing in terms of the (fictitious) enthalpy of mixing. Making use of Eq. (5.1.5), one obtains

$$\frac{(G - G^*)}{T} = - \lim_{T \to 0} (S - S^*) + \frac{(H - H^*)}{T}$$

$$- \int_0^T {}_{m,P \text{ const}} \frac{[\partial(H - H^*)/\partial T]_{m,P}}{T} dT. \quad (5.5.4)$$

By the third law of thermodynamics, the entropy of the solution at the zero of absolute temperature is a function of composition alone. In addition, S^* will have a constant value independent of composition at this temperature since it corresponds to the entropy of a composite of "pure" substances at the absolute zero of temperature, the constant for which may be taken to be the same for all substances. Hence, the (fictitious) entropy of mixing at the absolute zero of temperature is *independent of the reference state;* therefore, the latter may be chosen to make the solution ideal at the composition in question. Thus the entropy of mixing at the zero of absolute temperature is equal to the entropy of mixing of an ideal solution.

A comparison of Eqs. (5.5.3) and (5.5.4) then yields

$$RT \sum_{i=1}^{N} \left(\frac{m_i}{\overline{W}_i}\right) \ln \gamma_i = (H - H^*) - T \int_0^T {}_{m,P \text{ const}} \frac{[\partial(H - H^*)/\partial T]_{m,P}}{T} dT.$$

$$(5.5.5)$$

Because of the extensive character of $(H - H^*)$, it follows that

$$\frac{RT}{\overline{W}_i} \ln \gamma_i = \left[\frac{\partial(H - H^*)}{\partial m_i}\right]_{m \neq m_i; T,P} - T \int_0^T {}_{m,P \text{ const}} \left[\frac{\partial^2(H - H^*)}{\partial m_i \partial T}\right] \frac{dT}{T}.$$

$$(5.5.6)$$

In these terms it is evident that a linear dependence of $(H - H^*)$ on the masses will give a *constant* value of γ_i (i.e., independent of composition).

This value may be added simply to the chemical potential of the substance in the standard state; the net result amounts to a change in the standard state. Accordingly, we may assume that an appropriate choice of standard state has been made and $(H - H^*)$ contains no linear dependence on the masses. In that case it is necessary only to evaluate *some* enthalpy of mixing as a function of composition (as may be determined conveniently with real, pure substances) and measure the deviations which occur from *some* linear approximation to the result. The assumed linear approximation characterizes the standard state, and the deviations correspond to $(H - H^*)$ in Eq. (5.5.5).

While we shall not consider any specific examples, it should be evident that the integrals of either Eqs. (5.5.5) or (5.5.6) involve related heat capacities or specific heats of the various components. As a result, the integrand may be expected to be small, in which case the partial enthalpy of mixing will serve as a good approximation by which to estimate the activity coefficient.

The determination of activity coefficients may be carried out in still other ways. For example, the measurement of equilibrium constants may be employed to evaluate the activity coefficients in part. To apply the real chemical potentials to a problem of chemical equilibrium it is readily seen that the expression for the equilibrium constant in Eq. (5.3.3) is modified to

$$\frac{\prod_{\text{products}} x_i^{|\nu_i|}}{\prod_{\text{reactants}} x_i^{|\nu_i|}} \frac{\prod_{\text{products}} \gamma_i^{|\nu_i|}}{\prod_{\text{reactants}} \gamma_i^{|\nu_i|}} = \exp\left[-\frac{\Delta G^0(T, P)}{RT} \right] \equiv K_e(T, P). \quad (5.5.7)$$

This may be written as

$$K \text{ (measured)} \cdot \frac{\prod_{\text{products}} \gamma_i^{|\nu_i|}}{\prod_{\text{reactants}} \gamma_i^{|\nu_i|}} = K_e. \quad (5.5.8)$$

Since the activity coefficients are each unity at the standard state, it is evident that the indicated product ratio is determined by comparing the measured equilibrium constant with the value for the standard state. For a standard state of infinite dilution, an extrapolation procedure must be devised.

5.6 Summary. Having discussed earlier its role in characterizing the equilibria of chemical systems, we have dealt in this chapter with explicit expressions for the chemical potential.

To begin, ideal solutions are considered. These are defined as solutions which manifest no change in volume and in the enthalpy function when the pure components are mixed to form the solution at constant temperature and pressure. These criteria lead, immediately, to a form for the chemical potential which involves the chemical potential of the pure substance to which is added a composition-dependent part. Requiring that ideal chemical potentials have the same form, we find that the compositional dependence turns out to be a logarithmic function of an appropriate fraction of the relevant component. Further specification requires a model system, which is taken here to be an ideal gas. This then leads to the usual expression for the entropy of mixing of ideal gases.

The applications to various heterogeneous equilibria are considered. Raoult's law is obtained, as well as certain other colligative properties of ideal solutions. Chemical equilibrium is examined with the form of the ideal chemical potentials, and the thermodynamic expression for the equilibrium constant is obtained.

The choice of the standard state of reference is examined. The choice is shown to be arbitrary, permitting a wide range of ideal solutions as approximations to real solutions. It is shown that the essential approximation involved in the ideal solution theory is that the volume and enthalpy changes on mixing are thereby taken to be linear functions of the masses. The introduction of activity coefficients permits the form of ideal solution theory to be retained with simple modification. The means for determining the activity coefficients are described.

EXERCISES

1. Confirm Eqs. (5.1.4) and (5.1.5).

2. Confirm Eqs. (5.1.8) and (5.1.9).

3. Carry out the integrations leading to Eq. (5.1.10).

4. Complete the details of the analysis which leads to Eqs. (5.1.19).

5. Using Raoult's law as a starting point which defines ideal solutions, determine the chemical potentials of such components, especially their compositional dependence.

6. From Eq. (5.3.3) determine the temperature and pressure coefficient of the equilibrium constant. Compare with Exercises 17 and 18 of Chapter 4.

7. Confirm Eq. (5.5.2).

8. Consider a binary ideal solution for which the entropy of mixing of the pure substances may be taken as

$$\frac{\Delta S \text{ (mixing)}}{R} = (n_1 + n_2) - (n_1^2 + n_2^2)^{1/2},$$

where n_1 and n_2 are the number of gram-moles of the two substances. Derive the chemical potential of each component.

9. Derive an analog of Raoult's law, using the assumption that both phases have the same entropy of mixing given in Exercise 8.

10. Using the entropy of mixing given in Exercise 8, derive a relation between the depression of the freezing point of a dilute solution and the composition of the solution. Assume that pure solid is in equilibrium with the solution.

11. For substances satisfying the same entropy of mixing, obtain an expression for the equilibrium composition for the homogeneous reaction

$$2A + B \rightleftarrows A_2B.$$

12. Consider the distribution of a solute between two immiscible solvents, both of which are in contact. The solute may have different molecular weights in the two solvents. Derive the conditions of equilibrium and their consequences. Apply Eq. (5.4.7) to determine the equilibrium composition in terms of standard-state properties of the substances.

13. The energy of mixing of n moles of a substance in a fixed volume V of solvent (of molar volume $\overline{V}$) is given by

$$\frac{\Delta E \text{ (mixing; } T, V)}{V} = - \frac{C}{T^{1/2}} \left(\frac{n}{V} \right)^{3/2},$$

where C is a constant independent of T, V, and n. Determine the Helmholtz free energy of mixing.

14. Determine the entropy of mixing of the solution described in Exercise 13.

15. Determine the activity coefficient of the solute of the solution described in Exercise 13.

16. Justify the remark made in the text that, according to the third law, the entropy of a solution at the zero of absolute temperature is a function of composition alone.

17. When the activity coefficients are given by the first expression on the right side of Eq. (5.5.6) show that the entropy of mixing is the same as that of an ideal solution. Solutions with this behavior are called *regular solutions*.

18. Determine from Eq. (5.5.6) the *necessary* conditions for ideal solutions, as determined by the condition $\gamma_i = 1$ for all compositions, temperatures, and pressures.

19. Verify that Eq. (5.1.18) satisfies Eqs. (4.4.19) and (4.4.20).

CHAPTER 6

INTRODUCTION TO STATISTICAL MECHANICS

6.1 The scope of statistical mechanics. We have seen in the preceding chapters how thermodynamics deals with certain macroscopic properties of matter. Statistical mechanics is also concerned with macroscopic properties of matter. But in contrast to thermodynamic theory, statistical-mechanical theory begins with a basic postulate of the molecular constitution of matter. As a consequence, statistical mechanics may be regarded as concerned with the properties of large collections of molecules. As in the case of thermodynamics, the *equilibrium properties* of systems are a concern of statistical mechanics. However, statistical mechanics intrinsically is able to treat nonequilibrium phenomena, whereas thermodynamics, in spite of any connotations associated with the name, is not so constructed. In recent years statistical mechanics has furnished an impetus toward the creation of a thermodynamics capable of treating nonequilibrium phenomena. We shall not consider this aspect of either thermodynamics or statistical mechanics. We shall concern ourselves only with equilibrium properties of systems of molecules. In such cases it may be said that the most important aim of statistical mechanics is to furnish a rational foundation for thermodynamics. For this reason we may better refer to the subject at hand as *statistical thermodynamics.*

In any attempt to achieve this aim, one immediately is confronted with several conceptual difficulties. Thus, statistical mechanics is based on a mechanical description of natural phenomena, and such thermodynamic concepts as *temperature, heat,* and *entropy* are completely alien to it. Indeed, one might contend that the mechanical description of natural phenomena is all-inclusive and that any collection of particles is only a complicated system which is nevertheless capable of being accorded an accurate detailed description. As a result, nothing more would appear to be needed to calculate the various physical properties of the system. Hence, "Why thermodynamics?"

Such a point of view makes two assumptions: (1) the general principles are available for the complete description of physical systems; (2) these principles lead ultimately to soluble relations which comprise the aforementioned description. Conceding the first assumption, we have good reasons for questioning the validity of the latter. Since one cubic centimeter of a gas at ordinary temperatures and pressures contains about 10^{19} molecules, it is evident that an extraordinary number of mechanical degrees of freedom must be contended with, even for what amounts to microscopic quantities of substance. To solve the mechanical equations of motion—classical or quantum—in any realistic sense without some extraordinarily severe approximations is well nigh impossible. Conceding even that reasonably good approximations may be employed, one may venture to ask what may seem almost a philosophically directed question: what assurance is there that such a solution of the mechanical problem will assume a *recognizable* physical form? Inasmuch as we are interested in a physical theory, this question is very much to the point.

Statistical mechanics, as we shall be dealing with it, will be concerned specifically with transcribing a mechanical theory into terms more aptly regarded as physical. The transcription is effected in an heuristic manner of identification with the concepts of thermodynamics. From what we already have seen, the connections thereby established assure us of the relevance of the statistical-mechanical conclusions to the observable physical world. The breadth of thermodynamic theory then may be exploited to relate the knowledge we have of the microscopic structure of physical systems to all equilibrium properties of matter.

A consequence of this directed relationship between statistical mechanics and thermodynamics is the interesting parallel in the treatments given equilibrium by both these subjects. As we shall see, both statistical mechanics and thermodynamics view equilibrium in a similar manner with regard to the stationary properties of material systems. The net effect is to impart a better understanding of the common view.

6.2 Statistical distributions. At the outset, the viewpoint of statistical mechanics is microscopically oriented. That is, the description of any physical system is to be found and expressed in terms of the properties of its constituent particles (i.e., atoms, molecules, and the like). In an ultimate sense, as discussed previously, any immediate relation between these microscopic properties and the macroscopic properties of a physical system is bound to be obliterated. As a result, the validation of conclusions reached in statistical mechanics takes a more circuitous route than in thermodynamics.

From a practical point of view, it is extremely difficult to imagine that all the microscopic properties of a single molecule or atom can be measured directly. Nevertheless, it is inherently logical to suppose that these objects have well-defined measurable properties. The experiments which may be envisaged to effect a measurement of the properties of a single molecule usually have to be of a *conceptual* sort. In general, we can imagine a sequence of experiments in which smaller and smaller numbers of molecules are employed, the measured results on such systems permitting an extrapolation to the case of single molecules. Thereby we may suppose the properties of a single microscopic system to be measured. However, it is clear that the execution of such a series of experiments will usually become dubious as the number of molecules decreases. The introduction of a mechanical theory of the system guides the extrapolation procedure. The theory may be expected to yield solutions with fewer approximations for small numbers of particles. As a result, the extrapolated result may be known *in principle* from the mechanical theory. The function of the experiments, then, is to provide a basis for validating the principles of the mechanical theory itself. With this amalgamation of mechanical theory and conceptual experiment, the properties of individual microscopic systems may be regarded as measurable.

In terms of a collection of microscopic systems, each of which has a completely characterizable set of properties, as discussed, it should be apparent that the properties of the collection need not be simply a composite of the properties of the individual systems. The fact that individual systems may interact with one another will generally alter the properties of the collection from the properties expected from a simple composite of the *individual* properties. However, it will be possible in many cases, as we shall see, to impose just this restriction. The treatments which we shall consider initially will refer only to those collections in which the interaction between subsystems is justifiably negligible (negligible in comparison with *what* will be discussed presently). In this way the individual character of each system is preserved in spite of its presence in a collection. (This restriction will be relaxed in our later treatments.)

Under such a restriction there will be a number of properties of the collection which have a magnitude easily determined by summing the magnitudes of this property possessed by each microscopic system. Clearly, the mass of the collection is a simple illustration of just such a property. So also, for the restriction imposed here, is the energy of the collection. It is evident that the value of the macroscopic property can also be determined by the device of summing the products of each microscopic magnitude and the number of systems in the collection having that magnitude. The set of numbers corresponding to the latter is termed a *distribution.* The distribution of systems in the collection may be expected to depend on the property with which it is correlated.

In mathematical terms, however, a distribution may be regarded simply as a function of a variable having certain operational connotations. For simplicity in exposition we may regard the variable as having a discrete set of values. (When such is not the case, and the variables have continuous ranges of values, the formalism is easily modified.) Then, if α is a variable capable of assuming the values $(\alpha_1, \alpha_2, \ldots, \alpha_k, \ldots)$, the number of systems in a collection of the sort described having the value α_k is, evidently, $n(\alpha_k)$. Here $n(\alpha)$ is the *number distribution in* α. For a total number of N systems, we have

$$N = \sum_{k=1}^{\infty} n(\alpha_k).$$ (6.2.1)

In terms of this distribution, the total value of α for the collection is

$$A = \sum_{k=1}^{\infty} \alpha_k n(\alpha_k).$$ (6.2.2)

It is apparent that for bounded values of N, some $n(\alpha_k)$ must be zero.

It is sometimes more convenient to deal with the *average* properties of a system in the collection. Accordingly, the average value of the property is defined as

$$\bar{\alpha} \equiv \frac{\sum_{k=1}^{\infty} \alpha_k n(\alpha_k)}{\sum_{k=1}^{\infty} n(\alpha_k)} = \sum_{k=1}^{\infty} \alpha_k \left[\frac{n(\alpha_k)}{N} \right],$$ (6.2.3)

where, clearly,

$$1 = \sum_{k=1}^{\infty} \left[\frac{n(\alpha_k)}{N} \right].$$

In this instance $[n(\alpha)/N]$ is referred to as the *probability distribution in* α. For this purpose it is convenient to define

$$\left[\frac{n(\alpha)}{N} \right] \equiv f(\alpha).$$ (6.2.4)

It is evident that we can define the average of any finite power of α as

$$\overline{\alpha^m} \equiv \sum_{k=1}^{\infty} (\alpha_k)^m f(\alpha_k),$$ (6.2.5)

so that any function of α which is expressible as a power series in α may be said to have a meaningful average,

$$\overline{g(\alpha)} = \sum_{k=1}^{\infty} g(\alpha_k) f(\alpha_k).$$ (6.2.6)

Clearly, in general,

$$\overline{g(\alpha)} \neq g(\bar{\alpha}).$$ (6.2.7)

Because the introduction of a probability distribution is essential for a development of statistical mechanics, we must consider this quantity directly from the viewpoint of its measurability. Although we have regarded the distribution as dependent on the measured values of some microscopic physical property so that it thereby acquires a measurable status, we may regard the distribution as measurable itself in the following sense. Imagine a conceptual experiment in which one is able to select a system indiscriminately from the collection, and that this selection may be performed with a negligible influence on the values of the α-property. Then imagine the procedure to be repeated indefinitely, each time on a new *replica* of the original system. For each system selected, assume that the value of the α-property may be determined by measurement. In these circumstances we *assume* that as the number of selections becomes indefinitely great the fraction of selections which result in a measured value α_k approaches a limiting value. This limiting value is $f(\alpha_k)$. In mathematical terms, if $\phi_M(\alpha_k)$ is the fraction of M selections which have resulted in the value α_k, we assume that

$$\lim_{M \to \infty} \phi_M(\alpha_k) = f(\alpha_k). \qquad (6.2.8)$$

We may now regard the probability distribution as directly measurable. Moreover, it is clear that the means by which the values α_k are to be determined as well as the innate selection process will affect the determined values of the distribution.

Consider a collection which may be characterized as having a certain probability distribution in α. What can be said of the average value of some property of a system which is not a function of α? Here the expression given in Eq. (6.2.5) appears to be inapplicable. Obviously, to exploit the expression some sort of distribution that correlates with the property in question is needed. It seems apparent that for properties of a system that are independent, no difficulty is involved in referring to a joint distribution in the two properties. Thus, we may suppose that a collection of systems has a joint probability distribution in (α, β) such that, in the measurable sense we have described,

(Fraction of systems having values α_j and β_k) $= f(\alpha_j, \beta_k)$,   (6.2.9)

and

$$\bar{f}(\alpha_j) = \sum_{k=1}^{\infty} f(\alpha_j, \beta_k), \qquad (6.2.10)$$

which may be identified with the probability in Eq. (6.2.8). Clearly, the same sort of relation obtains for a distribution in β. Moreover, it is evident that a joint distribution in any number of independent properties is perfectly meaningful. In the sense of Eq. (6.2.10), any distribution may be regarded as obtainable from the joint distribution in all the independent properties of the system.

Now, all the independent properties of a system determine the *state* of a system. Hence, the joint distribution in all independent properties of the system may be recognized as a *distribution in states*. Such a distribution is the most comprehensive description of the collection which need be made for statistical purposes. A knowledge of it will enable us to determine the appropriate average value of any mechanical property of a system in a collection. To determine the distribution in states is the central problem in statistical mechanics.

6.3 Stationary distributions. For a collection of systems in "equilibrium" it seems reasonable to suppose that the distribution in states should not change with time. (Because the distribution refers to mechanical properties of the constituent systems, it is meaningful to refer here to temporal changes.) With such a restriction it is evident that all properties of the collection will also remain fixed in time.

The distribution in states, it must be remembered, is a property of the collection of systems which depends explicitly on the properties of a system. Under the conditions we have imposed on the collection, whereby the interactions between systems of the collection are negligible, we may suppose that the distribution in states will depend on those properties of an *isolated* system which are constant in time. These properties are called *constants of the motion* (of the system). It now is apparent why the interaction which has been assumed to exist between systems is to be negligible in comparison with their individual energies. Thereby, those properties which are constants of the motion for the isolated systems remain substantially so in the collection. We may anticipate that the distribution in states for "equilibrium" collections will depend on properties of the system such as its energy, total linear momentum, total angular momentum, etc. We note that the dependence on the energy of the system is by far the most important for the collections (i.e., macroscopic physical systems) we are to consider here. Nevertheless, the requirement of constancy in time cannot determine the distribution in energy. To accomplish this we will need to impose additional physical constraints on the collection.

Supposing that a stationary distribution in states can be determined, and that it will depend on the constants of the motion of the isolated system, what can be said of the individual systems of the collection? One may be inclined to view the distribution as a property of each system of the collection, whereupon it might be supposed that each system retains a fixed value of the energy, etc., thereby preserving the constancy in time of the distribution. Nothing could be further from the truth! The negligible interaction which has been supposed is nevertheless nonzero. In such a case the total energy of the isolated collection (in addition to other constants of the motion of the collection) must remain constant in time. Clearly, this will be assured also if the processes which occur on a microscopic level involve *exchanges* of energy between the systems of the collection, such exchanges resulting in no net change in energy whatever. Thus the stationary character of the "equilibrium" distribution is to be regarded as involving changes in the properties of the individual systems, but the number of each kind of system is fixed in time.

6.4 Determination of the equilibrium distribution. There are three well-known procedures for determining the equilibrium distribution in states. In the Boltzmann, or Maxwell-Boltzmann, procedure, it is recognized that a certain distribution may have a calculable probability associated with it. In other words, all stationary distributions in states may be imagined; for some reason, the likelihood that a real physical system may have some particular distribution associated with it may be imagined as depending on that distribution. Of all the possible distributions, there is imagined a most likely one, or a "most probable" distribution. The Boltzmann procedure attempts to determine the "most probable" distribution and *assumes* that the macroscopic properties of a collection calculated with this distribution will correspond to the observable properties.

We see here that an assumption of significance has been added and may immediately be questioned: why the most probable distribution? No *a priori* answer is entirely satisfactory. Only if we could establish that no other distribution exists with an appreciable probability could we satisfactorily answer the question. By way of anticipation, we observe that such turns out to be the case.

How is the most probable distribution determined? Although we shall consider this procedure in detail in Chapter 7, we mention its outlines here. To begin with, the probability of a specified distribution is defined as proportional to the number of different ways by which it may be constructed. This number of ways is maximized, subject to certain conditions of constraint. In the method of the most probable distribution, the constraints are those of constant total energy and total number of systems in the collection. The method is straightforward and the mathematics is simple. It is apparent from the procedure that only collections with negligible interactions between constituent systems may be treated.

By the procedure devised by Gibbs, the restriction to collections of slightly interacting systems is removed. Any collection of systems may be treated. To accomplish this, one essentially replaces each of the systems in the Boltzmann procedure by the macroscopic physical system of interest. That is, we refer to a distribution which correlates with the mechanical properties of the actual physical system being described. We imagine an indefinitely large number of replicas of the actual system being described.

Each replica may be imagined as differing in the value of the energy, configuration, etc. In other words, the replica here refers to a mechanically equivalent system. The resulting (indefinitely large) collection of replicas, termed an *ensemble*, is assumed to be in "equilibrium." Under the circumstances, the probability distribution is determined with ease. From the resulting probability distribution (which refers to the collection of the Boltzmann procedure), we determine the average properties of a system of the ensemble. These are presumed to correspond with the system's observable equilibrium properties.

Here, again, we note the intrusion of an important assumption relating the results of statistical computation to observable physical properties. In the Gibbs procedure the prescription for doing so is clear, but highly abstract, in relation to an observable system. Nevertheless, it turns out that the Gibbs procedure permits one to show that for systems of large number of degrees of (mechanical) freedom the distribution of systems in the ensemble is such as to give predominant importance to those of the same energy. This result is important in understanding the similarity of the results obtained by both the Boltzmann and the Gibbs methods. We shall consider this in detail in Chapter 9.

Although we shall not consider it in any detail, we mention the method of Darwin and Fowler for establishing the appropriate distribution function. The essential point in their treatment of the problem is to include all possible distributions, in the Boltzmann way of viewing a collection of systems. Thus the average of some particular property will depend on the particular distribution employed to determine the average. Since the distribution has a calculable probability, the average of all such averages may be computed by multiplying each average by the probability of the distribution and summing over all distributions. By insisting that the resulting average correspond to the physically observable property, we complete the formal aspect of the theory. To determine the *average* distribution in states, the Darwin-Fowler method fixes the total energy of the collection (termed *assembly* in this method) and the total number of systems, as in the Boltzmann method. The mathematics is somewhat elaborate, but the results obtained are precisely those achieved with the procedures already considered. We note, however, that the Darwin-Fowler method is strictly limited to a consideration of assemblies of weakly interacting systems. To treat any other situation we must appeal to the method of Gibbs.

6.5 Summary. The relation of statistical mechanics to thermodynamics has been considered in this chapter.

While both statistical mechanics and thermodynamics are concerned with systems in equilibrium, statistical mechanics is able to consider nonequilibrium situations. Nevertheless, such is not considered here; only what may be termed *statistical thermodynamics* is discussed. This subject refers to the use of statistical mechanics to provide a rational foundation for the subject of thermodynamics. The central problem of statistical thermodynamics is the determination of a stationary *distribution function*, which has the feature of enabling us to calculate all the stationary properties of a macroscopic physical system in terms of the properties of the microscopic systems of which it is constituted. The role of measurements in statistical mechanics is discussed. The need for an amalgamation of mechanical theory and *conceptual experiments* is necessary to provide the link between the theory and the physical world. The methods of Boltzmann, Gibbs, and Darwin and Fowler for determining the equilibrium distribution in states are described.

EXERCISES

1. Show that, in general, the *dispersion in* $g(\alpha)$ is

$$\overline{[g(\alpha) - \overline{g(\alpha)}]^2} = \overline{g^2(\alpha)} - [\overline{g(\alpha)}]^2.$$

2. Illustrate several $g(\alpha)$ and related probability distribution in α for which $\overline{g(\alpha)} = g(\bar{\alpha})$. Hence, determine the limitations on the distribution in order for this to hold for arbitrary $g(\alpha)$.

3. Using a joint distribution function, as in Eq. (6.2.9), show that

$$\overline{[u(\alpha, \beta) - \overline{u(\alpha, \beta)}]\,[v(\alpha, \beta) - \overline{v(\alpha, \beta)}]} = \overline{u(\alpha, \beta)v(\alpha, \beta)} - [\overline{u(\alpha, \beta)}][\overline{v(\alpha, \beta)}].$$

Determine, for a given distribution, the restrictions imposed on u and v in order that this quantity should vanish.

4. Taking

$$\bar{f}(\alpha) = \sum_{k=1}^{\infty} f(\alpha, \beta_k), \qquad \bar{f}(\beta) = \sum_{j=1}^{\infty} f(\alpha_j, \beta),$$

show that, generally,

$$f(\alpha, \beta) \neq \bar{f}(\alpha)\bar{f}(\beta) \qquad (\bar{f} \text{ is the same function}).$$

5. Show the general conditions under which $f(\alpha, \beta) = \bar{f}(\alpha)\bar{f}(\beta)$.

6. From Exercise 5, determine the form of $\bar{f}$ when $f(\alpha + \beta) = \bar{f}(\alpha)\bar{f}(\beta)$.

7. From Exercise 5, determine the form of $\bar{f}$ when $f(\alpha\beta) = \bar{f}(\alpha)\bar{f}(\beta)$.

8. Illustrate the statement made in Section 6.3 that "the requirement of constancy in time cannot determine the distribution in energy."

9. Formulate an expression analogous to Eq. (6.2.6) for a function of α and β, making use of Eq. (6.2.9) for the joint probability distribution in these quantities.

CHAPTER 7

THE MAXWELL-BOLTZMANN METHOD

7.1 Combinatorial mathematics. While we shall be concerned ultimately with the manner by which molecules may be classified according to their state, the present section will deal with some elementary mathematics pertaining thereto. For simplicity, but with no attending loss of generality, we shall consider a collection of identical objects each of which possesses certain characteristics that permit it to be classified. Homely illustrations are: a group of identical coins, a number of identical cubical dice, or a collection of marbles which differ only in color. In the first group, classification may be effected by the face of the coin (i.e., "head" or "tail"); in the second group, by the numerical face exhibited by the die; in the third group, by the color of the marble. We already have considered the relation between the classification and the experimental means for establishing it. Hence, we need only assume that experimental means are available to furnish an unambiguous result for the classification.

With the objects and the means for classifying them clearly in mind, we ask: in how many different ways can all of a fixed number of identical dice, say M, be placed on a surface so that m_1 have their $\boxdot$ face in contact with the surface, m_2 have their $\boxdot$ face in contact with the surface, etc.? Otherwise stated: in how many different ways can a specified distribution $(m_1, \ldots, m_6)$ of M identical dice be achieved? The answer to this question depends markedly on what is meant by "identical." In the sense intended here, the dice are identical in that any two having the same classification are regarded as *indistinguishable*; dice of different classifications are regarded as *distinguishable*. (We shall later consider completely indistinguishable systems.)

Considering the M dice as distinguishable, for the moment, it is evident that the group of m_1 dice may be made up in $[M(M-1)\ldots (M - m_1 + 1)]$ ways, the first number corresponding to the number of ways of choosing the first die, the second corresponding to the number of ways of choosing the second die, etc. However, inasmuch as the m_1 dice are to be regarded as indistinguishable, the order in which the m_1 dice have been selected is immaterial. There are $m_1!$ different orders of choosing the m_1 dice. Hence the number of different ways of constituting the m_1 group is

$$\binom{M}{m_1} = \frac{M!}{(M - m_1)!m_1!}. \tag{7.1.1}$$

We note that the m_1 group and the remainder appear symmetrically in Eq. (7.1.1). Now the procedure may be repeated to determine the number of different ways of choosing m_2 objects from a set of $(M - m_1)$ identical objects, regardless of order. With further repetition, the number of different ways of establishing the specified distribution is simply the product of the separate calculations:

$$W_1\left(\begin{matrix} M \\ m_1, \ldots, m_6 \end{matrix}\right) = \frac{M!}{\prod_{i=1}^{6} m_i!}, \tag{7.1.2}$$

with

$$\sum_{i=1}^{6} m_i = M. \tag{7.1.3}$$

It should be apparent that Eq. (7.1.2) is also the number of different ways in which the m_1 dice have their $\boxdot$ face exhibited, etc., because the m_1 dice have only one way of exhibiting this face, the m_2 have only one way of exhibiting the $\boxdot$ face, etc.

Often one is concerned with the relative frequency of the occurrence of a prescribed distribution of the dice. For dice which are unbiased (i.e., not "loaded" to favor the exhibition of certain faces), one might be inclined to *assume* that every possible arrangement will occur with equal likelihood. Under this assumption, the relative frequency of any prescribed distribution is found simply by dividing the appropriate number given by Eq. (7.1.2) by the sum of all possible arrangements. The latter may easily be determined for unbiased dice: since each die has six equally possible faces to exhibit, there will be

$$6^M = \prod_{i=1}^{6} 6^{m_i} \tag{7.1.4}$$

different arrangements possible for the M unbiased distinguishable dice. Hence the relative frequency of the originally prescribed distribution is

$$P\left(\begin{matrix} M \\ m_1, \ldots, m_6 \end{matrix}\right) = \left(\frac{M!}{\prod_{i=1}^{6} m_i!}\right) \prod_{i=1}^{6} \left(\frac{1}{6}\right)^{m_i}. \tag{7.1.5}$$

(The reason for writing the equation in this form will be clarified presently.)

Suppose, however, that the dice are indeed loaded. The frequency of any particular face occurring is no longer $(1/6)$. In fact, each face may be accorded a frequency of occurrence of ω_i. That is to say, in an indefinitely long sequence of experiments in which a die is selected from a collection indiscriminately and placed, also indiscriminately, on a surface, the number of times that the ith face will be exhibited will be taken as $N_i \to \omega_i N$, for $N \to \infty$. [Compare with Eq. (6.2.8).] Clearly,

$$\sum_{i=1}^{6} \omega_i = 1 \qquad (7.1.6)$$

and

$$0 \le \omega_i \le 1, \qquad \text{all } i. \qquad (7.1.7)$$

The ω_i's frequently are referred to as *a priori probabilities*. For a collection of biased identical dice, the relative frequency of the originally prescribed distribution is

$$P\left(\begin{matrix} M \\ m_1, \ldots, m_6 \end{matrix}\right) = M! \prod_{i=1}^{6} \left(\frac{\omega_i^{m_i}}{m_i!}\right), \qquad (7.1.8)$$

subject to Eqs. (7.1.3), (7.1.6) and (7.1.7).

As an aid to memory, Eq. (7.1.8) can be related to the *multinomial theorem*

$$\left(\sum_{i=1}^{f} \omega_i\right)^M = \sum_{\left(\substack{\text{all } m\text{'s} \\ \text{satisfying} \\ \sum_{i=1}^{f} m_i = M}\right)} P\left(\begin{matrix} M \\ m_1, \ldots, m_f \end{matrix}\right) \prod_{i=1}^{f} \omega_i^{m_i}, \qquad (7.1.9)$$

where the extension to f classifications has been made. When the ω's satisfy Eq. (7.1.6), the left side of Eq. (7.1.9) reduces to unity, a necessary result if the terms on the right side are to mean relative frequencies.

Our results depend markedly on the feature of distinguishability that we ascribed to the systems in the collection. We shall be interested in the situation in which the collections consist of entirely indistinguishable systems. In such cases, the previous results do not obtain. To see this, recognize that a "permutation of indistinguishable objects" cannot, in fact, be regarded as a permutation at all. As a result, the number of different ways of obtaining the originally specified distribution of dice expressed in Eq. (7.1.2) reverts to unity since Eq. (7.1.2) corresponds also to the number of permutations between systems in different classes, and such permutations are to be regarded as producing no observable change in the distribution. In the circumstances, there appears to be only one way of obtaining each and every distribution.

However, it so happens that there may be more than a single classification which can be accorded a system. Indeed, in the sense which has been discussed in Chapter 6, several classifications are generally available to physical systems; collectively they define the states of the system. In such cases the number of ways of achieving a distribution in one of the physical properties will depend on the classification of the states of the system. To illustrate, let us imagine that the procedure employed in classifying each die in a collection according to its face will result in different forms of the same classification. Thus, we may imagine a two-face appearing (as the result of the apparatus used) in the forms ⊡ or ⊡ . Similarly for the three-face and the six-face. To specify the distribution in faces is not the fullest specification which can be made. Each of the two-, three-, and six-face groups may be further distributed among two other classifications. In the case of identical dice, only in possibly different subdistributions can there be any variation in the number of ways of achieving different over-all distributions.

To illustrate further, for the present case the number of ways in which a collection of M identical and indistinguishable dice may have the distribution $(m_1, \ldots, m_6)$ will be identical to the number of different ways that each of the m_2, m_3, and m_6 dice can be distributed among two different categories. This number is simply the product of the number of ways m_2 things can be divided into two parts, m_3 things can be divided into two parts, and m_6 things can be divided into two parts. Each of these numbers can be computed easily from the number of distinguishable permutations possible among $(m_2 + 1)$ things of which m_2 are identical and indistinguishable. Similarly for the m_3 and m_6 quantities. The final result is

$$\frac{(m_2 + 1)!}{m_2!} \cdot \frac{(m_3 + 1)!}{m_3!} \cdot \frac{(m_6 + 1)!}{m_6!}.$$

It is readily seen that for a distribution $(m_1, \ldots, m_f)$ of M identical systems in which $(p_1, \ldots, p_f)$ represent the number of distinct subclassifications for each category, the number of ways of achieving that distribution is

$$W_2 \begin{pmatrix} M \\ m_1, \ldots, m_f \end{pmatrix} = \prod_{i=1}^{f} \frac{(m_i + p_i - 1)!}{m_i!(p_i - 1)!}, \qquad (7.1.10)$$

with, of course, $\sum_{i=1}^{f} m_i = M$. When each $p_i = 1$, the quantity on the right reduces to unity, as noted previously.

We shall need one more way of counting. For reasons which can be made clear only in quantum-mechanical terms, and hence to be deferred for the present, there are distributions of indistinguishable systems in which no more than one system may be in each state. Such an extraordinary correlation between identical systems affects the number of ways by which a specified distribution may be achieved. In the instance of the dice, it is apparent that only distributions for which

$$m_1 \leq 1, \ m_2 \leq 2, \ m_3 \leq 2, \ m_4 \leq 1, \ m_5 \leq 1, \ m_6 \leq 2$$

are possible. Hence we may generalize to the distribution $(m_1, \ldots, m_f)$ for M identical and indistinguishable systems in which $(p_1, \ldots, p_f)$ represent the number of distinct subclassifications for each category and no more than one system per state (i.e., ultimate classification). This latter restriction necessitates $m_i \leq p_i$. The number of different ways in which the m_i systems can be distributed among the p_i states, no more than one each, is simply the number of ways a group of m_i things can be picked from p_i things, regardless of their order. In other words, the number of ways of obtaining the aforementioned correlated distribution is

$$W_3 \left(\begin{matrix} M \\ m_1, \ldots, m_f \end{matrix} \right) = \prod_{i=1}^{f} \frac{p_i!}{m_i!(p_i - m_i)!}, \qquad (7.1.11)$$

with $\sum_{i=1}^{f} m_i = M$. Again, with $p_i = 1$, it is evident that W_3 can only be unity if nonzero.

Since the numbers usually encountered in statistical mechanics are extremely large, it will be convenient to take note of *Stirling's approximation* for asymptotic $(x \rightarrow \infty)$ values:

$$\ln x! \sim x \ln x - x + \tfrac{1}{2} \ln x + \tfrac{1}{2} \ln (2\pi) + \frac{1}{12x} + \cdots, \qquad (7.1.12)$$

the remaining terms vanishing no less rapidly than c/x^2. We shall frequently retain only the first two terms of this series.

7.2 The most probable distribution. We consider a collection of N identical but distinguishable systems (i.e., molecules or the like) for which the total energy is constant. Furthermore, we restrict the collection to one for which the energy of interaction between systems can be neglected as compared with the energy of an isolated system. The energy of the individual systems will be any one of the values, which are ordered for convenience,

$$\epsilon_0 \leq \epsilon_1 \leq \epsilon_2 \leq \cdots \leq \epsilon_n \leq \epsilon_{n+1} \leq \cdots.$$

For each value of the energy ϵ_j there will be n_j systems. It is clear that the total energy

$$E = \sum_{j=0}^{\infty} n_j \epsilon_j \qquad (7.2.1)$$

and

$$N = \sum_{j=0}^{\infty} n_j, \qquad (7.2.2)$$

in accord with Eqs. (6.2.1) and (6.2.2).

The ϵ's may usually be expected to depend on various external mechanical parameters such as the volume of a container, magnitudes of electric and magnetic fields, etc. It is apparent that a solution of the mechanical problem is implicit in the ϵ's whereby any parametric dependence referred to will have been made explicit and their values will be known precisely.

We now turn to the problem of finding the most probable distribution consistent with Eqs. (7.2.1) and (7.2.2). From the results of the preceding section it is evident that we seek that distribution which can be achieved in the greatest number of different ways. By an obvious extension of Eq. (7.1.2) we desire that distribution for which

$$W_1 = \frac{N!}{\prod_{j=0}^{\infty} n_j!} \tag{7.2.3}$$

is a maximum. In mathematical terms it proves to be more convenient to examine $\ln W_1$ which, because the logarithm is a monotonic function of its argument, obviously will have a maximum value when W does. Accordingly, we have the mathematical statement of the problem at hand:

$$\delta \ln W_1 \leq 0,$$

subject to

$$\left. \begin{array}{c} \\ \delta E = 0 \quad \text{and} \quad \delta N = 0. \end{array} \right\} \tag{7.2.4}$$

[Compare with Eqs. (4.3.7) through (4.3.10), noting that all external parameters including the volume are assumed to be fixed in Eqs. (7.2.4).]

To evaluate $\delta \ln W_1$ we must appreciate that the n's are restricted to integral values. Then, assuming $\delta n \geq 0$,

$$\delta \ln n! = \ln (n + \delta n)! - \ln n!$$

$$= \delta n \left[\frac{\ln (n + \delta n)!/n!}{\delta n} \right]$$

$$= \delta n \left[\frac{\ln \prod_{m=1}^{\delta n} (n + m)}{\delta n} \right].$$

Since

$$(n + \delta n)^{\delta n} \geq \prod_{m=1}^{\delta n} (n + m) \geq n^{\delta n},$$

we evidently obtain

$$\delta n \ln (n + \delta n) \geq \delta \ln n! \geq \delta n \ln n, \qquad \delta n \geq 0. \tag{7.2.5}$$

A corresponding expression obtains for $\delta n \leq 0$.

Since we shall be particularly concerned with extremely large values of n (i.e., $n \gg \delta n$), we may express Eqs. (7.2.4) as

$$\sum_{j=0}^{\infty} \delta n_j \ln n_j = 0, \qquad \sum_{j=0}^{\infty} \delta n_j \epsilon_j = 0, \qquad \sum_{j=0}^{\infty} \delta n_j = 0, \tag{7.2.6}$$

where terms $0(\delta n_j^2/n_j)$ have been neglected. The solution of these equations yields the most probable distribution. However, particular note is to be taken of the omission of any condition corresponding to a restriction of the δn_j to integral values. Since the values of the n_j *relative* to N prove to be the quantities of ultimate interest, no appreciable error is involved for sufficiently large N if the restriction to integral values is disregarded. The results then obtained are asymptotic ($N \to \infty$) solutions of Eq. (7.2.6). Proceeding then with Lagrange's method of undetermined multipliers, we obtain

$$\sum_{j=0}^{\infty} \delta n_j \, (\ln n_j + \beta \epsilon_j + \alpha) = 0,$$

whereupon

$$\ln n_j^0 + \beta \epsilon_j + \alpha = 0, \qquad \text{all } j, \tag{7.2.7}$$

which determines the most probable distribution. Clearly

$$n_j^0 = e^{-\beta \epsilon_j - \alpha}, \tag{7.2.8}$$

which is the celebrated Maxwell-Boltzmann distribution formula. From Eqs. (7.2.1) and (7.2.2)

$$E = \sum_{j=0}^{\infty} \epsilon_j e^{-\beta \epsilon_j - \alpha} \tag{7.2.9}$$

and

$$N = \sum_{j=0}^{\infty} e^{-\beta \epsilon_j - \alpha}. \tag{7.2.10}$$

Hence, defining the *partition function* for the (microscopic) system,

$$Z(\beta) \equiv \sum_{j=0} e^{-\beta \epsilon_j}, \tag{7.2.11}$$

we obtain

$$\alpha = \ln \left[\frac{Z(\beta)}{N} \right] \tag{7.2.12}$$

and

$$\bar{\epsilon} \equiv \left(\frac{E}{N} \right) = - \frac{\partial \ln Z(\beta)}{\partial \beta}. \tag{7.2.13}$$

These two equations serve to fix α and β as functions of E and N. From Eqs. (7.2.11) and (7.2.13) it is evident that β is determined by $\bar{\epsilon}$ alone. In these terms the Maxwell-Boltzmann probability distribution is given by

$$\left(\frac{n_j^0}{N} \right) = \frac{e^{-\beta \epsilon_j}}{Z(\beta)}. \tag{7.2.14}$$

For subsequent purposes, we may note that

$$\sum_{j=0}^{\infty} n_j^0 \, (\ln n_j^0 + \beta\epsilon_j + \alpha) = 0,$$

or

$$\beta E = - \sum_{j=0}^{\infty} n_j^0 \, (\ln n_j^0 + \alpha). \tag{7.2.15}$$

Presuming that β is an *intensive* function of the n's, a matter to be justified subsequently, the left side of this equation may be restricted to be an extensive function of the n's. All other extensive properties are to be regarded as fixed while the n's are altered. Hence, the right side must be an extensive function of the n's. Therefore

$$\frac{\partial(\beta E)}{\partial n_j^0} = -(\ln n_j^0 + \alpha).$$

But

$$\alpha = \alpha(N) = \frac{\partial}{\partial n_j^0} \int_0^N dN \, \alpha(N)$$

and

$$\ln n_j^0 = \frac{\partial}{\partial n_j^0} \left[\sum_{k=0}^{\infty} n_k^0 \, (\ln n_k^0 - 1) \right].$$

Hence we obtain

$$\beta E + \int_0^N dN\alpha(N) = - \sum_{j=0}^{\infty} n_j^0 \, (\ln n_j^0 - 1), \tag{7.2.16}$$

the integration being performed under conditions for which all extensive parameters other than N remain fixed in addition to β. Clearly,

$$\int_0^N dN\alpha(N) = (\alpha + 1)N, \tag{7.2.17}$$

in agreement with Eq. (7.2.12).

Under conditions when all the n's are indefinitely large, Stirling's approximation, Eq. (7.1.12), may be used (retaining only the first two terms) and Eq. (7.2.16) becomes for fixed values of β and extensive parameters other than N,

$$\beta E + \int_0^N dN\alpha(N) = \ln\left(\frac{W_1^0}{N!}\right), \qquad N \to \infty. \tag{7.2.18}$$

7.3 Characterization of distribution parameters. To obtain some insight into the nature of the parameters α and β which have been obtained for the most probable distribution, we consider a more elaborate collection of systems than previously.

Consider two collections of systems, each distinct from the other; to emphasize the distinction, each collection will consist of systems having different sets of allowed values of the energy. The two collections will be supposed to exchange energy. The two collections also will be supposed to exchange systems; to permit such an exchange, the differences between the two kinds of systems must be of a relatively restricted sort. Only the values of the energy are transferred. In an entirely equivalent view, the systems are substantially the same, but are classified as different according to the two sets of energy values. In these circumstances, the *joint* distribution may be treated by a simple extension of the previously considered case.

By defining

$$
\left.
\begin{aligned}
N &\equiv N_a + N_b = \sum_{j=0}^{\infty} n_j + \sum_{j=0}^{\infty} m_j, \\[2mm]
E &\equiv E_a + E_b = \sum_{j=0}^{\infty} n_j \epsilon_j + \sum_{j=0}^{\infty} m_j \eta_j, \\[2mm]
W_{ab} &= \frac{(N_a + N_b)!}{\prod_{j=0}^{\infty} n_j! \, \prod_{j=0}^{\infty} m_j!}
\end{aligned}
\right\}
\qquad (7.3.1)
$$

and

we evidently have to determine the joint distribution which satisfies the equations

$$
\delta \ln W_{ab} \leq 0, \qquad \delta E_a + \delta E_b = 0, \qquad \delta N_a + \delta N_b = 0, \qquad (7.3.2)
$$

which are formally identical with Eqs. (7.2.4). Substitution of Eqs. (7.3.1) into Eqs. (7.3.2) with the aid of Eq. (7.2.5) yields with Lagrange's method (We note again the lack of restriction of n and m to integral values.)

$$
\sum_{j=0}^{\infty} \delta n_j \left(\ln n_j + \beta \epsilon_j + \alpha \right) + \sum_{j=0}^{\infty} \delta m_j \left(\ln m_j + \beta \eta_j + \alpha \right) = 0
$$

or

$$
\ln n_j^0 + \beta \epsilon_j + \alpha = 0, \qquad \ln m_j^0 + \beta \eta_j + \alpha = 0. \qquad (7.3.3)
$$

As previously, the joint Maxwell-Boltzmann distribution is given by

$$
n_j^0 = e^{-\beta \epsilon_j - \alpha}, \qquad m_j^0 = e^{-\beta \eta_j - \alpha},
$$

and

$$\alpha = \ln \frac{Z_a(\beta)}{N_a} = \ln \frac{Z_b(\beta)}{N_b} = \ln \left[\frac{Z_a(\beta) + Z_b(\beta)}{N} \right], \qquad (7.3.4)$$

where

$$Z_a \equiv \sum_{j=0}^{\infty} e^{-\beta \epsilon_j}, \qquad Z_b \equiv \sum_{j=0}^{\infty} e^{-\beta \eta_j}.$$

Here α and β do not necessarily have the same values as the corresponding parameters obtained previously. We note here that a single system may be thought of as having a total partition function

$$Z = Z_a + Z_b. \qquad (7.3.5)$$

The most important consequence of Eqs. (7.3.3) is that α and β *are the same for both collections*. An alternate collection in which the exchange of systems, but not the exchange of energy, is prevented will give the same value of β, but not of α, for both collections. Hence, we may conclude that collections which are able to exchange energy but are *otherwise arbitrary* have most probable distributions with the same value of β. If the collections admit also of an exchange of systems so that the energy values of a system in one collection may be transferred to a system of the other, and vice versa, the two collections have also most probable distributions with the same value of α.

Now, thermodynamic systems of the most diverse sort in equilibrium, which can exchange energy, must have the same temperature value. We can anticipate that β will be related to temperature. Thermodynamic systems which also are in equilibrium with respect to the transfer of matter must have the same value of the chemical potential. Again, we may anticipate that α is related to this quantity. (See Section 4.3 for the thermodynamic parallel.)

In this connection, Eq. (7.3.4) gives immediately the relationship

$$\frac{N_a}{N_b} = \frac{Z_a(\beta)}{Z_b(\beta)},$$

providing an equilibrium restriction of the sort just considered is placed on the composition of collections. We may anticipate that the present model corresponds to a *chemical equilibrium* between two interconvertible chemical species, rather than to a heterogeneous equilibrium. Because of the restriction that interactions between systems are negligible, the latter model would appear to be excluded.

We turn now to the most important task of establishing the significance of α and β. Following Gibbs, we consider a collection of a large and variable number of systems, and permit the various allowed energies of each system to change due to changes in external (i.e., collection) parameters. Then, for simplicity, we define,

$$M \equiv N \ln\left[\frac{eZ(\beta)}{N}\right] + \phi(N), \qquad (7.3.6)$$

where $\phi(N)$ is an arbitrary differentiable function of N alone, to be considered later. Then, assuming that x_k denotes one of a set of extensive parameters affecting the energy values of each system,

$$dM = N \frac{\partial \ln Z(\beta)}{\partial \beta} d\beta + N \sum_k dx_k \frac{\partial \ln Z(\beta)}{\partial x_k} + \left\{\ln\left[\frac{Z(\beta)}{N}\right] + \phi'\right\} dN$$

$$= -E \, d\beta - \beta N \sum_k dx_k \left\{\frac{\sum_{j=0}^{\infty} (\partial \epsilon_j/\partial x_k) e^{-\beta \epsilon_j}}{\sum_{j=0}^{\infty} e^{-\beta \epsilon_j}}\right\} + \left\{\ln\left[\frac{Z(\beta)}{N}\right] + \phi'\right\} dN.$$

Now, the quantities

$$\frac{\sum_{j=0}^{\infty} (\partial \epsilon_j/\partial x_k) e^{-\beta \epsilon_j}}{\sum_{j=0}^{\infty} e^{-\beta \epsilon_j}}$$

represent changes in the energy due to changes in the parameter x_k, averaged over the distribution. These quantities represent the average force associated with the displacement dx_k. The sum over the differential displacements evidently is the differential work done upon the collection, $-dW$. Hence, one obtains

$$d(M + \beta E) = \beta \left\{dE + dW + \frac{1}{\beta}\left[\ln\left(\frac{Z(\beta)}{N}\right) + \phi'\right]dN\right\}. \qquad (7.3.7)$$

For a collection of a fixed number of systems (i.e., $dN = 0$),

$$dE + dW = dQ,$$

by the first and second laws of thermodynamics. Hence, we have the result that β is an integrating factor for the differential heat. We have seen already (Section 2.3) that the reciprocal of the absolute temperature is such an integrating factor. We may, therefore, set

$$\beta = \frac{1}{kT} \qquad (7.3.8)$$

and the differential of the entropy,

$$dS = k \, d(M + \beta E), \qquad (7.3.9)$$

where k is Boltzmann's constant, the value of which must be determined by experiment. It is evident that Eqs. (7.3.8) and (7.3.9) are *suggested* by the form of Eq. (7.3.7) and are *not proved*. The *identifications* made can be justified only in the light of subsequent developments.

Rewriting Eq. (7.3.7) with the previous identifications, we have

$$T \, dS = dE + dW + kT \left\{ \ln\left[\frac{Z(\beta)}{N}\right] + \phi'(N) \right\} dN.$$

When this is compared with Eqs. (4.3.2) and (4.3.3), it is evident that

$$-kT \left\{ \phi'(N) + \ln\left[\frac{Z(\beta)}{N}\right] \right\} = \left(\frac{\partial E}{\partial N}\right)_{S, \, \text{all} \, x_k} \tag{7.3.10}$$

is the chemical potential *per system*. From Eq. (7.2.12) it is apparent that

$$\alpha = -\phi'(N) - \frac{1}{kT}\left(\frac{\partial E}{\partial N}\right)_{S, \, \text{all} \, x_k}. \tag{7.3.11}$$

Furthermore, from Eq. (7.3.9) we may take

$$M = \frac{S}{k} - \frac{E}{kT} = -\frac{F}{kT}, \tag{7.3.12}$$

where F is the Helmholtz free energy function of the collection. Clearly

$$\left(\frac{\partial F}{\partial N}\right)_{T, \, \text{all} \, x_k} = -kT \left\{ \phi'(N) + \ln\left[\frac{Z(\beta)}{N}\right] \right\},$$

so that

$$\alpha = -\phi'(N) - \frac{1}{kT}\left(\frac{\partial F}{\partial N}\right)_{T, \, \text{all} \, x_k}. \tag{7.3.13}$$

From a thermodynamic aspect, the relation between α and the chemical potential is only incompletely established at this point. Alternatively, we may state that the statistical *analog* of the chemical potential per system is

$$\mu = -kT[\alpha + \phi'(N)], \tag{7.3.14}$$

where $\phi'(N)$ is an arbitrary function of N. Nevertheless, the properties of the chemical potential require it to be an intensive function; if α is such, $\phi'(N)$ can only be a constant.

A more important requirement of this restriction, according to Eq. (7.2.12), is that the partition function for the microscopic system *must* be an extensive property. This will require the allowed values of the energy of a system in the collection to depend in some manner on the size of the collection. This matter will be considered in Section 7.5; for the present we turn to an examination of the statistical role played by the indistinguishability of identical systems.

7.4 Indistinguishability. We noted in Section 7.1 the number of ways by which a specified distribution in some particular property is affected when the systems are indistinguishable. In fact, it is necessary to examine other properties of the systems in such instances to arrive at any result which will differ from unity. In the present instance, we wish to examine a distribution in energy for a collection of identical, indistinguishable systems. For reasons which are deeply rooted in the quantum-mechanical aspects of indistinguishability of identical systems, the procedure of counting the number of subdistributions which we have designated as W_2 in Eq. (7.1.10) will be referred to as *Bose-Einstein* statistics. Here it will be noted that the subclassifications correspond to groups of states all of which have the same value of the energy of the system. We shall occasionally refer to each such group as *degenerate in energy*, and their number as the *degeneracy* or *multiplicity* of the energy value. The essential physical feature involved in the Bose-Einstein statistics is that there are no restrictions as to the numbers of indistinguishable systems which may have the same identical subclassification (i.e., state). Then, following the procedure in Section 7.2, we have

$$\delta \ln W_2 = \sum_{i=0}^{\infty} \delta n_i \left[\ln \left(\frac{n_i + p_i - 1}{n_i} \right) \right] = 0,$$

$$\delta E = \sum_{i=0}^{\infty} \delta n_i \epsilon_i = 0, \qquad \delta N = \sum_{i=0}^{\infty} \delta n_i = 0.$$

Carrying out Lagrange's method, we obtain (α and β here are possibly different parameters than have been introduced previously) for arbitrary δn_i

$$\ln \left(\frac{n_i^0 + p_i - 1}{n_i^0} \right) + \beta \epsilon_i + \alpha = 0. \tag{7.4.1}$$

Hence, assuming $p_i \gg 1$ for simplicity,

$$n_i^0 = \frac{p_i}{e^{\beta \epsilon_i + \alpha} - 1}, \tag{7.4.2}$$

which is the Bose-Einstein distribution formula.

Before examining Eq. (7.4.2) we shall consider another important way in which the statistics is affected by distinguishability. In the so-called *Fermi-Dirac* statistics the number of systems in each subclassification may not exceed unity. The reasons, as mentioned, will be discussed later in quantum-mechanical terms. The number of ways of obtaining a specified distribution in energy of the system is given by W_3 in Eq. (7.1.11).

Then, following the previous procedure for the Bose-Einstein statistics, we have

$$\delta \ln W_3 = \sum_{i=0}^{\infty} \delta n_i \left[\ln \left(\frac{n_i}{p_i - n_i} \right) \right] = 0,$$

$$\delta E = \sum_{i=0}^{\infty} \delta n_i \epsilon_i = 0, \qquad \delta N = \sum_{i=0}^{\infty} \delta n_i = 0.$$

Hence, it may be shown for arbitrary δn_i that

$$\ln \left(\frac{n_i^0}{p_i - n_i^0} \right) + \beta \epsilon_i + \alpha = 0, \tag{7.4.3}$$

whereupon,

$$n_i^0 = \frac{p_i}{e^{\beta \epsilon_i + \alpha} + 1}, \tag{7.4.4}$$

which is the Fermi-Dirac distribution formula. The similarity to the Bose-Einstein distribution formula permits a parallel treatment of the two cases.

It can be shown that relations analogous to Eq. (7.2.18) obtain. Since

$$\ln W_2 \cong \sum_{i=0}^{\infty} \left[(n_i + p_i) \ln (n_i + p_i) - n_i \ln n_i - p_i \ln p_i \right]$$

$$= \sum_{i=0}^{\infty} \left[n_i \ln \left(1 + \frac{p_i}{n_i} \right) + p_i \ln \left(1 + \frac{n_i}{p_i} \right) \right],$$

one obtains with the aid of Eq. (7.4.2)

$$\ln W_2^0 \cong \beta E + N\alpha - \sum_{i=0}^{\infty} p_i \ln (1 - e^{-\beta \epsilon_i - \alpha}). \tag{7.4.5}$$

Similarly it can be shown that

$$\ln W_3^0 \cong \beta E + N\alpha + \sum_{i=0}^{\infty} p_i \ln (1 + e^{-\beta \epsilon_i - \alpha}). \tag{7.4.6}$$

Note, now, that for both cases (β, as well as each ϵ, is kept constant in the integration)

$$\int_{\infty}^{\alpha} N(\alpha) \, d\alpha = \int_{\infty}^{\alpha} d\alpha \sum_{i=0}^{\infty} \frac{p_i}{e^{\beta \epsilon_i + \alpha} \pm 1} = \sum_{i=0}^{\infty} p_i \int_{\infty}^{\alpha} \frac{e^{-\beta \epsilon_i - \alpha}}{1 \pm e^{-\beta \epsilon_i - \alpha}} \, d\alpha$$

$$= \mp \sum_{i=0}^{\infty} p_i \ln (1 \pm e^{-\beta \epsilon_i - \alpha}).$$

Since

$$\int_\infty^\alpha N(\alpha)\, d\alpha = N\alpha - \int_0^N \alpha(N)\, dN,$$

one obtains the formal equation [using Eq. (7.2.18)] for $N \to \infty$,

$$\beta E + \int_0^N \alpha(N)\, dN = \begin{cases} \ln\left(\dfrac{W_1^0}{N!}\right), & \text{Maxwell-Boltzmann statistics,} \\[2mm] \ln W_2^0, & \text{Bose-Einstein statistics,} \\[2mm] \ln W_3^0, & \text{Fermi-Dirac statistics,} \end{cases}$$

$$= \frac{S}{k} - \phi(N), \qquad (7.4.7)$$

indicating that α and β assume the same role, regardless of the specific statistics. The entropy, however, is calculated differently and depends on the statistics.

We may stress here the presence of $\phi(N)$, which is arbitrary at this point. However, we shall see in Section 7.5 that $\phi(N)$ must be an extensive function of N. Therefore the entropy per particle is determined from Eq. (7.4.7) to within an arbitrary additive constant. When it can be shown that the left side of Eq. (7.4.7) vanishes for $\beta \to \infty$, the constant term must correspond to the entropy per particle at the absolute zero of temperature. Then statistical mechanics only determines the entropy as measured from the value at absolute zero. As a result, the $\phi(N)$ may be suppressed in Eq. (7.4.7) with the understanding that the entropy then vanishes at the absolute zero of temperature. (Compare with Section 2.6.)

The relation between the statistics is made especially clear when $\alpha \gg 1$. Then for both Bose-Einstein and Fermi-Dirac statistics we obtain,

$$n_i^0 \cong p_j e^{-\beta \epsilon_j - \alpha}, \qquad \alpha \gg 1, \qquad (7.4.8)$$

which, clearly, differs from the Maxwell-Boltzmann distribution formula, Eq. (7.2.8), only by the presence of the p's. However, such a difference is purely a formal one since the index in the Boltzmann case corresponds to *states* while that of the Bose-Einstein or Fermi-Dirac statistics corresponds to values of the energy for which there are p degenerate states. Thus, from Eqs. (7.2.11) and (7.2.12) we may expect identity of all three statistics for $\beta \to 0$, all other parameters fixed.

7.5 Properties of statistical-thermodynamic functions. The thermodynamic utility of statistical mechanics is emphasized in the opportunity
provided for calculating values of the thermodynamic functions in absolute
terms. While this has been indicated already, we wish to examine this
aspect of statistical thermodynamics more closely.

The thermodynamic functions of particular interest are the free energy
functions. A full knowledge of either the Helmholtz or the Gibbs function permits a determination to be made of the others. In the present
connection, the Helmholtz function may be determined from Eq. (7.4.7) as

$$F = E - TS = -kT \int_0^N dN\alpha(N), \qquad N \to \infty, \qquad (7.5.1)$$

regardless of the kind of statistics. Clearly the thermodynamic properties
of F require it to be extensive, but not in the sense we have been considering. In the present context all *extensive* parameters and the temperature were regarded as fixed and N was imagined as altered. In the
thermodynamic sense, all *intensive* variables are regarded as fixed while N
is altered. It seems evident that $\alpha(N)$ must be intensive in the latter sense
while not necessarily so in the former.

For very large temperatures ($\beta \to 0$), all three forms of statistics are
identical, and Eq. (7.2.12) gives us the value of α. From this expression
we see that when the extensive parameters of the collection are kept
fixed, $Z(\beta)$ will be fixed. Hence, as $N \to \infty$, α becomes unbounded.
Clearly α is not an intensive function in these circumstances. However,
from the thermodynamic aspect it must be. Thus, we must anticipate
that $Z(\beta)$ will be a homogeneous function of the extensive parameters of
the collection (excluding N), of the first order. For lower temperatures
($\beta \neq 0$), the differences in the three kinds of statistics must be kept in
mind. From Eqs. (7.4.2) and (7.4.4) we see that

$$N = \sum_{i=0}^{\infty} \frac{p_i}{e^{\beta\epsilon_i + \alpha} \pm 1}.$$

From a formal aspect we assume ($\beta\epsilon_0 + \alpha$) > 0, in which case we obtain

$$N = \sum_{i=0}^{\infty} p_i e^{-\beta\epsilon_i - \alpha} \sum_{n=0}^{\infty} (\mp e^{-\beta\epsilon_i - \alpha})^n$$

$$= \sum_{n=0}^{\infty} (\mp)^n e^{-(n+1)\alpha} \sum_{i=0}^{\infty} e^{-(n+1)\beta\epsilon_i}$$

$$= \sum_{n=0}^{\infty} (\mp)^n e^{-(n+1)\alpha} Z[(n+1)\beta]. \qquad (7.5.2)$$

As a result,

$$1 = \sum_{n=0}^{\infty} (\mp)^n e^{-(n+1)\alpha} \left\{ \frac{Z[(n+1)\beta]}{N} \right\},$$

so that if $Z(\beta)/N$ [and hence $Z\{(n+1)\beta\}/N$] is intensive in the thermodynamic sense, as discussed just previously, α evidently will be such an intensive function. Thus, for the free energy function of Helmholtz to be an extensive function in the thermodynamic sense, it appears sufficient that the partition function be an extensive function. This result applies to the three kinds of statistics which have been described.

That such is, in fact, the case for the systems which may be treated by the method of the most probable distribution is associated with the nature of the energy values of the systems. The energy of a system which we have been considering may be regarded at the outset as consisting of two separate kinds: that related to the motion of the center of mass of each system and that related to the motion of the parts of the system relative to its center of mass. For simplicity of terminology, the first kind will be referred to as *translational energy*, corresponding to the motion of each system throughout the region of space which confines the collection. The second kind will be referred to as *internal energy*. This separation may be shown to be exact. It may be supposed that the internal energy does not depend on the extent of the collection. (No confusion with the *internal energy function* of thermodynamics should result in spite of the similarity in terminology.) In mathematical terms, a value of the energy of a system

$$\epsilon_{ij} = \epsilon_i \text{ (translation)} + \epsilon_j \text{ (internal)}, \tag{7.5.3}$$

where, of course, the ϵ's are quite different in their dependence on the subscript. With this separation, it is evident that the partition function is expressible as

$$Z(\beta) = \sum_{\substack{i=0 \\ j=0}}^{\infty} e^{-\beta\epsilon_{ij}} = \sum_{i=0}^{\infty} e^{-\beta\epsilon_i(\text{trans})} \cdot \sum_{j=0}^{\infty} e^{-\beta\epsilon_j(\text{int})}$$

$$= Z_{\text{trans}}(\beta) \cdot Z_{\text{int}}(\beta). \tag{7.5.4}$$

In these terms Eq. (7.2.12) becomes for the Maxwell-Boltzmann statistics

$$\alpha = \ln \frac{Z_{\text{trans}}(\beta)}{N} + \ln Z_{\text{int}}(\beta).$$

From the nature of the internal energy values, $Z_{\text{int}}(\beta)$ may be supposed to be independent of the extent of the collection. Thus, the translational partition function assumes the burden of providing the extensive characteristics called for.

It is well worth noting that any further separation of the internal energy into terms which may be attributed to independent modes of motion of the parts of the system will give rise to a further factorization of the partition function. But each of these factors will make only an intensive contribution to α.

What can be said of those collections for which $Z_{\text{trans}}(\beta)$ ostensibly is not an extensive function? Such a partition function might be expected if the values of the translational energy for each system are independent of the extension of the collection. Systems with this sort of independence will be referred to as *localized*. It is a moot point as to whether or not a system can be localized in a complete sense; for sufficiently large translational energies it would appear to be unlikely that the systems should be restricted in their motion in any way other than that provided by the confines of the collection. This point will be taken up presently. As a concept, however, localization can be useful as a means for approximating the behavior of real (macroscopic) physical systems. The thermodynamic transcription which has been effected in Section 7.3 must be modified for localized systems. This is apparent because the changes in the energy values brought about by changes in the values of the extensive parameters of the collection have not been defined. To examine this question we must specify a relation between the extensive parameters of the collection and those of the separate systems.

For simplicity, we consider the behavior of a set of N localized systems for which the extensive parameters of interest are the sum of the values for the separate systems. Such a situation obtains for the volume of a collection of identical localized systems. Then

$$x_k = N\bar{x}_k, \quad \text{all } k,$$

where $\bar{x}_k$ is the value of the extensive parameter for one system. Inasmuch as ϵ_j depends on the $\bar{x}$ quantities,

$$\frac{\partial \epsilon_j}{\partial x_k} = \frac{1}{N}\left(\frac{\partial \epsilon_j}{\partial \bar{x}_k}\right)$$

while

$$\left(\frac{\partial \epsilon_j}{\partial N}\right)_{\text{all } x_k} = \sum_k \left[-\frac{\bar{x}_k}{N}\left(\frac{\partial \epsilon_j}{\partial \bar{x}_k}\right)\right].$$

Hence,

$$\left(\frac{\partial Z(\beta)}{\partial N}\right)_{\text{all } x_k} = -\sum_k \left[\frac{\beta \bar{x}_k}{N} \sum_{j=0}^{\infty} \left(\frac{\partial \epsilon_j}{\partial \bar{x}_k}\right) e^{-\beta \epsilon_j}\right].$$

As a result, we can verify that Eq. (7.3.7) will be modified to

$$d(M + \beta E) = \beta \left\{ dE + dW + \left\{ \sum_k X_k \bar{x}_k + \frac{1}{\beta}\left[\ln \frac{Z(\beta)}{N} + \phi'(N)\right]\right\} dN\right\},$$

$$(7.5.5)$$

where

$$X_k \equiv - \frac{\sum_{j=0}^{\infty} (\partial \epsilon_j / \partial \bar{x}_k) e^{-\beta \epsilon_j}}{Z(\beta)}.$$

In the present instance the chemical potential per system is evidently

$$-kT \left\{ \ln\left[\frac{Z(\beta)}{N} \right] + \phi'(N) \right\} - \sum_k X_k \bar{x}_k = \left(\frac{\partial E}{\partial N} \right)_{S,\, \text{all } x_k}. \qquad (7.5.6)$$

Apart from the appearance of the term $(-\sum_k X_k \bar{x}_k)$, this expression is not substantially different from Eq. (7.3.7). (Note that zero values for the X_k are not precluded, and for the localized systems we shall consider explicitly such will be the case.)

To assure the intensive character of the chemical potential requires, in view of the foregoing analysis, something more drastic. Now, while we have made mention of an inherent inability to completely localize a collection of (microscopic) systems, we have not exploited this inadequacy. Indeed, we must consider that this very possibility makes it necessary to regard each system as ultimately capable of assuming the properties associated with each *locale*. It will simplify matters if each locale is such as to impart to each system a set of energy values which is different from those of any other locale. Indeed, we may then justifiably regard each different set of energy values as characterizing the locale (for a single kind of system). But now we observe that the entire set of values of the energy of a single system is considerably greater than that to be ascribed to a single locale. As a consequence, the partition function which we have been considering must be constructed in such a way as to include this enlarged set of energy values.

Since the energy values for a single system now include every set from each locale, we may express

$$\epsilon_i = \epsilon_i^{(m)}, \qquad (7.5.7)$$

where the superscript refers to the mth locale. Hence the partition function becomes, for N different locales,

$$Z(\beta) = \sum_{m=1}^{N} \sum_{i=0}^{\infty} e^{-\beta \epsilon_i^{(m)}} = \sum_{m=1}^{N} Z_m(\beta), \qquad (7.5.8)$$

where $Z_m(\beta)$ is the partition function for the system in the mth locale. Clearly Eq. (7.5.8) is simply an extension of Eq. (7.3.5). When the *locales are identical*, we have, evidently,

$$Z(\beta) = N Z_1(\beta). \qquad (7.5.9)$$

The extension to the corresponding quantities in the Bose-Einstein and

Fermi-Dirac statistics is apparent. By our previous considerations, $Z_1(\beta)$ may be regarded as independent of the extensive properties of the collection. As a result, the partition function for a collection of localized systems also is extensive. Hence we may now generally take $\phi'(N)$ to be a constant (which we disregard) in Eq. (7.5.6). Accordingly, we may write for the chemical potential for localized systems

$$\mu = -kT\alpha - \sum_k X_k \bar{x}_k, \qquad (7.5.10)$$

the sum being omitted for nonlocalized systems. In either case, α is generally determined by Eqs. (7.2.12) or (7.5.2).

We now are in a position to determine several statistical-thermodynamic functions for simple collections of systems.

7.6 Summary. The method of the *most probable distribution* has been discussed in the present chapter.

Collections of systems which have a negligible mutual interaction are classified in terms of the values of the energy possessed by their systems. The number of ways in which a specified distribution in energy may be achieved depends on whether the systems are *distinguishable*. In any case, the mathematics involves a combinatorial procedure to evaluate the degeneracy of the distribution. The case of distinguishable systems leads to Maxwell-Boltzmann statistics; two cases of indistinguishable systems are considered: one leads to Bose-Einstein statistics, the other to Fermi-Dirac statistics.

The mathematical formulation of the equilibrium problem in statistical mechanics is in terms of variational equations. The similarity of the statistical equations to the thermodynamic conditions for equilibrium is a marked one. The distribution which, for fixed values of the energy of the collection and the number of systems, has the greatest number of ways of being achieved is determined with Lagrange's method of undetermined multipliers. In each of the three statistics considered, the most probable distribution depends on two parameters. Intuitively, it is shown that one of these plays a role akin to temperature while the other is related to the chemical potential. A general treatment along the lines employed by Gibbs enables a comparison to be made with the first and second laws of thermodynamics. A formal similarity of each of the three statistics permits the various parameters to be related to one another. One of the two parameters is *identified* as proportional to the reciprocal of the absolute temperature. The other distribution parameter is related to the chemical potential in a linear fashion; it is, however, subject to some arbitrariness. This arbitrariness is resolvable through the condition that the chemical potential be an intensive function of the number of systems of the collection in the ordinary thermodynamical sense. For conditions identified as asymptotic in the temperature ($T \to \infty$), all three statistics merge to the same result. This corresponds also to indefinitely large, negative values of the chemical potential.

The identification of various thermodynamic functions is achieved. In an asymptotic sense ($N \to \infty$), the entropy functions for the various statistics are simply related to the degeneracy of the most probable distribution. The requirement that the Helmholtz free energy function be an extensive function requires no separate means for computing the chemical potential for localized, or other, systems. Rather, the partition function is shown to be extensive for localizable systems, so that in both instances the chemical potential proves to be an intensive function in the extent of the collection.

EXERCISES

1. Supply the details to show that Eq. (7.1.2) does not obtain with indistinguishable objects.

2. Establish the expression analogous to Eq. (7.2.5) for $\delta n \leq 0$.

3. Show that the quadratic terms omitted from Eq. (7.2.6) yield the condition that W_1 is a maximum.

4. Show that Eq. (7.2.17) leads to Eq. (7.2.12) insofar as the dependence on N is concerned.

5. Carry through the analysis in the beginning of Section 7.3, which leads to Eqs. (7.3.3) with the condition only that the two collections may exchange energy.

6. Supply the details leading to Eq. (7.4.2) for the Bose-Einstein distribution.

7. Supply the details leading to Eq. (7.4.4) for the Fermi-Dirac distribution.

8. Establish Eq. (7.4.6).

9. Carry through the analysis of Section 7.3 to identify the distribution parameters for the Bose-Einstein and Fermi-Dirac statistics. Hence justify the entropy identification made in Eq. (7.4.7).

10. Show that the different modes of motion of a system which give rise to separable energies make an additive contribution to the extensive thermodynamic functions.

11. Construct a "collection" partition function Q to satisfy an expression analogous to Eq. (7.2.13), namely,

$$E = -\frac{\partial \ln Q}{\partial \beta}.$$

Hence construct the "collection" partition function of a collection of collections of diverse systems open only to exchange of energy.

12. Determine the value of the entropy contribution made by the internal motion of a system at the absolute zero of temperature.

13. Obtain a general expression for the heat capacity of a collection.

14. The *fluctuation* in a quantity is defined as the average of the square less the square of the average. Determine the fluctuation in the energy of a collection. Relate this quantity to the heat capacity.

15. Determine the energy, entropy, and heat capacity for a collection of localized systems each of which has only two values of the energy, $\pm\epsilon$; use Maxwell-Boltzmann statistics.

16. Carry through the analysis for a determination of the entropy of the collection described by Eqs. (7.3.3) and (7.3.4).

17. Determine the joint equilibrium distribution for the collection of two kinds of systems such that $N' = N_a + 2N_b$ is fixed during an otherwise arbitrary exchange of systems. [See Eqs. (7.3.1) and (7.3.2).]

18. Determine the equilibrium composition of the collection of Exercise 17.

19. Determine the *average* probability that a system has a specified energy value. Why is the value not identically unity? Determine, as well, the fluctuation in this probability.

20. Show that $[Z(\beta)]^2 \geq Z(2\beta)$.

21. Show that $Z(\beta)Z(3\beta) \geq [Z(2\beta)]^2$.

22. Justify the disregard of a constant ϕ' in Eq. (7.5.6).

23. Derive the expressions analogous to Eq. (7.5.9) for the Bose-Einstein and Fermi-Dirac statistics.

24. Show that the left side of Eq. (7.4.7) vanishes as $\beta \rightarrow \infty$ when Eq. (7.5.9) is satisfied.

25. Show that the left side of Eq. (7.4.7) does not vanish as $\beta \rightarrow \infty$ if the partition function given by Eq. (7.2.11) is independent of N.

CHAPTER 8

STATISTICAL-THERMODYNAMIC FUNCTIONS FOR SIMPLE SYSTEMS

8.1 The ideal gas: Maxwell-Boltzmann statistics. The ideal gas assumes an important role in many discussions of the equilibria of chemical systems. Some indication of that role already has been given in connection with our previous thermodynamic considerations. It is taken up here to indicate how connections of the microscopic properties with the macroscopic properties are ultimately made.

To begin, we shall obtain an expression for the Gibbs free energy function for a collection of structureless particles, of negligible interaction, enclosed in a rectangular parallelepiped of uniform potential energy. From quantum mechanics, as we shall see later, the energy values of a particle in the box which has been indicated are restricted to

$$\epsilon_{ijl} = \frac{h^2}{8m}\left(\frac{i^2}{a^2} + \frac{j^2}{b^2} + \frac{l^2}{c^2}\right), \tag{8.1.1}$$

where h is Planck's constant; m is the mass of the particle; i, j, and l are nonzero positive integers; and a, b, and c are the lengths of the rectangular parallelepiped. Equation (8.1.1) represents what has been referred to previously as the translational energy of a more complex system; we are examining, of course, the translational partition function and allied quantities.

We consider first the partition function. We have

$$Z_{\text{trans}} = \sum_{i=1}^{\infty} \sum_{j=1}^{\infty} \sum_{l=1}^{\infty} \exp\left[-\frac{h^2}{8mkT}\left(\frac{i^2}{a^2} + \frac{j^2}{b^2} + \frac{l^2}{c^2}\right)\right], \tag{8.1.2}$$

which evidently may be written as

$$Z_{\text{trans}} = Z_a Z_b Z_c,$$

with

$$Z_a \equiv \sum_{i=1}^{\infty} \exp\left[-\frac{h^2}{8mkT}\left(\frac{i^2}{a^2}\right)\right], \tag{8.1.3}$$

the partition function for the motion in the a-direction; the remaining Z's are defined analogously. Clearly we need consider only one of the latter

119

in any detail. For that purpose we note that the series with which we must contend is very simply related to one of the *elliptic theta functions*,

$$\theta_3(0, q) = \sum_{n=-\infty}^{+\infty} q^{n^2}, \qquad q < 1. \qquad (8.1.4)$$

In these terms

$$Z_a = \frac{\theta_3(0, q_a) - 1}{2},$$

with

$$q_a \equiv \exp\left(- \frac{h^2}{8ma^2kT}\right).$$

The advantages derivable from the introduction of the theta function lie in its *inversion* properties. Thus, in particular, if $q = e^{-\sigma_a}$,

$$\theta_3(0, e^{-1/\sigma_a}) = \left(\frac{\sigma_a}{\pi}\right)^{1/2} \theta_3(0, e^{-\sigma_a}), \qquad (8.1.5)$$

which permits the partition function to be represented as a rapidly convergent series whenever $\sigma \ll 1$ or $\sigma \gg 1$. The case of usual interest is one for which

$$\sigma_a \equiv \frac{h^2}{8ma^2kT} \ll 1,$$

and warrants the partition function being expressed as

$$Z_a = \left(\frac{2\pi mkT}{h^2}\right)^{1/2} a \sum_{n=-\infty}^{+\infty} \exp\left(- \frac{8mkTa^2}{h^2} n^2\right) - \frac{1}{2}. \qquad (8.1.6)$$

The last series converges rapidly when that of Eq. (8.1.3) is slow to converge, and vice versa. Since we shall ultimately be interested in asymptotic values of Z (that is, $a, b, c \to \infty$), the constant term may be disregarded. Then to a good approximation,

$$Z_{\text{trans}} = \left(\frac{2\pi mkT}{h^2}\right)^{3/2} abc$$

$$\times \sum_{i=-\infty}^{+\infty} \sum_{j=-\infty}^{+\infty} \sum_{l=-\infty}^{+\infty} \exp\left[- \left(\frac{8mkT}{h^2}\right)(a^2i^2 + b^2j^2 + c^2l^2)\right], \qquad (8.1.7)$$

which is to be compared with Eq. (8.1.2).

From Eqs. (7.2.12) and (7.5.1) we obtain for the ideal gas the Helmholtz function

$$- \frac{F}{kT} = N \ln\left[\frac{e\,(2\pi mkT/h^2)^{3/2}V}{N}\right] + N \ln\,(\Sigma),$$

where V has been written for abc and $\sum$ has been used for the triple sum in Eq. (8.1.7). Under the conditions that V and N increase indefinitely but in a constant ratio, the last term vanishes and

$$F = -NkT \ln\left(\frac{V}{N}\right) - \frac{3}{2} NkT \ln T - \frac{3}{2} NkT \ln\left(\frac{2\pi mke^{2/3}}{h^2}\right). \quad (8.1.8)$$

From Eqs. (2.5.2), we obtain for the ideal gas

$$S = Nk \ln\left(\frac{V}{N}\right) + \frac{3}{2} Nk \ln T + \frac{3}{2} Nk \ln\left(\frac{2\pi mke^{5/3}}{h^2}\right), \quad (8.1.9)$$

$$P = \frac{NkT}{V}, \quad (8.1.10)$$

$$E = F + TS = \tfrac{3}{2}NkT. \quad (8.1.11)$$

Finally, the Gibbs free energy function

$$G = NkT \ln P - \tfrac{5}{2}NkT \ln T - \tfrac{3}{2}NkT \ln\left(\frac{2\pi mk^{5/3}e^{5/3}}{h^2}\right), \quad (8.1.12)$$

and the chemical potential per system

$$\mu = \left(\frac{\partial G}{\partial N}\right)_{T,P} = \frac{G}{N},$$

as expected for a pure substance.

From Eq. (8.1.12) we have a value for the entropy constant discussed in Section 3.1. It is

$$S_0 = \frac{3Nk}{2} \ln\left(\frac{2\pi mk^{5/3}e^{5/3}}{h^2}\right), \quad (8.1.13)$$

a result first obtained by Sackur and Tetrode. The last six equations may be compared with the results of Chapter 3. Note that the equation of state, Eq. (8.1.10), enables us to evaluate the numerical value of k, Boltzmann's constant, from measured values of P, V, N, and T. We consider next the case when

$$\sigma_a \equiv \frac{h^2}{8ma^2kT} \gg 1,$$

for which the original expression for the partition function, Eq. (8.1.2), is a rapidly convergent series. As a good approximation we may take

$$Z_{\text{trans}} \cong \exp\left(-\frac{3h^2}{8mkTV^{2/3}}\right)\left[1 + 3\exp\left(-\frac{4h^2}{3mkTV^{2/3}}\right)\right], \quad (8.1.14)$$

where, for simplicity, we have taken $a = b = c = V^{1/3}$. Proceeding as previously, we note immediately that Z_{trans} is not an extensive function under the present circumstances. Nevertheless we shall proceed in a formal manner to evaluate certain of the thermodynamic functions. From Eqs. (7.2.12) and (7.5.1) we have

$$F = \frac{3Nh^2}{8mV^{2/3}} - NkT \ln\left[1 + 3\exp\left(-\frac{4h^2}{3mkTV^{2/3}}\right)\right] + NkT \ln\frac{N}{e}.$$

(8.1.15)

The entropy is

$$S = Nk\ln\left[1 + 3\exp\left(-\frac{4h^2}{3mkTV^{2/3}}\right)\right]$$

$$+\left[\frac{(4Nh^2/mTV^{2/3})\exp(-4h^2/3mkTV^{2/3})}{1 + 3\exp(-4h^2/3mkTV^{2/3})}\right] - Nk\ln\frac{N}{e}.$$

(8.1.16)

The pressure is given by

$$P = \frac{Nh^2}{4mV^{5/3}}\left[\frac{1 + (41/3)\exp(-4h^2/3mkTV^{2/3})}{1 + 3\exp(-4h^2/3mkTV^{2/3})}\right].$$

(8.1.17)

The energy

$$E = F + TS = \frac{3Nh^2}{8mV^{2/3}}\left[\frac{1 + (41/3)\exp(-4h^2/3mkTV^{2/3})}{1 + 3\exp(-4h^2/3mkTV^{2/3})}\right].$$

(8.1.18)

For fixed N and V, note that P and E do not vanish for vanishing T, in contrast to Eqs. (8.1.10) and (8.1.11). Also, apart from the $Nk\ln(N/e)$ term, the entropy vanishes. However, the lack of extensive behavior for F warrants that these conclusions be used with caution.

8.2 The ideal gas: Fermi-Dirac statistics. We now consider the same collection as immediately preceding but apply the Fermi-Dirac statistics. For any reasonable size of container, the important values of

$$\frac{h^2}{8mkTV^{2/3}}$$

are generally considerably less than unity. In that case we may utilize the results of the previous section and Eq. (7.5.2). Taking, for simplicity,

$$Z_{\text{trans}} = \left(\frac{2\pi mkT}{h^2}\right)^{3/2} V,$$

(8.2.1)

we have for

$$\left(\frac{3h^2}{8mkTV^{2/3}} + \alpha\right) > 0,$$

$$N = \left(\frac{2\pi mkT}{h^2}\right)^{3/2} V \sum_{n=0}^{\infty} (-1)^n (n+1)^{-3/2} e^{-(n+1)\alpha}.$$

(8.2.2)

Our problem now is to evaluate the sum. This cannot be accomplished for all values of α with no approximation. Accordingly, we shall examine first the conditions under which $\alpha \gg 1$. We proceed to *reverse* the series

$$y = \sum_{n=1}^{\infty} a_n x^n$$

by regarding

$$x = \sum_{n=1}^{\infty} b_n y^n.$$

Substitution yields

$$y = \sum_{n=1}^{\infty} a_n \left(\sum_{m=1}^{\infty} b_m y^m \right)^n$$

$$= a_1 b_1 y + (a_1 b_2 + a_2 b_1^2) y^2 + (a_1 b_3 + 2a_2 b_1 b_2 + a_3 b_1^3) y^3 + \cdots,$$

so that

$$b_1 = \frac{1}{a_1}, \qquad b_2 = -\frac{a_2}{a_1^3}, \qquad b_3 = -\frac{a_3}{a_1^4} + \frac{2a_2^2}{a_1^5}, \qquad \text{etc.} \qquad (8.2.3)$$

Hence, identifying $e^{-\alpha}$ with x and identifying N/Z_{trans} with y, we obtain

$$e^{-\alpha} = \left(\frac{Z_{\text{trans}}}{N} \right)^{-1} + \frac{1}{2^{3/2}} \left(\frac{Z_{\text{trans}}}{N} \right)^{-2} + \left(\frac{1}{4} - \frac{1}{3^{3/2}} \right) \left(\frac{Z_{\text{trans}}}{N} \right)^{-3} + \cdots,$$

$$(8.2.4)$$

where Z_{trans} is given by Eq. (8.2.1). Higher terms may be determined by the procedure which has been given. The first term evidently is that expected from the Maxwell-Boltzmann value for α. To estimate the effect on the thermodynamic properties, we take the approximation

$$\alpha \cong \ln \frac{Z_{\text{trans}}}{N} - \ln \left[1 + \frac{1}{2^{3/2}} \left(\frac{Z_{\text{trans}}}{N} \right)^{-1} \right].$$

From Eq. (7.5.1), we obtain

$$F_{\text{FD}} \cong F_{\text{MB}} + kT(N + 2^{3/2} Z_{\text{trans}}) \ln \left(1 + \frac{N}{2^{3/2} Z_{\text{trans}}} \right) - NkT, \quad (8.2.5)$$

where F_{MB} is given by Eq. (8.1.8). The remaining terms evidently represent a correction to the Maxwell-Boltzmann result.

We can obtain for this approximation:

$$S_{\text{FD}} = S_{\text{MB}} - Nk \left[\left(1 + \frac{5}{2} \frac{2^{3/2} Z_{\text{trans}}}{N} \right) \ln \left(1 + \frac{N}{2^{3/2} Z_{\text{trans}}} \right) - \frac{5}{2} \right],$$

$$(8.2.6)$$

$$P_{FD} = P_{MB} - \frac{NkT}{V} \cdot 2^{3/2} Z_{trans} \left[\ln \left(1 + \frac{N}{2^{3/2} Z_{trans}} \right) - \frac{N}{2^{3/2} Z_{trans}} \right].$$

$$(8.2.7)$$

The subscript MB refers to the Maxwell-Boltzmann result. For sufficiently large temperatures one can show that the effect of the Fermi-Dirac statistics is to decrease the entropy and increase the pressure of the Maxwell-Boltzmann ideal gas.

The previous results apply in those circumstances where there is no major distinction between the results of each of the statistics [that is, Eq. (7.4.8)]. The more interesting properties of the Fermi-Dirac ideal gas occur for $\alpha < 0$. For such values the expansion of Eq. (7.5.2) may not be justified. As a result we may represent the series in Eq. (8.2.2) in terms which will permit our determining its values under the conditions stated. One may show that the series

$$-\sum_{n=0}^{\infty} \frac{(-e^{-\alpha})^{n+1}}{(n+1)^{3/2}} = \frac{2}{\sqrt{\pi}} \int_0^{\infty} \frac{t^{1/2} \, dt}{e^{t+\alpha} + 1} .$$

$$(8.2.8)$$

This integral occurs in the usual treatment of the Fermi-Dirac ideal gas. We may now attempt to develop an expansion for $\alpha \ll 0$. Letting $\gamma = -\alpha \gg 0$, $t = \gamma u$, we have

$$\int_0^{\infty} \frac{t^{1/2} \, dt}{e^{t+\alpha} + 1} = \gamma^{3/2} \int_0^{\infty} \frac{u^{1/2} \, du}{e^{\gamma(u-1)} + 1}$$

$$= \gamma^{3/2} \left[\int_0^1 \frac{u^{1/2} \, du}{e^{\gamma(u-1)} + 1} + \int_1^{\infty} \frac{u^{1/2} \, du}{e^{\gamma(u-1)} + 1} \right]$$

$$= \gamma^{3/2} \left[\int_0^1 u^{1/2} \, du - \int_0^1 \frac{u^{1/2} \, du}{1 + e^{\gamma(1-u)}} + \int_1^{\infty} \frac{u^{1/2} \, du}{1 + e^{\gamma(u-1)}} \right].$$

Changing variables, we obtain

$$\int_0^{\infty} \frac{t^{1/2} \, dt}{e^{t+\alpha} + 1}$$

$$= \gamma^{3/2} \left[\frac{2}{3} - \int_0^1 \frac{(1-w)^{1/2} \, dw}{1 + e^{\gamma w}} + \int_0^1 \frac{(1+w)^{1/2} \, dw}{1 + e^{\gamma w}} + \int_1^{\infty} \frac{(1+w)^{1/2} \, dw}{1 + e^{\gamma w}} \right]$$

$$= \gamma^{3/2} \left[\frac{2}{3} + \int_0^1 dw \, \frac{(1+w)^{1/2} - (1-w)^{1/2}}{1 + e^{\gamma w}} + \int_1^{\infty} \frac{(1+w)^{1/2} \, dw}{1 + e^{\gamma w}} \right].$$

$$(8.2.9)$$

Now

$$(1 + w)^{1/2} - (1 - w)^{1/2} = (1 + \tfrac{1}{2}w - \tfrac{1}{8}w^2 - \tfrac{1}{16}w^3 + \cdots)$$
$$- (1 - \tfrac{1}{2}w - \tfrac{1}{8}w^2 + \tfrac{1}{16}w^3 + \cdots)$$
$$= w - \tfrac{1}{8}w^3 + \cdots,$$

and

$$\int_1^\infty \frac{(1 + w)^{1/2}\, dw}{1 + e^{\gamma w}} < \int_1^\infty e^{w/2} e^{-\gamma w}\, dw = \frac{e^{-(\gamma - 1/2)}}{\gamma - \tfrac{1}{2}}.$$

Hence for $\gamma \gg 0$,

$$\int_0^\infty \frac{t^{1/2}\, dt}{1 + e^{t+\alpha}} \cong \gamma^{3/2} \left[\frac{2}{3} + \int_0^1 \frac{dw(w - \tfrac{1}{8}w^3 + \cdots)}{1 + e^{\gamma w}} + 0\left(\frac{e^{-\gamma}}{\gamma}\right) \right]$$

$$= \gamma^{3/2} \left[\frac{2}{3} + \frac{1}{\gamma^2} \int_0^\gamma \frac{dx\, x}{1 + e^x} + 0\left(\frac{1}{\gamma^4}\right) \right].$$

For $\gamma \gg 0$, the upper limit of the integral may be replaced by infinity with no undue loss of accuracy. Since

$$\int_0^\infty dx\, \frac{x}{1 + e^x} = \frac{\pi^2}{12},$$

we have the asymptotic ($\alpha \ll 0$) approximation

$$\int_0^\infty \frac{t\, dt}{1 + e^{t+\alpha}} \cong (-\alpha)^{3/2} \left[\frac{2}{3} + \frac{\pi^2}{12\alpha^2} + 0\left(\frac{1}{\alpha^4}\right) \right]. \qquad (8.2.10)$$

Hence, substitution of Eqs. (8.2.8) and (8.2.10) into Eq. (8.2.2) yields

$$\frac{3\sqrt{\pi}\, N}{4Z_{\text{trans}}} \cong (-\alpha)^{3/2} \left(1 + \frac{\pi^2}{8\alpha^2}\right), \qquad (8.2.11)$$

neglecting higher-order terms.

We may approximate the solution for $(-\alpha)$ as follows:

$$-\alpha \cong \frac{(3\sqrt{\pi}\, N/4Z_{\text{trans}})^{2/3}}{[1 + (\pi^2/8\alpha^2)]^{2/3}} \doteq \left(\frac{3\sqrt{\pi}\, N}{4Z_{\text{trans}}}\right)^{2/3} \left[1 - \frac{\pi^2}{12}\left(\frac{3\sqrt{\pi}\, N}{4Z_{\text{trans}}}\right)^{-4/3}\right].$$

Substitution of Eq. (8.2.1) gives

$$-\alpha \doteq \left(\frac{3N}{4\pi V}\right)^{2/3} \frac{h^2}{2mkT} \left[1 - \left(\frac{3N}{4\pi V}\right)^{-4/3} \frac{(\pi mkT)^2}{3h^4}\right].$$

The Helmholtz free energy function is

$$F = -kT \int_0^N \alpha(N) \, dN$$

$$= \frac{3N}{10} \left(\frac{3N}{4\pi V}\right)^{2/3} \frac{h^2}{m} - N \left(\frac{4\pi V}{3N}\right)^{2/3} \frac{\pi^2 m k^2 T^2}{2h^2}. \qquad (8.2.12)$$

The entropy

$$S = N \left(\frac{4\pi V}{3N}\right)^{2/3} \frac{\pi^2 m k^2 T}{h^2}. \qquad (8.2.13)$$

As a consequence, the heat capacity at constant volume

$$C_V = S. \qquad (8.2.14)$$

The energy

$$E = F + TS$$

$$= \frac{3N}{10} \left(\frac{3N}{4\pi V}\right)^{2/3} \frac{h^2}{m} + N \left(\frac{4\pi V}{3N}\right)^{2/3} \frac{\pi^2 m k T^2}{2h^2}. \qquad (8.2.15)$$

The pressure

$$P = \frac{1}{5} \left(\frac{3}{4\pi}\right)^{2/3} \frac{h^2}{m} \left(\frac{N}{V}\right)^{5/3} + \left(\frac{4\pi}{3}\right)^{2/3} \frac{\pi^2 m k^2 T^2}{3h^2} \left(\frac{N}{V}\right)^{1/3}. \qquad (8.2.16)$$

It is interesting to note the formal resemblance of Eqs. (8.2.15) and (8.2.16) to Eqs. (8.1.17) and (8.1.18).

The behavior just described of the Fermi-Dirac ideal gas generally is termed *strongly degenerate*. This behavior simply corresponds to an almost complete filling of the subclassifications for each energy value. (See Section 7.4.) At the absolute zero, this filling is presumably complete, for the entropy vanishes. By Eq. (7.4.7), W_3 is substantially unity. The contrast with the usual behavior expected from an ideal gas is very marked.

The theory of the strongly degenerate Fermi-Dirac ideal gas has been applied by Sommerfeld to the model of a free electron gas in metals. Because of the very high electron density, one verifies that the above theory should be relevant. However, the nature of the energy values of electrons in a metallic environment is apt to be altered considerably from that which has been given. Nevertheless, the experimental behavior of the heat capacity of metals at very low temperatures indicates the general validity of the model.

8.3 The ideal gas: Bose-Einstein statistics. We may take advantage of some of the previous results in a description of the Bose-Einstein ideal gas. Thus, from Eq. (7.5.2) we see that only the positive sign must be used. Hence, a simple transcription is possible. For $\alpha \gg 0$, we can obtain

$$F_{BE} \cong F_{MB} + kT(N - 2^{3/2}Z_{trans}) \ln\left(1 - \frac{N}{2^{3/2}Z_{trans}}\right) - NkT. \quad (8.3.1)$$

As a consequence, to this approximation,

$$S_{BE} = S_{MB} - Nk\left[\left(1 - \frac{5}{2}\frac{2^{3/2}Z_{trans}}{N}\right)\ln\left(1 - \frac{N}{2^{3/2}Z_{trans}}\right) - \frac{5}{2}\right], \quad (8.3.2)$$

$$P_{BE} = P_{MB} + \frac{NkT}{V} \cdot 2^{3/2}Z_{trans}\left[\ln\left(1 - \frac{N}{2^{3/2}Z_{trans}}\right) + \frac{N}{2^{3/2}Z_{trans}}\right]. \quad (8.3.3)$$

The behavior here is opposite to that noted for the Fermi-Dirac ideal gas. For sufficiently large temperatures, the effect of the Bose-Einstein statistics is to increase the entropy and decrease the pressure of the Maxwell-Boltzmann ideal gas.

As previously, it is necessary to express the sum in Eq. (7.5.2) in a form which will allow approximations other than those above. In a manner analogous to Eq. (8.2.8), one may show for Bose-Einstein statistics that

$$\frac{N}{Z_{trans}} = \sum_{n=0}^{\infty} (n+1)^{-3/2}e^{-(n+1)\alpha} = \frac{2}{\sqrt{\pi}}\int_0^\infty \frac{t^{1/2}\,dt}{e^{t+\alpha} - 1}. \quad (8.3.4)$$

Note that the integral diverges for $\alpha < 0$. As a result, any finite density will correspond to $\alpha \geq 0$. To attempt an approximation which gives the density as a function of α in the vicinity of the maximum density, we note that a power series expansion in α is not possible about this value of α, each derivative of the integral with respect to α diverging in the limit of vanishing α. However, we may effect an approximation by observing that

$$\frac{1}{Z_{trans}}\frac{\partial N}{\partial \alpha} = -\sum_{n=0}^{\infty}(n+1)^{-1/2}e^{-(n+1)\alpha}$$

and

$$\sum_{n=0}^{\infty}\frac{e^{-(n+1)\alpha}}{(n+1)^{1/2}} \leq \int_0^\infty \frac{e^{-\alpha x}}{x^{1/2}}\,dx = \frac{1}{\alpha^{1/2}}\int_0^\infty y^{-1/2}e^{-y}\,dy.$$

The last series diverges, as α tends toward zero, in a manner which can be estimated from the last integral. This integral is a representation of the *gamma function*

$$\Gamma(x) = \int_0^\infty y^{x-1} e^{-y} \, dy.$$

Hence

$$\sum_{n=0}^\infty \frac{e^{-(n+1)\alpha}}{(n+1)^{1/2}} \leq \alpha^{-1/2} \Gamma(\tfrac{1}{2}) = \sqrt{\frac{\pi}{\alpha}}.$$

Using this result as an approximation, we have

$$\frac{1}{Z_{\text{trans}}} \frac{\partial N}{\partial \alpha} \doteq -\sqrt{\frac{\pi}{\alpha}}$$

and

$$\frac{N}{Z_{\text{trans}}} \doteq \frac{N_0}{Z_{\text{trans}}} - 2\sqrt{\pi\alpha}, \tag{8.3.5}$$

where

$$\frac{N_0}{Z_{\text{trans}}} = \sum_{n=0}^\infty (n+1)^{-3/2} = \zeta(\tfrac{3}{2}) \doteq 2.612. \tag{8.3.6}$$

Here

$$\zeta(x) = \sum_{n=0}^\infty (n+1)^{-x}$$

is the Riemann ζ-function. Combining the previous results, we obtain

$$\alpha \doteq \frac{[\zeta(\tfrac{3}{2}) - (N/Z_{\text{trans}})]^2}{4\pi}. \tag{8.3.7}$$

The Helmholtz free energy function, to this approximation, cannot be determined directly from Eqs. (7.5.1) and (8.3.7) since N is bounded. However, we generally may determine

$$F = -kT \int_0^N dN \alpha(N) = -kT \int_0^{N_0} dN \alpha(N) + kT \int_N^{N_0} dN \alpha(N), \tag{8.3.8}$$

where N_0 is given by Eq. (8.3.6). Now

$$-kT \int_0^{N_0} dN \alpha(N) = -kT \int_\infty^0 d\alpha \, \alpha \frac{\partial N}{\partial \alpha}$$

$$= -kT \alpha N(\alpha) \Big|_\infty^0 + kT \int_\infty^0 d\alpha N(\alpha)$$

$$= kT Z_{\text{trans}} \sum_{n=0}^\infty (n+1)^{-3/2} \int_\infty^0 d\alpha e^{-(n+1)\alpha}$$

$$= -kT Z_{\text{trans}} \sum_{n=0}^\infty (n+1)^{-5/2} = -kT Z_{\text{trans}} \zeta(\tfrac{5}{2}).$$

Hence the Helmholtz function for vanishing α,

$$F_0 \doteq -1.341 kT Z_{\text{trans}}. \tag{8.3.9}$$

Thus, to this approximation,

$$F = -1.341 kT Z_{\text{trans}} + \frac{kT}{12\pi} Z_{\text{trans}} \left[\varsigma \left(\frac{3}{2} \right) - \frac{N}{Z_{\text{trans}}} \right]^3. \tag{8.3.10}$$

The entropy determined from Eq. (8.3.10) is

$$S = - \left(\frac{5}{2} \frac{F}{T} + \frac{3}{2} Nk\alpha \right), \tag{8.3.11}$$

from which the energy

$$E = F + TS = -\tfrac{3}{2}(F + NkT\alpha). \tag{8.3.12}$$

The pressure is

$$P = - \left(\frac{F}{V} + \frac{NkT\alpha}{V} \right). \tag{8.3.13}$$

Under the conditions that we have been considering (α small), the Bose-Einstein ideal gas is referred to as *strongly degenerate*. Certain peculiarities are to be noted. The density of the gas has an extreme value at each temperature; the pressure then depends only on the temperature. The last feature is, perhaps, not too surprising in view of the upper limit to the density. Indeed, one can show that when α vanishes,

$$\left(\frac{PV}{N_0} \right) = \frac{\varsigma(\frac{5}{2})}{\varsigma(\frac{3}{2})} kT \sim \frac{kT}{2}, \tag{8.3.14}$$

(N_0/V) being determined as the extreme density from Eq. (8.3.6). One of the most unusual properties is that at the extreme density ($\alpha = 0$) all the partial quantities

$$\left(\frac{\partial F}{\partial N} \right)_{T,V}, \quad \left(\frac{\partial S}{\partial N} \right)_{T,V}, \quad \left(\frac{\partial E}{\partial N} \right)_{T,V}$$

vanish, suggesting that the addition of more systems to the collection makes no contribution whatever to the extensive properties of the collection. It is reasonable to suppose that the properties of the added systems (under equilibrium conditions) correspond to the states of zero entropy and energy. For this reason the phenomenon described is sometimes referred to as a Bose-Einstein *condensation*. London has considered the possible application of these considerations to the interesting properties of liquid helium.

8.4 The ideal gas: systems with internal motion. In the previous sections of this chapter we have seen how the properties of a collection of structureless particles can be related to the translational partition function for such systems. In general, the systems with which we deal are highly structured and have internal motions associated with this structure. We have indicated [Eq. (7.5.4)] that in such instances the partition function is expressible as a product of partition functions, one factor of which is the translational partition function. The other factor refers only to the values of the energy associated with the internal motions; when these are separable into completely independent modes, the internal partition function factors further.

In terms of the treatment which has been given, there is no simple way to determine the influence of internal motion of the systems on the statistical-thermodynamic properties of the collection. Only in the case of the Maxwell-Boltzmann statistics is a general treatment possible. The basis for such is contained in the expression which obtains for the parameter α,

$$\alpha = \ln \frac{Z_{\text{trans}}}{N} + \ln Z_{\text{int}} \tag{8.4.1}$$

Thereby, the contribution made by the internal modes of motion to the statistical-thermodynamic functions is simply an additive one. We shall consider in a later section different partition functions for different kinds of internal motion.

How can we proceed with such more complex systems obeying either Fermi-Dirac or Bose-Einstein statistics? Clearly the problem is formally solved in terms of Eq. (7.5.2). However, unless the dependence of the internal partition function on $(1/kT)$ is sufficiently simple, it will be quite impossible to effect a simplification which can lead to an equation like Eq. (8.2.2). Perhaps the best that can be hoped for is a statement of the problem in terms that make the difficulty prominent.

Making use of Eq. (7.5.3) in Eq. (7.5.2), we obtain

$$N = \sum_{j=0}^{\infty} P_j \,(\text{int}) \sum_{n=0}^{\infty} (\mp)^n \exp\left\{-(n+1)[\alpha + \beta\epsilon_j \,(\text{int})]\right\} Z_{\text{trans}}[(n+1)\beta],$$
$$\tag{8.4.2}$$

where the multiplicity has been taken as the product of that for translational motion and internal motion. Following the procedure we have employed previously, but omitting the details, we obtain for both Fermi-Dirac and Bose-Einstein statistics

$$N = \frac{2Z_{\text{trans}}}{\sqrt{\pi}} \sum_{j=0}^{\infty} P_j \int_0^{\infty} \frac{t^{1/2}\,dt}{\exp(t + \alpha + \beta\epsilon_j) \pm 1}, \tag{8.4.3}$$

the sum being taken over the values of the internal energy. From Eq. (7.5.1) and the development following Eq. (7.4.6) we evidently obtain the Helmholtz function

$$F = \pm \frac{2kT}{\sqrt{\pi}} Z_{\text{trans}} \sum_{j=0}^{\infty} P_j \int_0^{\infty} dt \, t^{1/2} \ln \left(1 \pm e^{-\beta\epsilon_j - \alpha - t}\right), \quad (8.4.4)$$

$(+)$ corresponding to Fermi-Dirac statistics, $(-)$ to Bose-Einstein statistics. It is apparent that the summation will be especially difficult to carry through in general terms.

8.5 Partition function for the harmonic oscillator. One of the kinds of internal motion that needs consideration is vibratory motion. This generally consists of a periodic relative motion of the various parts of a system. In the cases of interest, molecular systems, the relative motion of atoms and groups of atoms is an important characteristic of such systems. The possible values of the energy associated with vibratory motion depend on the nature of the forces acting between the various parts. In the simplest situation, the force satisfies a Hooke's law and is simply proportional to the extent of displacement from a so-called equilibrium position. The motion associated with this kind of force law is characteristic of the so-called (linear) *harmonic oscillator*. We shall see later that the energy values of a harmonic oscillator in one dimension are simply

$$\epsilon_n = (n + \tfrac{1}{2})h\nu, \quad n = 0, 1, 2, \ldots, \quad (8.5.1)$$

where h is Planck's constant and ν is the vibration frequency of a classical harmonic oscillator.

The partition function associated with this sort of motion is

$$Z_v = \sum_{n=0}^{\infty} \exp\left[-\frac{(n+\tfrac{1}{2})h\nu}{kT}\right] = \exp\left(-\frac{h\nu}{2kT}\right) \sum_{n=0}^{\infty} \left[\exp\left(-\frac{h\nu}{kT}\right)\right]^n$$

$$= \frac{\exp\left(-h\nu/2kT\right)}{1 - \exp\left(-h\nu/kT\right)}, \quad (8.5.2)$$

since the series is a geometric series. Particular note should be taken that Z_v is an intensive function, in accord with our earlier expectations. The contribution to the Helmholtz function in the case of Maxwell-Boltzmann statistics is

$$F_v = -NkT \ln Z_v = N \frac{h\nu}{2} + NkT \ln\left[1 - \exp\left(-\frac{h\nu}{kT}\right)\right]. \quad (8.5.3)$$

The entropy contribution is

$$S_v = Nk \left\{ \frac{h\nu}{kT} \frac{\exp\left(-h\nu/kT\right)}{1 - \exp\left(-h\nu/kT\right)} - \ln\left[1 - \exp\left(-\frac{h\nu}{kT}\right)\right] \right\}. \quad (8.5.4)$$

The energy contribution is

$$E_v = \frac{Nh\nu}{2} + Nh\nu \left[\frac{\exp\,(-h\nu/kT)}{1 - \exp\,(-h\nu/kT)} \right]. \tag{8.5.5}$$

The heat capacity associated with this motion is

$$C_v = Nk \left(\frac{h\nu}{kT}\right)^2 \frac{\exp\,(-h\nu/kT)}{[1 - \exp\,(-h\nu/kT)]^2}. \tag{8.5.6}$$

Both S_v and C_v tend toward zero as the absolute zero of temperature is reached; correspondingly, F_v and E_v then assume the *zero-point energy* value of $(Nh\nu/2)$. Note, however, that the latter cannot be confirmed on the basis of purely thermal measurements.

For very large temperatures $(T \to \infty)$,

$$C_v \sim Nk, \qquad E_v \sim \frac{Nh\nu}{2} + NkT, \qquad S_v \sim Nk \left(1 + \ln \frac{kT}{h\nu}\right). \tag{8.5.7}$$

In concluding this section, we note that any number of vibration frequencies may be accommodated easily in the case of Maxwell-Boltzmann statistics, for the contribution to each of the statistical thermodynamic properties is simply the sum due to each of the frequencies. Thus if there are M such frequencies for each system, the vibrational energy would consist of

$$E_v = N \sum_{i=1}^{M} \frac{h\nu_i}{2} + N \sum_{i=1}^{M} \frac{h\nu_i \exp\,(-h\nu_i/kT)}{1 - \exp\,(-h\nu_i/kT)}, \tag{8.5.8}$$

while the heat capacity attributable to such motion is

$$C_v = Nk \sum_{i=1}^{M} \frac{(h\nu_i/kT)^2 \exp\,(-h\nu_i/kT)}{[1 - \exp\,(-h\nu_i/kT)]^2}. \tag{8.5.9}$$

Equation (8.5.9) serves as the basis for the model of an atomic solid introduced by Einstein. To construct that theory it is necessary to ascribe to each system of the collection three identical vibration frequencies. In such a case Eq. (8.5.9) reduces to Eq. (8.5.6) with $3N$ replacing N. From Eq. (8.5.7) we see that when N is replaced by $3N_A$ (N_A being Avogadro's number), the high-temperature value of the molal heat capacity of an atomic solid approaches the value $3R$, the law of Dulong and Petit. This value is evidently independent of the vibration frequency. The low-temperature behavior is only qualitatively in agreement with experiment. An improved model due to Debye will be considered later.

8.6 Partition functions for rotational motion. We shall consider here only rotational motion of the very simplest kind. We shall restrict our considerations to the so-called *linear rigid rotor*, which is exemplified by a fixed linear array of mass points. As we shall see later, the motion of such an array about its center of mass has special energy values associated with it. In the simplest possible situation, the linear array is confined to a prescribed plane and has the energy values

$$\epsilon_K = \frac{\hbar^2}{2I} K^2, \qquad K = 0, \pm 1, \pm 2, \ldots, \tag{8.6.1}$$

where $\hbar = h/2\pi$ and the moment of inertia of the linear array of P masses

$$I = \sum_{i=1}^{P} m_i(x_i - \bar{x})^2,$$

$(x_i - \bar{x})$ being the distance of the ith mass, m_i, measured from the center of mass of the array, $\bar{x}$.

For such a rotor, the partition function

$$Z_r = \sum_{K=-\infty}^{+\infty} \exp\left(-\frac{\hbar^2 K^2}{2IkT}\right) \equiv \theta_3\left[0, \exp\left(-\frac{\hbar^2}{2IkT}\right)\right], \tag{8.6.2}$$

by Eq. (8.1.4). From Eq. (8.1.5) we may represent

$$Z_r = \left(\frac{8\pi IkT}{h^2}\right)^{1/2} \sum_{K=-\infty}^{+\infty} \exp\left(-\frac{2IkT}{\hbar^2} K^2\right). \tag{8.6.3}$$

Either of the two series may be used, but usually one will converge more rapidly than the other. The statistical-thermodynamic properties of such a rotor, in the case of Maxwell-Boltzmann statistics, is easily seen to correspond to that contributed by one direction of translational motion.

A more realistic description of the linear rigid rotor would give the energy values

$$\epsilon_K = \frac{\hbar^2}{2I} K(K + 1), \qquad K = 0, 1, 2, \ldots, \tag{8.6.4}$$

with, however, a multiplicity or degeneracy of

$$P_K = 2K + 1. \tag{8.6.5}$$

Hence, the partition function for the rotational motion is

$$Z_r = \sum_{K=0}^{\infty} (2K + 1) \exp\left[-\frac{\hbar^2}{2IkT} K(K + 1)\right]. \tag{8.6.6}$$

For $(\hbar^2/2IkT) \gg 1$, the series converges rapidly. For most cases of physical interest this condition is not satisfied. (Clearly this condition is bound to be satisfied at sufficiently small values of T.) In these circumstances the partition function may be approximated by an integral. In fact, all the partition functions of the present chapter may be so approximated for sufficiently large values of T.

We make use of a general means for evaluating an integral in terms of a sum, known as the *Euler-Maclaurin* expansion. It is

$$\int_a^b f(x)\, dx = h \sum_{n=0}^{R-1} f(a + nh) - \sum_{r=0}^{\infty} \frac{h^{r+1}}{(r+1)!} B_{r+1}[f^{(r)}(b) - f^{(r)}(a)],$$

(8.6.7)

where $a + Rh = b$, $f^{(r)}(x)$ is the rth derivative of $f(x)$, and the B's are the *Bernoulli numbers* defined through the relation

$$\sum_{r=0}^{\infty} B_r \frac{x^r}{r!} = \frac{x}{e^x - 1}.$$

(8.6.8)

The first few Bernoulli numbers are:

$$B_0 = 1, \quad B_1 = -\tfrac{1}{2}, \quad B_2 = \tfrac{1}{6}, \quad B_4 = -\tfrac{1}{30}, \quad B_6 = \tfrac{1}{42},$$
$$B_{2r+1} = 0, \quad r \geq 1.$$

In the present instance, we have $h = 1$, and taking $R = \infty$,

$$\sum_{K=0}^{\infty} (2K + 1) \exp\left[-\left(\frac{\hbar^2}{2IkT}\right) K(K+1)\right]$$
$$= \int_0^{\infty} dx\, (2x + 1) \exp\left[-\frac{\hbar^2}{2IkT} x(x+1)\right]$$
$$- B_1 - \frac{B_2}{2}\left(2 - \frac{\hbar^2}{2IkT}\right)$$
$$- \frac{B_4}{4!}\left[-12\left(\frac{\hbar^2}{2IkT}\right) + 12\left(\frac{\hbar^2}{2IkT}\right)^2 - \left(\frac{\hbar^2}{2IkT}\right)^3\right] + \cdots$$
$$\doteq \left(\frac{2IkT}{\hbar^2}\right) + \frac{1}{3} + \frac{1}{15}\left(\frac{\hbar^2}{2IkT}\right) + 0\left[\left(\frac{\hbar^2}{2IkT}\right)^2\right].$$

(8.6.9)

With this approximation,

$$F_r \doteq -NkT \ln\left(\frac{2IkT}{\hbar^2}\right) - NkT \ln\left[1 + \frac{1}{3}\left(\frac{\hbar^2}{2IkT}\right) + \frac{1}{15}\left(\frac{\hbar^2}{2IkT}\right)^2\right].$$

(8.6.10)

For $T \to \infty$, up to but not including terms $0[(\hbar^2/2IkT)^2]$,

$$S_r \doteq Nk \ln T + Nk \ln \left(\frac{2Ike}{\hbar^2}\right), \qquad (8.6.11)$$

whereupon

$$E_r \doteq NkT\left[1 - \frac{1}{3}\left(\frac{\hbar^2}{2IkT}\right)\right], \qquad (8.6.12)$$

and

$$C_r \doteq Nk. \qquad (8.6.13)$$

Frequently there arise restrictions on the values of K to be summed over in the partition function. These restrictions are related to the symmetry of the rotator and will be discussed in a later section. However, these restrictions reduce for the linear rotor to exclusion of either odd or even values of K. For the approximation considered here, it seems evident that the partition function computed only with even values of K will be essentially equal to one-half the value obtained when all values of K are employed. With the exception of the Helmholtz function and the chemical potential, the thermodynamic functions are unaffected thereby.

8.7 Chemical equilibrium among ideal gases of diatomic molecules. The developments of the preceding sections can be exploited to estimate the equilibrium constants of gaseous substances when the latter may be approximated by ideal gases consisting of diatomic molecules.

We already have discussed (Section 5.3) how the equilibrium constant is determined by the chemical potential of the reacting substances in their standard states. For the present, we may take the standard state to be the pure substances at the temperature and pressure of the equilibrium mixture. We note that the chemical potentials of Eq. (5.3.2), which refer to a unit of mass, are multiplied by the molecular weight of the pertinent species. Accordingly, the chemical potential per particle, which occurs in the statistical-thermodynamic expressions, may be multiplied by Avogadro's number N_A to make the two chemical potentials correspond. That is, we identify, for the case of Maxwell-Boltzmann statistics,

$$\overline{W}_i \mu_i^0(T, P) \equiv -N_A kT\alpha_i = -N_A kT \ln \left(\frac{Z_i}{N_i}\right), \qquad (8.7.1)$$

the i referring to the appropriate species. With Eq. (5.3.3) we obtain the formal expression

$$K_e(T, P) = \frac{\prod_{\text{products}} (Z_i/N_i)^{|\nu_i|}}{\prod_{\text{reactants}} (Z_i/N_i)^{|\nu_i|}}. \qquad (8.7.2)$$

For Eq. (8.7.2) to be correct, it is necessary that all energy values be measured from a common origin. Thus, for some particular species we should represent

$$\epsilon_{qrst} = \epsilon^0 + \epsilon_q \text{ (trans)} + \epsilon_r \text{ (vib)} + \epsilon_s \text{ (rot)} + \epsilon'_t,$$

where ϵ^0 is a constant which adjusts the energy of all species to a common origin; ϵ'_t is an energy value attributable to motions other than those which have been listed. The equilibrium constant may now be simplified. Using Eqs. (8.1.7), (8.1.10), and (8.6.9), it is convenient to give an expression for the logarithm of the equilibrium constant (noting that ν's are positive for reactants and negative for products) which is valid for the ideal gas approximation at not too large temperatures:

$$\ln K_e = \sum_i \left(\frac{\nu_i \epsilon_i^0}{kT}\right) - \frac{7}{2}\left(\sum_i \nu_i\right) \ln T + \left(\sum_i \nu_i\right) \ln P$$

$$- \sum_i \nu_i j_i - \sum_i \nu_i \ln [Z_i \text{ (vib) } Z'_i], \qquad (8.7.3)$$

where the *chemical constants*

$$j_i = \ln\left(\frac{2^{9/2} \pi^{7/2} m_i^{3/2} I_i k^{7/2}}{h^5}\right). \qquad (8.7.4)$$

Sometimes Z'_i, to a good approximation, is constant and equal to the multiplicity of the so-called ground state of the molecular system. It then may be included in the expression for the chemical constant. Moreover, each partition function for vibration, at not too large temperatures, will be approximated by $\exp(-hf_i/2kT)$. As a result the chemical constant will be augmented by $(hf_i/2kT)$. (The f_i here refers to the classical vibration frequency.)

Now, on the basis of Eq. (8.7.3) it is possible to test the hypothesis that there exists a zero-point vibrational energy. From the equilibrium constants for similar reactions involving *isotopic* species, the changes can be correlated with the changes in the masses. (The frequencies f_i depend implicitly on the masses. See Section 12.6.) As a result, one can verify the presence of the zero-point energy contribution in $[\sum_i \nu_i \ln Z_i \text{ (vib)}]$.

8.8 Summary. The statistics of the most probable distribution have been applied in the present chapter to determine statistical-thermodynamic functions for simple systems.

The model of an ideal gas as consisting of a collection of noninteracting structureless particles enclosed in a container is treated by Maxwell-Boltzmann, Fermi-Dirac, and Bose-Einstein statistics. The properties of such ideal gases are found to depend on the partition function for such a system. The partition function is evaluated for a structureless particle in a box and found to be simply related to an elliptic theta function. The mathematical properties of the theta function permit the partition function for translation to be represented by either of two series, of which one is generally more rapidly convergent than the other.

The Maxwell-Boltzmann ideal gas is treated in detail. The high-temperature behaviors of the Fermi-Dirac and Bose-Einstein ideal gases are established in relation to the Maxwell-Boltzmann ideal gas.

The low-temperature behaviors of all three models of an ideal gas are considered. A marked similarity is noted between the Maxwell-Boltzmann and the Fermi-Dirac gases, especially as to the form of pressure-density and energy-density dependence. The degenerate regions of both the Fermi-Dirac and Bose-Einstein ideal gases are considered in detail. In each of the treatments the procedure adopted is one devoted simply to a mathematical evaluation or approximation of the pertinent quantities; no attempt is made to introduce any additional physical information other than that which is associated with the energy values of the systems of the collection.

The nature of the statistical-mechanical problem when systems possess internal structure and corresponding motion is examined. Except for the case of Maxwell-Boltzmann statistics, no simple and general procedure is available for determining the effect of internal motions on the statistical thermodynamic functions.

The partition function for the vibratory motion of a linear harmonic oscillator is constructed, and statistical-thermodynamic functions associated with this motion in the Maxwell-Boltzmann statistics are determined. The low- and high-temperature behavior are examined explicitly. Likewise, the partition function for the rotational motion of a linear rigid rotor is evaluated and the statistical-thermodynamic functions determined.

The partition functions for ideal diatomic gases are employed to estimate equilibrium constants for the chemical equilibrium of such gases. The chemical equilibrium properties are thus related to the microscopic properties of the chemical reactants and products.

EXERCISES

1. Establish the asymptotic form $(T \to \infty)$ of the translational partition function using the Euler-Maclaurin expansion. Compare with Eq. (8.1.7).

2. Show that the triple sum in Eq. (8.1.7) has a logarithm which vanishes more rapidly than $(1/N)$ when $N \to \infty$ and $\lim_{N \to \infty} (N/V)$ is finite.

3. Derive Eq. (8.3.4) from the Bose-Einstein distribution formula Eq. (7.4.4) and the expression for the translational energy values Eq. (8.1.1), using the Euler-Maclaurin expansion. (Note that this will require a triple integral.)

4. Assume a collection of noninteracting structureless particles which are *localized* in contiguous regions of uniform potential energy such that the volume of the total collection is the sum of the volumes of the individual regions. Determine, for $(N/V) \gg 1$, the heat capacity at constant volume of such a collection.

5. Establish the validity of Eqs. (8.2.3).

6. Establish explicitly that for sufficiently large temperature the molal entropy of a Bose-Einstein ideal gas is greater than the entropy of a Maxwell-Boltzmann ideal gas which, in turn, is greater than the entropy of a Fermi-Dirac ideal gas. (Assume structureless particles.) Make a similar comparison of the pressures of the three ideal gases.

7. Establish Eq. (8.2.8).

8. Verify Eq. (8.2.9).

9. The increase in entropy $(\partial S/\partial N)_{T,V}$ of a Fermi-Dirac ideal gas at the absolute zero of temperature vanishes. Hence, one concludes that the subclassifications for each energy value are filled. Show that such is also the case for the localized collection of Exercise 4.

10. Establish that the integral of Eq. (8.3.4) diverges for $\alpha < 0$.

11. Carry out the analysis leading to Eq. (8.3.5), using the Euler-Maclaurin expansion to obtain a better approximation for the chemical potential.

12. Determine the isothermal variation of pressure with volume for a fixed number of particles of a Bose-Einstein ideal gas.

13. Determine the pressure for the collection of Exercise 4 and compare with Eq. (8.2.16).

14. Determine the variation of heat capacity at constant volume with the temperature for a Bose-Einstein gas.

15. Establish Eq. (8.4.2).

16. Use the Einstein model of a solid mentioned following Eq. (8.5.9) and the Maxwell-Boltzmann ideal gas to obtain an expression for the vapor pressure of a solid. (Make certain to refer all energies to a common origin.)

17. From given values of the temperature variation of the chemical equilibrium constant for ideal gases, indicate how the vibrational zero-point energy differences may be determined. For explicitness, consider the reactions

$$H_2 + I_2 \leftrightarrows 2HI,$$

and

$$D_2 + I_2 \rightleftarrows 2DI.$$

18. Determine the average value of the (quantum) number K for a linear rigid rotor of energy values

$$\frac{\hbar^2}{2I} K (K + 1).$$

Determine also the most probable value of K.

19. Determine the average value of *one* of the (quantum) numbers for translational motion.

20. Evaluate *exactly* the chemical potential of a two-dimensional collection of structureless particles, using the strongly degenerate forms of the Fermi-Dirac and Bose-Einstein statistics.

21. Show that for sufficiently large temperatures the rotational partition function computed only with odd K-values is equal to that computed only with even K-values.

22. Determine the Helmholtz free energy function for a strongly degenerate Fermi-Dirac gas of particles having the internal energy values $\pm\epsilon$, which are nondegenerate.

23. Determine the Helmholtz free energy function for a strongly degenerate Bose-Einstein gas of particles which have the nondegenerate internal energy values of $\pm\epsilon$.

24. Estimate the equilibrium constant for the dissociation of a diatomic molecule into atoms: $AB \rightleftarrows A + B$.

25. Justify the approximation of Section 8.3, as stated explicitly in Eq. (8.3.5), by using the *Euler-Maclaurin* expansion of Section 8.6 to estimate the neglected terms.

26. Verify Eq. (7.4.7) explicitly for the Maxwell-Boltzmann ideal gas.

CHAPTER 9

THE METHOD OF GIBBS

9.1 The canonical ensemble. We have seen how the properties of microscopic systems can be employed to construct statistical-thermodynamical functions for collections of such systems. These systems have been idealized to the extent that we have neglected their interactions in a collection. This neglect has enabled us to refer to the individual systems in a meaningful way. Any other simplification has been introduced only for reasons of convenience. Hence, we may suppose that a knowledge of the internal energy values of molecular systems will enable us to determine precise statistical-thermodynamical functions for ideal gases. In principle, nothing more appears possible.

The systems of greatest interest would thus appear to be beyond consideration. However, the brilliant contribution made by Gibbs was that of regarding the actual physical system, with all its intermolecular interactions, as assuming the role of the noninteracting system which we have been considering until now. That is, in Gibbs' view, the term *system* will be understood to refer to any mechanical system whatever. It may consist of a single molecule or a collection of molecules. The term *ensemble* will be understood to refer to a collection of *replicas* of a system. Each replica is such in a precise and formal sense: they all have identical mechanical descriptions, but the values of the mechanical properties may vary from one replica to another. Furthermore, the ensemble consists of an indefinitely great number of replicas. In addition, the energy of interaction between systems of the ensemble may be regarded as negligible (but not actually zero). With regard to the latter point, there seems to be no serious objection to its reasonableness for macroscopic systems as contrasted with microscopic systems. In terms of our previous considerations, we now have to deal with an infinite *collection of collections*.

In the Gibbs scheme there is no need to refer to the number of systems having any particular value of the energy, etc. In fact, such a number is indefinitely great and, as a result, meaningless. The Gibbs method is especially simple in that it deals with *probabilities* directly. [In terms of our earlier discussion, we are to deal with fractions of the ensemble of systems which have the stipulated properties. See Eq. (6.2.8).] Accordingly, we shall concern ourselves shortly with probability distributions; in particular, probability distributions in energy will interest us because they may be presumed to be stationary in time. Then, distributions that refer, presumably, to *equilibrium* distributions of systems will

140

be termed *canonical* distributions and describe the probability distribution in *canonical ensembles*.

Suppose that the probability of finding a system in the states having the energy E_s in a canonical ensemble is $P(E_s)$. We shall evidently require (noting that the summation extends over the *states* of the system) that

$$\sum_s P(E_s) = 1. \tag{9.1.1}$$

The ensemble average of some property of the system that depends on the state s is taken as

$$\bar{\alpha} = \sum_s \alpha_s P(E_s). \tag{9.1.2}$$

We may note that for two different states, s and s', but for which $E_s = E_{s'}$, it is intended that

$$P(E_s) = P(E_{s'}), \tag{9.1.3}$$

which is fundamental; unless indicated to the contrary, two states having the same energy are equally probable.

The most important assumption of the Gibbs method is that the ensemble averages, as indicated by Eq. (9.1.2), correspond to the physically observable properties of a system in thermal equilibrium. This assumption may appear initially to be arbitrary to an extent exceeding physical reasonableness. However, because the canonical ensemble is constructed to provide the thermal transfer of energy between systems, replacing any system by what may be regarded as its thermal equivalent will do nothing to alter the canonical distribution. Each system may be regarded, from this point of view, as immersed and in thermal contact with a thermostat comprising the remaining (infinite) portion of the canonical ensemble. In contrast with the most probable distribution, the averages of the canonical ensemble include values of the energy which differ from the average value. Indeed, while we shall not consider them in any detail, Gibbs did consider *microcanonical ensembles* which involved an equilibrium ensemble of systems each of which has the same energy. The microcanonical ensemble would appear to be more closely related to the collections considered by the method of the most probable distribution than it is to the canonical ensemble. In spite of these differences, we shall see that the canonical ensemble provides a reasonable statistical description of equilibrium phenomena. (See Section 9.2.)

We now turn to a determination of the canonical distribution. Suppose we wish to determine the probability that a "double system" may be selected from the ensemble. Such a system may be supposed to have an energy which is the sum of the energies of the two constituent systems.

Since the "double system" may be selected by selecting first one system and then, independently, the other, the probability of doing so is evidently the probability of selecting the "double system." In fact, we require that

$$P(E_1 + E_2) = P(E_1)P(E_2), \tag{9.1.4}$$

regardless of the values of E_1 and E_2. This then determines the form of the distribution in energy for the canonical distribution, for

$$\frac{\partial P(E_1 + E_2)}{\partial E_1} = P'(E_1 + E_2) = P'(E_1)P(E_2)$$

and

$$\frac{\partial P(E_1 + E_2)}{\partial E_2} = P'(E_1 + E_2) = P(E_1)P'(E_2).$$

Hence, regardless of the values of E_1 and E_2,

$$\frac{P'(E_1)}{P(E_1)} = \frac{P'(E_2)}{P(E_2)} = -\frac{1}{\Theta},$$

where Θ in a constant independent of E_s. As a result, the canonical distribution may be expressed as

$$P(E_s) = e^{(F - E_s)/\Theta}, \tag{9.1.5}$$

where Eq. (9.1.1) requires

$$e^{-F/\Theta} = \sum_s e^{-E_s/\Theta}. \tag{9.1.6}$$

Note the similarity with the Maxwell-Boltzmann distribution; note also the difference, namely that here E_s refers to the energy of the macroscopic system. Clearly, if the values of E_s may become indefinitely large, then Θ must be restricted to positive values. We refer to Θ as the *modulus of the distribution*. (When E_s is bounded in magnitude, there is no reason for Θ to be restricted to positive values. This gives rise to the possibility of "negative temperatures" for such systems. In spite of an interest which has arisen recently in this phenomenon, no discussion of it will be attempted here.)

From our previous results we can guess the physical significance to be attached to F and Θ, but we repeat the Gibbs argument of thermodynamic analogy. Since

$$e^{-F/\Theta} = \sum_s e^{-E_s/\Theta},$$

$$e^{-F/\Theta}\left(\frac{F}{\Theta^2}d\Theta - \frac{dF}{\Theta}\right) = \sum_s \frac{E_s}{\Theta^2}e^{-E_s/\Theta}d\Theta - \frac{1}{\Theta}\sum_k dx_k \sum_s \frac{\partial E_s}{\partial x_k}e^{-E_s/\Theta},$$

where we have assumed that the energy values of the system may be altered by changes in a set of extensive parameters x_k. Rearranging, we have

$$\frac{F}{\Theta^2}\, d\Theta - \frac{dF}{\Theta} = \frac{1}{\Theta^2}\sum_s E_s e^{(F-E_s)/\Theta}d\Theta - \frac{1}{\Theta}\sum_k dx_k \sum_s \frac{\partial E_s}{\partial x_k}e^{(F-E_s)/\Theta},$$

and writing the ensemble averages, we find

$$-dF = -\left(\frac{F-\overline{E}}{\Theta}\right)d\Theta - \left[\sum_k dx_k \overline{\left(\frac{\partial E}{\partial x_k}\right)}\right].$$

The last series can be recognized as the ensemble average of the differential work done on the system. Since

$$d\left(\frac{\overline{E}-F}{\Theta}\right) = \frac{d\overline{E}}{\Theta} - \frac{dF}{\Theta} - \frac{\overline{E}-F}{\Theta^2}\,d\Theta,$$

$$\Theta d\left(\frac{\overline{E}-F}{\Theta}\right) = d\overline{E} + d\overline{W}, \tag{9.1.7}$$

which is the differential expression of the first and second laws of thermodynamics for systems which are closed with respect to the exchange of matter. Clearly, we shall identify

$$\Theta = kT \tag{9.1.8}$$

and

$$kd\left(\frac{\overline{E}-F}{\Theta}\right) = d\overline{S}, \tag{9.1.9}$$

which gives us a new form for the entropy. Since

$$\ln P_s = \frac{F-E_s}{\Theta},$$

we have

$$\overline{S} = -k\sum_s P_s \ln P_s, \tag{9.1.10}$$

or the entropy is proportional to the *average* of the logarithm of the *probability distribution*. In the method of the most probable distribution, it will be recalled, the entropy was simply related to the *degeneracy* of the most probable distribution. [See Eq. (7.4.7).]

In the method of Maxwell-Boltzmann there was no question that the quantity identified as the entropy was maximal. In the case of the present identification we can verify also that the entropy, so defined, is a maximum with respect to arbitrary changes in the distribution, which, however, leave the energy unaltered. To see this, consider the quantity

$$H = \sum_s P_s \ln P_s, \tag{9.1.11}$$

with

$$\overline{E} = \sum_s E_s P_s \tag{9.1.12}$$

and

$$1 = \sum_s P_s. \tag{9.1.13}$$

Developing H in a Taylor's series, we obtain

$$\delta H = \sum_s \frac{\partial H}{\partial P_s} \delta P_s + \tfrac{1}{2} \sum_{s,t} \frac{\partial^2 H}{\partial P_s \, \partial P_t} \delta P_s \, \delta P_t + \cdots,$$

to second-order terms. Substituting Eq. (9.1.11), we obtain

$$\frac{\partial H}{\partial P_s} = (1 + \ln P_s),$$

$$\frac{\partial^2 H}{\partial P_s \, \partial P_t} = \frac{1}{P_s}, \qquad s = t,$$

$$= 0, \qquad s \neq t.$$

Hence

$$\delta H = \sum_s (1 + \ln P_s) \, \delta P_s + \tfrac{1}{2} \sum_s \frac{1}{P_s} (\delta P_s)^2.$$

Now, if we refer to deviations from the canonical distribution, Eq. (9.1.5) may be employed. Then, by Eqs. (9.1.12) and (9.1.13), the first variation vanishes. Since the probabilities are nonnegative, we obtain [compare with Eq. (4.1.4)]

$$\delta H_E \geq 0, \tag{9.1.14}$$

or the canonical value of H is a minimum. If we take Eq. (9.1.10) as a *general definition* of entropy, then we are entitled to say that the canonical value of the entropy is a maximum.

The result just obtained is related to a celebrated theorem due to Boltzmann, namely that the quantity H cannot increase with time. Inasmuch as we have not considered the temporal variation at all, we cannot claim to have demonstrated the H-theorem. Nevertheless, the parallel seems clear: if equilibrium is a state of affairs which ultimately may be achieved by a system of fixed energy, regardless of the initial set of circumstances, H achieves thereby its minimum possible value.

9.2 Dispersions in statistical-thermodynamic properties. A consequence of the new statistical analog for the entropy is that we now can inquire into the dispersions in the average values of all statistical-thermodynamic properties. While it is possible to determine the dispersion in energy for a single system in terms of the most probable distribution, no other thermodynamic properties may be so treated insofar as they pertain to the collection.

We consider, first, the dispersion in energy. Let

$$\overline{(\Delta E)^2} = \sum_s E_s^2 P(E_s) - \overline{E}^2$$

$$= e^{F/\Theta} \left(\Theta^2 \frac{\partial}{\partial \Theta} \right) \left(\Theta^2 \frac{\partial}{\partial \Theta} \right) \sum_s e^{-E_s/\Theta} - \overline{E}^2,$$

using the canonical distribution. From the relation

$$\overline{E} = \sum_s E_s e^{(F-E_s)/\Theta} = e^{F/\Theta} \left(\Theta^2 \frac{\partial}{\partial \Theta} \right) \sum_s e^{-E_s/\Theta} \qquad (9.2.1)$$

and Eq. (9.1.6), we have

$$\overline{(\Delta E)^2} = \Theta^2 \frac{\partial \overline{E}}{\partial \Theta}. \qquad (9.2.2)$$

Since

$$\overline{(\Delta E)^2} = \overline{E^2} - \overline{E}^2,$$

$$\left(\frac{\overline{\Delta E}}{\overline{E}} \right)^2 = \frac{\overline{E^2}}{\overline{E}^2} - 1 = \frac{\Theta^2}{\overline{E}^2} \frac{\partial E}{\partial \Theta}.$$

With Eq. (9.1.8), the relative dispersion in energy is

$$\left(\frac{\overline{\Delta E}}{\overline{E}} \right)^2 = \frac{kT^2 \overline{C}}{\overline{E}^2}, \qquad (9.2.3)$$

where $\overline{C}$ is the heat capacity of the system. Since both $\overline{C}$ and $\overline{E}$ are extensive, the relative dispersion in energy vanishes for indefinitely large systems.

The dispersion in entropy may be determined in a similar manner. Taking Eq. (9.1.10), we may express the entropy as

$$\overline{S} = \overline{-k \ln P(E)} = -k \overline{\left(\frac{F-E}{\Theta} \right)} = -\frac{k}{\Theta} (F - \overline{E}).$$

In this sense,

$$\overline{S^2} = \overline{k^2 \, [\ln \, P(E)]^2} = \frac{k^2}{\Theta^2} (\overline{F^2} - 2F\overline{E} + \overline{E^2}).$$

Hence the dispersion in entropy is

$$\overline{(\Delta S)^2} = \overline{S^2} - \overline{S}^2 = \frac{k^2}{\Theta^2} \overline{E^2} - \overline{E}^2 = \frac{k^2}{\Theta^2} \overline{(\Delta E)^2}, \qquad (9.2.4)$$

and the relative dispersion in entropy is

$$\overline{\left(\frac{\Delta S}{\overline{S}}\right)^2} = \frac{k\overline{C}}{\overline{S}^2}, \qquad (9.2.5)$$

by Eqs. (9.2.2) and (9.1.8). The relative dispersion in entropy thus vanishes for indefinitely large systems.

One might view the above calculations of dispersion as corresponding to the relative dispersion in these quantities which would result from measurements made on systems withdrawn from a canonical ensemble. According to this view, the fact that the relative dispersion tends toward zero means that such distributions as do occur in the various properties are relatively *precise* for indefinitely large systems. In this sense, the canonical distribution tends toward the microcanonical, and the probability distribution in any thermodynamic property is essentially singular about the average or most probable value of the property.

We can express the probability of finding a system of the canonical ensemble in a certain state as

$$P_i = \exp\left[\frac{\overline{S}}{k} - \frac{(E_i - \overline{E})}{kT}\right].$$

If, now, we consider a set of all systems of the same energy, the probability of finding such a group of systems (that is, a *microcanonical subensemble*) in a canonical ensemble is

$$\overline{P}(E_i) \equiv \sum_{\substack{i \\ E_i \, \text{const.}}}' P_i = \sum_{\substack{i \\ E_i \, \text{const.}}}' \exp\left[-\frac{\overline{S}}{k} - \frac{(E_i - \overline{E})}{kT}\right]$$

$$= W(E_i) \exp\left[-\frac{\overline{S}}{k} - \frac{(E_i - \overline{E})}{kT}\right], \qquad (9.2.6)$$

where the prime denotes a summation over states of constant energy and $W(E_i)$ is the degeneracy of the microcanonical subensemble for an energy E_i. Inasmuch as the relative dispersion in energy is vanishingly small, we may suppose that $\overline{P}(E_i)$ essentially vanishes unless $E_i = \overline{E}$; but then to satisfy Eq. (9.1.1), it must follow that

$$\overline{P}(\overline{E}) = W(\overline{E})e^{-\overline{S}/k} \sim 1, \qquad (9.2.7)$$

which leads to

$$\ln W(\overline{E}) - \frac{\overline{S}}{k} \sim 0, \qquad (9.2.8)$$

in accord with Eqs. (7.4.7). This suggests the *assumption* that the *entropy of a microcanonical subensemble* in the canonical ensemble be taken as (following Gibbs)

$$S_i = k \ln W(E_i), \qquad (9.2.9)$$

whereupon the probability of finding a microcanonical subensemble, with prescribed energy and entropy, in the canonical ensemble, is

$$\overline{P}(E_i, S_i) = \exp\left[\frac{(S_i - \overline{S})}{k} - \frac{(E_i - \overline{E})}{kT}\right].$$

[Note that this expression requires that $\overline{S} > k \ln W(\overline{E}) = S(\overline{E})$, in order that Eq. (9.1.1) be satisfied. Nevertheless, the difference in the two entropies may be relatively negligible.] To bring this into a useful form, we may distinguish between changes in the energy attributable to changes in certain extensive parameters and those which are not. Then, in terms of deviations from the ensemble average values,

$$\overline{P}\,(\delta E, \delta S, \delta x_k) = \exp\left(-\,\frac{\delta E - \sum_k X_k\,\delta x_k - T\,\delta S}{kT}\right), \qquad (9.2.10)$$

where, clearly, we must have

$$\delta E - \sum_k X_k\,\delta x_k - T\,\delta S \geq 0. \qquad (9.2.11)$$

Comparing this expression with that for thermodynamic equilibrium, Eq. (4.1.5), we see that the deviations from the ensemble average values of the thermodynamic properties are not attainable by real physical processes. We see here the relation between thermodynamic and statistical equilibrium, namely that the distribution of microcanonical subensembles in a canonical ensemble is stable if all deviations from the canonical thermodynamic state correspond to microcanonical thermodynamic states which cannot be attained from the former by real physical processes.

Equation (9.2.10) may be used to determine the dispersion in the value of any thermodynamic property. We may illustrate its use by determining the dispersion in energy under conditions of constant volume.

Since the deviations in energy and entropy are measured from the canonical average values, we have for $\delta x_k = \delta V = 0$

$$\delta S_V = [S(\overline{E}) - \overline{S}] + \left(\frac{\partial \overline{S}}{\partial \overline{E}}\right)_V \delta E + \frac{1}{2}\left(\frac{\partial^2 \overline{S}}{\partial \overline{E}^2}\right)_V (\delta E)^2 + \cdots$$

$$\doteq [S(\overline{E}) - \overline{S}] + \frac{1}{T}\, \delta E - \left(\frac{1}{2C_V T^2}\right)(\delta E)^2.$$

As noted earlier, the first term is negative and represents the difference in the entropies for a microcanonical ensemble and a canonical ensemble of the same energy. To this approximation,

$$\overline{P}\,(\delta E,\, \delta S,\, 0)\, \propto\, \exp\left[-\left(\frac{1}{2kT^2 C_V}\right)(\delta E)^2\right].$$

Now, to simplify matters, we express the normalization of $\overline{P}$ by an integral:

$$1 = \sum_{\delta E} \overline{P}\,(\delta E,\, \delta S,\, 0)$$

$$\doteq A \int_{-\infty}^{+\infty} d(E - \overline{E}) \exp\left[-\frac{(E - \overline{E})^2}{2kT^2 C_V}\right],$$

whereupon we require

$$A = \frac{1}{\sqrt{2kT^2 C_V \pi}}.$$

In this respect,

$$\overline{P}\,(\delta E,\, \delta S,\, 0)\, d(E - \overline{E}) = \frac{e^{-(E-\overline{E})^2/(2kT^2 C_V)}}{\sqrt{2kT^2 C_V \pi}}\, dE$$

is the probability that a microcanonical subensemble in a canonical ensemble of systems of fixed volume will have an energy between E and $E + dE$ (with entropy between S and $S + dS$). The dispersion in the energy is

$$\overline{(E - \overline{E})^2} = \frac{1}{\sqrt{2kT^2 C_V \pi}} \int_{-\infty}^{+\infty} d(E - \overline{E})(E - \overline{E})^2 \exp\left[-\frac{(E - E_V)^2}{2kT^2 C_V}\right]$$

$$= kT^2 C_V,$$

in agreement with Eq. (9.2.2). The dispersion in other thermodynamic quantities is easily computed along the lines indicated.

9.3 The grand canonical ensemble. Before any extensive use can be made of Gibbs' procedure, the energy values of the macroscopic system must be specified. For the procedure to be particularly useful for chemical purposes, it also is necessary to consider the statistical equilibrium of systems which are open to the exchange of matter. While Gibbs' main line of investigation dealt with closed systems, he did not neglect open systems. These he treated under what he termed *grand canonical ensembles* (to be contrasted with the *petit ensembles* considered to this point).

A grand canonical ensemble may be regarded as an indefinitely large collection of petit ensembles, but the composition of the systems may vary from one ensemble to another. In fact, there no longer is any need for requiring the ensemble to consist of replicas of any system, except in the most general sense. We simply require that each system of the ensemble have states which determine the energy of the system and its composition. For simplicity we restrict our considerations to two kinds of molecular species, α and β. Then a given system will have the energy E_s; the number of α-species will be N_s^α; the number of β-species will be N_s^β. Following our earlier line of argument, the probability of finding a system in the ensemble in the state s will be given by $P(E_s, N_s^\alpha, N_s^\beta)$. Then, as previously,

$$P(E_1 + E_2, N_1^\alpha + N_2^\alpha, N_1^\beta + N_2^\beta) = P(E_1, N_1^\alpha, N_1^\beta)P(E_2, N_2^\alpha, N_2^\beta),$$

(9.3.1)

from which it follows that

$$P(E_s, N_s^\alpha, N_s^\beta) = \exp\left(\frac{L + \mu^\alpha N_s^\alpha + \mu^\beta N_s^\beta - E_s}{\Theta}\right), \qquad (9.3.2)$$

subject to

$$\sum_s P(E_s, N_s^\alpha, N_s^\beta) = 1, \qquad (9.3.3)$$

or

$$e^{-L/\Theta} = \sum_s \exp\left(\frac{\mu^\alpha N_s^\alpha + \mu^\beta N_s^\beta - E_s}{\Theta}\right). \qquad (9.3.4)$$

It must be kept in mind that E_s generally is not entirely independent of the values of the N's. The ensemble averages now are to be computed on the basis of the grand canonical distribution.

The procedure of identifying the statistical parameters through the first and second laws of thermodynamics may be carried out. We can readily verify that

$$\Theta = kT,$$

$$-k\left(\frac{L + \mu^\alpha \overline{N}^\alpha + \mu^\beta \overline{N}^\beta - \overline{E}}{\Theta}\right) = \overline{S}, \qquad (9.3.5)$$

and μ^α, μ^β are the chemical potentials per particle. In these terms, we see that

$$F = L + \mu^\alpha \overline{N^\alpha} + \mu^\beta \overline{N^\beta}. \tag{9.3.6}$$

One may show, further, that (the x_k standing for extensive parameters referring to work)

$$\overline{N^\alpha} = - \left(\frac{\partial L}{\partial \mu^\alpha} \right)_{\Theta, \mu^\beta, x_k}, \tag{9.3.7}$$

$$\overline{E} = (L + \mu^\alpha \overline{N^\alpha} + \mu^\beta \overline{N^\beta}) - \Theta \left(\frac{\partial L}{\partial \Theta} \right)_{\mu^\alpha, \mu^\beta, x_k}. \tag{9.3.8}$$

Hence

$$\overline{S} = k \left(\frac{\partial L}{\partial \Theta} \right)_{\mu^\alpha, \mu^\beta, x_k}. \tag{9.3.9}$$

One can show also that

$$\mu^\alpha = \left(\frac{\partial \overline{E}}{\partial \overline{N^\alpha}} \right)_{\overline{S}, x_k}. \tag{9.3.10}$$

Since

$$\left(\frac{\partial L}{\partial \mu^\alpha} \right)_{\Theta, \mu^\beta, x_k} \left(\frac{\partial \mu^\alpha}{\partial \overline{N^\alpha}} \right)_{\Theta, \mu^\beta, x_k} = \left(\frac{\partial L}{\partial \overline{N^\alpha}} \right)_{\Theta, \mu^\beta, x_k},$$

Eq. (9.3.7) yields

$$\left(\frac{\partial L}{\partial \overline{N^\alpha}} \right)_{\Theta, \mu^\beta, x_k} = - \overline{N^\alpha} \left(\frac{\partial \mu^\alpha}{\partial \overline{N^\alpha}} \right)_{\Theta, \mu^\beta, x_k}. \tag{9.3.11}$$

We are now in a position to evaluate the dispersion in N for a grand canonical ensemble.

$$\overline{(N^\alpha - \overline{N^\alpha})^2}$$

$$= e^{L/\Theta} \sum_s (N_s^\alpha - \overline{N^\alpha})^2 \exp\left(\frac{\mu^\alpha N_s^\alpha + \mu^\beta N_s^\beta - E_s}{\Theta} \right)$$

$$= e^{L/\Theta} \sum_s \left[\Theta^2 \frac{\partial^2}{\partial \mu^{\alpha 2}} - 2\overline{N^\alpha} \Theta \frac{\partial}{\partial \mu^\alpha} + \overline{N^\alpha}^2 \right] \exp\left(\frac{\mu^\alpha N_s^\alpha + \mu^\beta N_s^\beta - E_s}{\Theta} \right)$$

$$= e^{L/\Theta} \left[\Theta^2 \frac{\partial^2}{\partial \mu^{\alpha 2}} - 2\Theta \overline{N^\alpha} \frac{\partial}{\partial \mu^\alpha} + \overline{N^\alpha}^2 \right] e^{-L/\Theta}.$$

Hence, one can show that

$$\overline{(N^\alpha - \overline{N^\alpha})^2} = -\Theta \left(\frac{\partial^2 L}{\partial \mu^{\alpha 2}}\right)_{\Theta, \mu^\beta, x_k} = \Theta \left(\frac{\partial \overline{N^\alpha}}{\partial \mu^\alpha}\right)_{\Theta, \mu^\beta, x_k}$$

and

$$1 - \overline{\left(\frac{N^\alpha}{\overline{N^\alpha}}\right)^2} = \frac{\Theta}{\overline{N^\alpha}^2} \left(\frac{\partial \overline{N^\alpha}}{\partial \mu^\alpha}\right)_{\Theta, \mu^\beta, x_k}. \tag{9.3.12}$$

Since $\overline{N^\alpha}$ is extensive while μ^α and Θ are intensive, the relative dispersion in N tends towards zero for indefinitely large $\overline{N^\alpha}$. In this case, the grand canonical ensemble approaches the canonical. But, as we have seen, the canonical ensemble then approaches the microcanonical.

The distribution of systems in terms of their thermodynamic properties may be augmented to include changes in composition. Following the procedure of Section 9.2, we can show that the probability of finding a microcanonical subensemble in a grand canonical ensemble with a set of properties different from the ensemble average values of these properties is

$$P(\delta E, \delta S, \delta x_k, \delta N) = \exp\left(-\frac{\delta E - \sum_k X \delta x_k + \sum_i \mu^i \delta N^i - T \delta S}{kT}\right),$$

$$\tag{9.3.13}$$

where, now,

$$\delta E - \sum_k X_k \delta x_k + \sum_i \mu^i \delta N^i - T \delta S \geq 0,$$

in agreement with our expectations from equilibrium considerations. This expression may be employed to determine the dispersion in the value of any thermodynamic property of a system in a grand canonical ensemble.

It is interesting to examine the maximum term in N^α in the series in Eq. (9.3.4). From Eq. (9.3.12) we know that this must correspond to a value of N^α which differs from its average value by a relatively negligible amount. First we express Eq. (9.3.4) as

$$e^{-L/\Theta} = \sum_{N_\alpha, N_\beta} \exp\left(\frac{\mu^\alpha N^\alpha + \mu^\beta N^\beta}{\Theta}\right) \sum_s \exp\left[-\frac{E_s(N^\alpha, N^\beta)}{\Theta}\right]. \tag{9.3.14}$$

The last series may be expressed as

$$\sum_s \exp\left[-\frac{E_s(N^\alpha, N^\beta)}{\Theta}\right] = \exp\left[-\frac{F(N^\alpha, N^\beta)}{\Theta}\right],$$

by Eq. (9.1.6). Thus

$$e^{-L/\Theta} = \sum_{N_\alpha, N_\beta} \exp\left(\frac{\mu^\alpha N^\alpha + \mu^\beta N^\beta}{\Theta}\right) \exp\left[-\frac{F(N_\alpha, N_\beta)}{\Theta}\right]. \quad (9.3.15)$$

The maximum term in the series evidently corresponds to that for which

$$\mu^\alpha = \frac{\partial F(N^\alpha, N^\beta)}{\partial N^\alpha} \quad \text{and} \quad \mu^\beta = \frac{\partial F(N^\alpha, N^\beta)}{\partial N^\beta}, \quad (9.3.16)$$

in accord with our thermodynamic expectations. The N's here may be replaced by their average values, in view of Eq. (9.3.12), with no significant loss of accuracy.

9.4 Gibbs statistics for ideal gases. The previous sections have shown an asymptotic relationship between the Gibbs results and those of the most probable distribution. In the case where the macroscopic system is, in fact, an ideal gas, we may expect the two procedures to lead to identical results. For this purpose we examine the ideal gas consisting of structureless particles and derive the Maxwell-Boltzmann, Fermi-Dirac, and Bose-Einstein distribution formulas.

The energy of such a system of N particles is

$$E = \sum_{p=1}^{N} \epsilon_\sigma^{(p)}, \quad (9.4.1)$$

where $\epsilon_\sigma^{(p)}$ may be given by Eq. (8.1.1) regardless of p. [A state of the macroscopic system evidently is one of the set of all $3N$-sets $(i_1 \ldots i_p \ldots i_N, j_1 \ldots j_p \ldots j_N, l_1 \ldots l_p \ldots l_N)$.] Clearly, for one species, noting that we include *zero particles* as a state,

$$e^{-L/\Theta} = \sum_s \exp\left(\frac{\mu N_s - E_s}{\Theta}\right)$$

$$= \sum_{N_s=0}^{\infty} \exp\left(\frac{\mu N_s}{\Theta}\right) \sum_{\text{all } \sigma} \exp\left[-\frac{\sum_{p=1}^{N_s} \epsilon_\sigma^{(p)}}{\Theta}\right]$$

$$= \sum_{N_s=0}^{\infty} \exp\left(\frac{\mu N_s}{kT}\right) (Z_{\text{trans}})^{N_s}$$

$$= \sum_{N_s=0}^{\infty} (e^{\mu/kT} Z_{\text{trans}})^{N_s} = \frac{1}{1 - e^{\mu/kT} Z_{\text{trans}}}. \quad (9.4.2)$$

From Eq. (9.3.6), we obtain

$$\overline{N} = \frac{e^{\mu/kT}Z_{\text{trans}}}{1 - e^{\mu/kT}Z_{\text{trans}}},$$

or

$$e^{\mu/kT}Z_{\text{trans}} = \frac{\overline{N}}{\overline{N}+1} \to 1 \qquad (N \to \infty). \tag{9.4.3}$$

By Eqs. (7.2.12) and (7.3.11) we clearly have an inconsistency. However, the inconsistency is not due to Gibbs. We emphasize that we have treated the individual particles as if they were distinguishable while, in fact, they are not. Gibbs pointed out that it was in the spirit of the statistical method to regard two states as identical if they were related to each other by the exchange of entirely similar particles. For systems thus constituted, he suggested that Eq. (9.3.2), for example, be replaced by

$$P(E_s, N_s^\alpha, N_s^\beta) = \frac{e^{(L+\mu^\alpha N_s^\alpha + \mu^\beta N_s^\beta - E_s)/\Theta}}{N_s^\alpha! N_s^\beta!}, \tag{9.4.4}$$

to account for the obviously redundant permutations of identical objects. This change will not affect the identifications which have been made. However, for the Maxwell-Boltzmann statistics we shall take

$$e^{-L_{\text{MB}}/\Theta} = \sum_s \frac{e^{(\mu^\alpha N_s^\alpha + \mu^\beta N_s^\beta - E_s)/\Theta}}{N_s^\alpha! N_s^\beta} \tag{9.4.5}$$

instead of Eq. (9.3.4). For the present case of an ideal gas, we obtain, instead of Eq. (9.4.2),

$$e^{-L_{\text{MB}}/kT} = \sum_{N_s=0}^{\infty} \frac{(e^{\mu/kT}Z_{\text{trans}})^{N_s}}{N_s!} = \exp\,(e^{\mu/kT}Z_{\text{trans}}) \tag{9.4.6}$$

and

$$L_{\text{MB}} = -kTZ_{\text{trans}}\,e^{\mu/kT}. \tag{9.4.7}$$

From Eq. (9.3.7) we have

$$\overline{N} = Z_{\text{trans}}\,e^{\mu/kT},$$

or

$$\mu = -kT \ln\left(\frac{Z_{\text{trans}}}{\overline{N}}\right),$$

in agreement with our previous result.

The average occupation number of a microscopic state with energy ϵ_σ is

$$\overline{n_{\epsilon_\sigma}} = \sum_s n_\sigma \frac{\exp\left[\dfrac{L_{\mathrm{MB}} + \mu N_s - \sum_{p=1}^{N_s} \epsilon_\sigma^{(p)}}{\Theta}\right]}{N_s!}$$

$$= \sum_s \frac{e^{L_{\mathrm{MB}}/\Theta}}{N_s!}\left(-\Theta\frac{\partial}{\partial\epsilon_\sigma}\right)\exp\left(\frac{\mu N_s - \sum_{p=1}^{N_s}\epsilon_\sigma}{\Theta}\right)$$

$$= e^{L_{\mathrm{MB}}/\Theta}\left(-\Theta\frac{\partial}{\partial\epsilon_\sigma}\right)e^{-L_{\mathrm{MB}}/\Theta},$$

or

$$\overline{n_{\epsilon_\sigma}} = e^{\mu/kT}\frac{\partial Z_{\mathrm{trans}}}{\partial\epsilon_\sigma} = e^{(\mu-\epsilon_\sigma)/kT}, \tag{9.4.8}$$

in agreement with Eq. (7.2.8) with the *difference* that here we refer to *average* occupation numbers.

We may now employ the Gibbs statistics to obtain the distribution for indistinguishable particles. Following a method due to Pauli, the energy of the system may be written as

$$E_s = \sum_\sigma n_\sigma^{(s)}\epsilon_\sigma, \tag{9.4.9}$$

with

$$N_s = \sum_\sigma n_\sigma^{(s)}. \tag{9.4.10}$$

Here again σ is a set of labels which describes the microscopic *state*, as in Eq. (8.1.1). Each E_s is included only once for any distribution or set $n_\sigma^{(s)}$. Hence no counting occurs over indistinguishable permutations as previously; the probability is then given by Eq. (9.3.2). We have

$$e^{-L/\Theta} = \sum_s \exp\left[\frac{\mu N_s - \sum_\sigma n_\sigma^{(s)}\epsilon_\sigma}{\Theta}\right]$$

$$= \sum_s \exp\left[\frac{\sum_\sigma n_\sigma^{(s)}(\mu - \epsilon_\sigma)}{\Theta}\right].$$

We now imagine the summation over macroscopic states to be carried out by first summing the n_σ in accordance with the restrictions of the Fermi-Dirac or Bose-Einstein statistics and then carrying out the summation over the microscopic states σ. That is, we express

$$e^{-L/\Theta} = \prod_\sigma\left[{\sum_{n_\sigma}}' e^{n_\sigma(\mu-\epsilon_\sigma)/\Theta}\right], \tag{9.4.11}$$

the prime denoting:

$$n_\sigma = 0, 1, 2, 3, \ldots, \qquad \text{for Bose-Einstein statistics,}$$

$$n_\sigma = 0, 1, \qquad\qquad\qquad \text{for Fermi-Dirac statistics.}$$

Hence

$$e^{-L_{\mathrm{BE}}/kT} = \prod_\sigma \sum_{n_\sigma=0}^{\infty} \left[\exp\left(\frac{\mu - \epsilon_\sigma}{kT} \right) \right]^{n_\sigma}$$

$$= \prod_\sigma \left[1 - \exp\left(\frac{\mu - \epsilon_\sigma}{kT} \right) \right]^{-1}. \qquad (9.4.12)$$

From this the average occupation number is

$$\overline{n_{\sigma,\mathrm{BE}}} = e^{L_{\mathrm{BE}}/kT} \left(-kT \frac{\partial}{\partial \epsilon_\sigma} \right) e^{-L_{\mathrm{BE}}/kT}$$

$$= \frac{e^{(\mu-\epsilon_\sigma)/kT}}{1 - e^{(\mu-\epsilon_\sigma)/kT}} = \frac{1}{e^{(\epsilon_\sigma-\mu)/kT} - 1}, \qquad (9.4.13)$$

in agreement with Eq. (7.4.2) with the difference here, again, that average occupation numbers are involved.

For the Fermi-Dirac statistics we evidently have

$$e^{-L_{\mathrm{FD}}/kT} = \prod_\sigma \sum_{n_\sigma=0}^{1} \left[\exp\left(\frac{\mu - \epsilon_\sigma}{kT} \right) \right]^{n_\sigma}$$

$$= \prod_\sigma \left[1 + \exp\left(\frac{\mu - \epsilon_\sigma}{kT} \right) \right]. \qquad (9.4.14)$$

Hence

$$\overline{n_{\sigma,\mathrm{FD}}} = e^{L_{\mathrm{FD}}/kT} \left(-kT \frac{\partial}{\partial \epsilon_\sigma} \right) e^{-L_{\mathrm{FD}}/kT}$$

$$= \frac{1}{e^{(\epsilon_\sigma-\mu)/kT} + 1}, \qquad (9.4.15)$$

again, with the restriction that average occupation numbers are involved, in agreement with Eq. (7.4.4).

In the foregoing terms, we reproduce entirely the results of the method of the most probable distribution.

9.5 Transition to classical statistical mechanics. We turn now to the most important applied aspect of the Gibbs statistical mechanics, namely, the way it can be used to deal with systems of interacting subsystems. Since we restrict our considerations to the case of Maxwell-Boltzmann statistics, the results obtained may be applied reliably only for temperatures which are not too small.

It is evident, once the energy values of the system of interacting subsystems are known, that the formal solution of the statistical-mechanical problem is complete. However, the problem of determining these energy values is a formidable one for which general solutions free from approximations are not yet available. One approximation which we shall consider has the noteworthy feature that it comprises the results attainable when classical, rather than quantum, mechanics is employed; as such it has a feature of general applicability.

Imagine that the physical system of interest is confined to a fixed region of space. Imagine, also, that this region is divided into a number of contiguous regions, each of which may be presumed to contain a single molecular system. In such a *localized* model of the physical system, each molecule will have a value for its energy which may be associated with the region of space in which it is found. For simplicity, we assume that the variation of the potential energy in each region is negligibly small; in that case, the energy of a molecular system may be seen to consist of one of the values of its kinetic energy in the pertinent region and the pertinent potential energy. The latter, it must be noted, reflects the interaction of the given molecule and all the others, as well as the effects intrinsically associated with the region. We may write one of the energy values for the t-th molecule in the s-th region as

$$\epsilon_s^{(t)} = \frac{h^2}{8m} \left[\left(\frac{n_x^{(t)}}{x_{st}}\right)^2 + \left(\frac{n_y^{(t)}}{y_{st}}\right)^2 + \left(\frac{n_z^{(t)}}{z_{st}}\right)^2 \right] + v_t(s) + \epsilon_i^{(t)}. \qquad (9.5.1)$$

Here the first group of terms corresponds to the kinetic energy of motion in a box, Eq. (8.1.1), with x_{st}, y_{st}, and z_{st} the sides of the rectangular parallelopiped enclosing the region; $v_t(s)$ is presumed to be uniform throughout the sth region; $\epsilon_i^{(t)}$ refers to one of the internal energy values of the t-th molecule. Now we make the important additional approximation that the set of all energy values given by Eq. (9.5.1) *for different s* comprise the localized energy values of a molecule of the system. That is, we imagine that each molecule of the system may be found in any region, whereupon it acquires one of the energy values associated with that region. In this connection, we may emphasize that the so-called potential energy of the region $v_t(s)$ depends implicitly on the location of the other regions (and, thus, on the disposition of the other molecules).

The partition function for a single configuration may be constructed. We shall do so, assuming that the appropriate sum may be replaced by an integral with no undue loss of accuracy [see Eq. (8.6.7)]:

$$Z_s = \prod_{t=1}^{N} \frac{x_{st} y_{st} z_{st}}{h^3} \exp\left[-\frac{v_t(s)}{kT}\right] \sum_i \exp\left[-\frac{\epsilon_i^{(t)}}{kT}\right]$$

$$\times \int_{-\infty}^{+\infty} dp_x^{(t)} \int_{-\infty}^{+\infty} dp_y^{(t)} \int_{-\infty}^{+\infty} dp_z^{(t)} \exp\left\{-\frac{[p_x^{(t)}]^2 + [p_y^{(t)}]^2 + [p_z^{(t)}]^2}{2mkT}\right\},$$

$$(9.5.2)$$

where we have introduced the classical momenta through the definition

$$[p_x^{(t)}]^2 = \left[\frac{h^2 n_x^{(t)}}{4 x_{st}}\right]^2,$$

with analogous definitions for $[p_y^{(t)}]^2$ and $[p_z^{(t)}]^2$. Because of the localized character of the molecules, we now permute them from one region to another. As discussed in Section 7.5, this results in an additive contribution to the partition function. In Eq. (9.5.2) this corresponds to a summation over all s for each t:

$$Z_{\text{class}} = \frac{[Z_{(\text{int})}]^N}{h^{3N}} \sum_{\substack{s \\ t=1}} \cdots \sum_{\substack{s \\ t=N}} \exp\left[-\sum_{t=1}^{N} \frac{v_t(s)}{kT}\right] \prod_{t=1}^{N} x_{st} y_{st} z_{st}$$

$$\times \int_{-\infty}^{+\infty} \cdots \int \exp\left\{-\sum_{t=1}^{N} \frac{[p_x^{(t)}]^2 + [p_y^{(t)}]^2 + [p_z^{(t)}]^2}{2mkT}\right\} \prod_{t=1}^{N} dp_x^{(t)} \, dp_y^{(t)} \, dp_z^{(t)}.$$

$$(9.5.3)$$

Note, now, that since the t's and s's are correlated to the extent that only one molecule occurs in each region, $\sum_{t=1}^{N} v_t(s)$ is simply the sum of the potential energies experienced by all N molecules. It may be regarded as a function of the coordinates of each of the molecules. If now the sum over the regions can be replaced by an integral with no undue loss of accuracy, we have (disregarding the indistinguishable permutations)

$$e^{-F_{\text{class}}/kT} = \frac{[Z_{(\text{int})}]^N}{h^{3N}} \int \cdots \int e^{-H/kT} \prod_{i=1}^{3N} dp_i \, dq_i, \qquad (9.5.4)$$

the integral being taken over the relevant *phase space;* also we have introduced the classical Hamiltonian,

$$H = \sum_{i=1}^{3N} \frac{p_i^2}{2m} + v(q_1 \ldots q_{3N}), \qquad (9.5.5)$$

and have employed the canonical variables p_i and their conjugate coordinates q_i. Apart from the factor $[Z_{(\text{int})}]^N/h^{3N}$, Eq. (9.5.4) is the expression introduced by Gibbs for the canonical ensemble. For the grand canonical ensemble (taking into account the permutations),

$$e^{-L_{\text{class}}/kT} = \sum_{N=0}^{\infty} \frac{[Z_{(\text{int})}]^N e^{\mu N/kT}}{h^{3N} N!} \int \cdots \int e^{-H/kT} \prod_{i=1}^{3N} dp_i \, dq_i. \qquad (9.5.6)$$

Now, one of the great conveniences of the classical form is that the kinetic energy and the potential energy can be separated in the cases of usual interest. In such cases, we have (again omitting $N!$)

$$e^{-F_{\text{class}}/kT} = \left[\frac{Z_{(\text{int})} Z_{\text{trans}}}{V} \right]^N \int \cdots \int \exp\left[-\frac{v(q_1 \ldots q_{3N})}{kT} \right] \prod_{i=1}^{3N} dq_i, \qquad (9.5.7)$$

where Z_{trans} is given by Eq. (8.2.1). Clearly when $v(q_1 \ldots q_{3N})$ is zero, as in the case of the ideal gas, we recover the theory of the ideal gas. For the solution of the problem of interacting molecules in the classical approximation we may express Eq. (9.5.7) as

$$e^{-F_{\text{class}}/kT} = e^{-F_{\text{ideal}}/kT} \frac{e^{-F_{\text{config}}/kT}}{V^N}, \qquad (9.5.8)$$

where the configurational integral

$$Q \equiv \int \cdots \int \exp\left[-\frac{v(q_1 \ldots q_{3N})}{kT} \right] \prod_{i=1}^{3N} dq_i \equiv e^{-F_{\text{config}}/kT} \qquad (9.5.9)$$

has been related to the "configurational part" of the Helmholtz function. The evaluation of Eq. (9.5.9) itself is a formidable undertaking and generally cannot be effected without some approximations. We shall see several instances of how this may be done in the following chapter.

The extension of the foregoing to more than a single species readily is carried out.

9.6 Summary. The method of Gibbs in statistical mechanics has been considered.

From a formal point of view, the essential concept of Gibbs is that of considering an ensemble of replicas of the physical system of interest. In this way the macrophysical system assumes the role of the microphysical system in the method of the most probable distribution. The most important consequence of this point of view is that it permits the consideration of systems of interacting molecules. The ensemble is an unlimited number of systems which, though mechanically identical, may have different configurations and velocities of its constituent parts. If the distribution of systems is determined by the energies of the systems, the equilibrium ensemble is termed a canonical ensemble.

The canonical ensemble involves the equilibrium among systems capable of exchange of energy but closed to the transfer of matter. In spite of its apparently abstract character, the canonical ensemble furnishes the thermodynamic analog of the first and second laws of thermodynamics, as in the case of the method of the most probable distribution. The relation to the most probable distribution is established when, under the circumstances that the system becomes indefinitely great in extent, the dispersion in energy is shown to be negligible, relative to the square of the average energy determined for a system of the ensemble. In such a case, the difference between the most probable and average distribution can only be insignificant. In any case, the Gibbs procedure is equipped to evaluate canonical ensemble averages of various properties, and these are taken to correspond with the physically observable equilibrium properties of systems. The dispersion in thermodynamic properties of microcanonical subensembles in equilibrium is examined and related to the entropy definitions employed in the most probable distribution. The thermodynamic condition for equilibrium is seen to be identical with the condition that the canonical distribution of microcanonical subensembles be stable.

To consider systems open to the transfer of matter, Gibbs introduced the grand canonical ensemble. Such an ensemble consists of systems of the most diverse composition and energy. The grand canonical ensemble may be regarded as an ensemble of canonical ensembles, the composition of each of the latter regarded as fixed but varying from one canonical ensemble to the next. Averages of a system in a grand canonical ensemble are taken to correspond with physically observable equilibrium properties of systems. The relative dispersion in numbers of each species in a grand canonical ensemble is shown to become vanishingly small when the average number of each species is increased indefinitely. Under these conditions, the average composition of a system in the grand canonical ensemble corresponds essentially to the only composition. In this sense, the grand canonical ensemble reduces to the canonical. As previously, the dispersion in the thermodynamic properties of open systems in equilibrium requires the thermodynamic condition for the equilibrium of such systems to be satisfied in order that the grand canonical distribution be a stable one.

The explicit evaluation of the distribution formulas in the cases of Maxwell-Boltzmann, Fermi-Dirac, and Bose-Einstein statistics is carried out with the aid of the grand canonical distribution. The results obtained previously are reproduced, with the important difference that the grand canonical derivation gives ensemble averaged occupation numbers.

The utility of Gibbs' statistical mechanics is made apparent by bringing the form we have considered into that invoking classical mechanics—the form originally introduced by Gibbs. The problem of statistical-mechanical equilibrium of interacting molecules is shown to reduce to the evaluation of the configuration integral.

161

1. The probability of finding a molecule of an ideal gas with the velocity components v_x to $v_x + dv_x$, v_y to $v_y + dv_y$, v_z to $v_z + dv_z$ is often referred to as *Maxwell's distribution law*. Derive this from the classical distribution formula for an ideal gas.

2. Assume that an ideal gas nevertheless has molecules which have a potential energy that depends on their location in space. From the classical distribution formula, determine the Boltzmann distribution formula which relates to the probability per unit volume of finding a molecule in a certain region in space.

3. Derive Eq. (9.3.2).

4. Determine the dispersion in temperature for systems in equilibrium and with fixed volume and composition.

5. Determine the dispersion in density for systems in equilibrium at constant temperature and fixed composition.

6. Carry out the detailed analysis leading to Eqs. (9.3.5).

7. Show directly that for homogeneous systems,

$$L = -PV,$$

where P is the pressure exerted by the system and V is its volume. Evaluate L for an ideal gas, using Eq. (9.5.6).

8. Verify Eqs. (9.3.7) through (9.3.10).

9. Derive the classical distribution formula for two species α and β, analogous to Eq. (9.4.4).

10. In terms of Eq. (9.4.11) it is possible to obtain various distribution formulas. Determine such a one for which $n_\sigma = 0$, 1, or 2.

11. The classical form of statistical mechanics may be used to estimate the internal partition function for molecules. Consider a harmonic oscillator which has a kinetic energy $p^2/2m$ and a potential energy $cq^2/2$, c being a positive constant. Evaluate the contribution made to the heat capacity of this classical oscillator. Compare with Section 8.5.

12. Consider a "canonical" distribution in which some other property of a system which is independent of its energy and is constant in time is required in addition to the energy to classify the various systems of an equilibrium ensemble. Determine the relevant distribution formula and how any and all parameters are to be evaluated.

13. Show, in terms of the illustration of Section 9.2, that $[S(\overline{E}) - \overline{S}]$ is negligible in comparison with $\overline{S}$.

14. Verify that the μ's in Eq. (9.3.5) can be identified as the chemical potential per particle, as asserted in the text.

CHAPTER 10

STATISTICAL-THERMODYNAMIC FUNCTIONS
FOR NONSIMPLE SYSTEMS

10.1 Slightly nonideal monatomic gases. We have seen in the preceding chapter how systems consisting of interacting molecules may be treated statistically. Here we shall examine in some detail the effect of intermolecular interactions on the equation of state of a gas. For simplicity we shall restrict our attention to the translational part of the thermodynamic properties and, hence, consider a model for a monatomic gas.

Using the canonical distribution, we have for N identical molecules by Eq. (9.5.8),

$$e^{-F_{class}/kT} = e^{-F_{ideal}/kT} \cdot \frac{e^{-F_{config}/kT}}{V^N},\qquad (10.1.1)$$

where

$$e^{-F_{config}/kT} = \int \cdots \int \exp\left[-\frac{\upsilon(q_1 \ldots q_{3N})}{kT}\right] \prod_{i=1}^{3N} dq_i$$

and V is the volume containing the system while $\upsilon(q_1 \ldots q_{3N})$ is the intermolecular potential. We have already evaluated the Helmholtz function for an ideal gas (Chapter 7).

For simplicity we shall confine our attention to intermolecular potentials consisting entirely of *pair potentials*. That is, we consider only

$$\upsilon(q_1 \ldots q_{3N}) = \sum_{i>j}^{N} \sum_{j=1}^{N} \phi(r_{ij}),\qquad (10.1.2)$$

where r_{ij} is the distance between the molecules (atoms, in the present case). It seems clear that $\phi(r)$ must be specified if any definite results are to be achieved. But since we wish to keep the treatment simple, we shall defer specification of $\phi(r)$ until later stages of the analysis. For the present we need to exploit the properties that: (1) $\phi(r)$ increases enormously when r becomes smaller than some nonzero value, and (2) $\phi(r)$ vanishes extremely rapidly as r increases beyond some finite value. In other words, we must assume that the intermolecular potentials have strongly repulsive parts and negligible values for large intermolecular distances. We may anticipate that some region of attractive potential energy must be manifest also, but we need not elaborate on this aspect for the present.

We now attempt to evaluate the configurational integral. It seems apparent that an exact evaluation is quite unlikely for general $\phi(r)$. When the latter vanishes, of course, the evaluation of the integral is trivial. We attempt, therefore, to take advantage of this circumstance. Consider that

$$\exp\left[-\frac{v(q_1 \ldots q_{3N})}{kT}\right] = \prod_{j=1}^{N} \prod_{i>j}^{N} \exp\left[-\frac{\phi(r_{ij})}{kT}\right] \quad (10.1.3)$$

when the intermolecular potential has the form of Eq. (10.1.2). Clearly we may define

$$f(r_{ij}) = 1 - \exp\left[-\frac{\phi(r_{ij})}{kT}\right], \quad (10.1.4)$$

whereupon

$$\exp\left[-\frac{v(q_1 \ldots q_{3N})}{kT}\right] = \prod_{j=1}^{N} \prod_{i>j}^{N} [1 - f(r_{ij})]. \quad (10.1.5)$$

It is evident that when the intermolecular potential vanishes, so does the appropriate f. We may utilize this feature to render Eq. (10.1.5) into a more tractable form. We have

$$\exp\left[-\frac{v(q_1 \ldots q_{3N})}{kT}\right] = \prod_{j=1}^{N}\left[1 - \sum_{i>j}^{N} f(r_{ij}) + \sum_{i>k>j}^{N} \sum_{k>j}^{N} f(r_{ij})f(r_{kj}) + \cdots\right]$$

$$= 1 - \sum_{j=1}^{N} \sum_{i>j}^{N} f(r_{ij}) + \sum_{j=1}^{N}\left[\sum_{i>k>j}^{N} f(r_{ij})f(r_{kj})\right]$$

$$+ \sum_{j=1}^{N} \sum_{k>j}^{N}\left[\sum_{i>j}^{N} f(r_{ij})\right]\left[\sum_{i>k}^{N} f(r_{ik})\right] + O(f^3). \quad (10.1.6)$$

Other ways of grouping the terms are possible, but we shall here be concerned only with the so-called first-order terms, those linear in the f's. The systematic representation of the configurational integral in terms of f's involving 2, 3, etc., groups of atoms is due to Ursell and Mayer.

Retaining only the linear terms in Eq. (10.1.6), we obtain as an approximation to the configurational integral:

$$e^{-F_{\text{config}}/kT} = V^N - \int \cdots \int \prod_{i=1}^{N} dx_i \, dy_i \, dz_i \sum_{j=1}^{N} \sum_{i>j}^{N} f(r_{ij}), \quad (10.1.7)$$

where we have changed to cartesian coordinates for the sake of clarity. It is possible to carry out the integrations one at a time. Inasmuch as $\phi(r)$ is negligibly small for intermolecular distances greater than some finite value which, in turn, is extremely small compared with macroscopic dimensions, the integrations over the coordinates of each atom may be extended to include all of space. Then the integral in Eq. (10.1.7) is easily converted to

$$\int \cdots \int \prod_{i=1}^{N} dx_i\, dy_i\, dz_i \sum_{j=1}^{N} \sum_{i>j}^{N} f(r_{ij})$$

$$= N(N-1)V^{N-1} 2\pi \int_0^\infty dr\, r^2 [1 - e^{-\phi(r)/kT}], \quad (10.1.8)$$

where advantage has been taken of the spherically symmetric property of $\phi(r)$. Defining

$$B(T) \equiv 2\pi \int_0^\infty dr\, r^2 [1 - e^{-\phi(r)/kT}], \quad (10.1.9)$$

we obtain the asymptotic approximation $(N \to \infty)$ for the configurational integral:

$$e^{-F\,\text{config}/kT} \cong V^N \left[1 - \frac{N^2}{V} B(T) \right]. \quad (10.1.10)$$

Because of the neglect of higher powers of f, this approximation would appear to be limited to intermolecular configurations for which the interaction of more than two molecules at a time makes a negligible contribution. It appears that Eq. (10.1.10) is thus limited to *dilute gases*. [For instance, $N^2 B(T)/V < 1$, since the left side cannot be negative.]

From Eqs. (10.1.1) and (10.1.10), we may define a nonideal contribution to the Helmholtz function as

$$V^{-N} e^{-F\,\text{config}/kT} = e^{-F\,\text{nonideal}/kT} \cong 1 - \frac{N^2}{V} B(T).$$

Since

$$F = F_\text{ideal} + F_\text{nonideal},$$

it follows that if F is to be extensive then F_nonideal must be extensive. This can be assured only if we *approximate*

$$F_\text{nonideal} \cong \frac{N^2 kT B(T)}{V}. \quad (10.1.11)$$

Then

$$P = P_\text{ideal} - \left(\frac{\partial F_\text{nonideal}}{\partial V} \right)_{T,N} \doteq \frac{NkT}{V} \left[1 + \frac{N}{V} B(T) \right]. \quad (10.1.12)$$

This expression can be recognized as the beginning of a virial expansion. (See Section 3.3.) The second virial coefficient may be recognized as $kT B(T)$. Integrals involving higher powers of the f's will yield expressions for the higher virial coefficients, but we shall not consider them here.

Instead we shall consider a special form for $\phi(r)$ which will give us some value of $B(T)$ that will be useful in a semiquantitative way.

Consider an intermolecular potential for which

$$\phi(r) = +\infty \quad (r < r_0)$$
$$\leq 0 \quad (r \geq r_0)$$
$$\rightarrow 0 \quad (r \rightarrow \infty). \quad (10.1.13)$$

Then

$$B(T) = 2\pi \int_0^\infty dr\, r^2[1 - e^{-\phi(r)/kT}]$$

$$= \frac{2\pi r_0^3}{3} + \int_{r_0}^\infty dr\, r^2[1 - e^{-\phi(r)/kT}]$$

$$= 4v_0 - \frac{\alpha}{kT}, \quad (10.1.14)$$

where v_0 is the volume of one atom. (Note that $r_0/2$ is essentially the radius of an atom in the present model.) We have taken the form indicated for Eq. (10.1.14), since $T \rightarrow \infty$

$$\int_{r_0}^\infty dr\, r^2[1 - e^{-\phi(r)/kT}] \sim \int_{r_0}^\infty dr\, r^2 \frac{\phi(r)}{kT} + 0\left(\frac{1}{T^2}\right) \sim -\frac{\text{const}}{kT}.$$

We may anticipate that α of Eq. (10.1.13) will be positive and nearly constant for sufficiently large temperatures.

Now if we represent the van der Waals equation [Eq. (3.2.1), where it was expressed in terms of molecules per unit volume] in terms of a virial expansion, then

$$P_{\text{vdW}} = \frac{kT}{(V/N) - b} - \frac{a}{(V/N)^2}$$

$$= \frac{NkT}{V} + \frac{N^2}{V^2}(kTb - a) + \frac{N^3}{V^3}kTb^2 + \cdots.$$

If this expression is compared with that obtained from Eqs. (10.1.12) and (10.1.14), the physical significance of the van der Waals constants may be inferred. However, we note regrettably that the van der Waals equation of state will require considerably higher approximation than we have considered.

10.2 Mixtures of slightly nonideal monatomic gases. We extend the considerations of the previous section to include a mixture of two species α and β. We use the classical approximation. Taking into account the indistinguishability of the respective species, the canonical distribution gives for N_α α-species and N_β β-species

$$e^{-F/kT} = \frac{1}{N_\alpha! N_\beta! h^{3(N_\alpha+N_\beta)}} \int \cdots \int \exp\left(-\sum_{i=1}^{3N_\alpha} \frac{p_i^2}{2m_\alpha kT}\right) \prod_{i=1}^{3N_\alpha} dp_i$$

$$\times \int \cdots \int \exp\left(-\sum_{i=1}^{3N_\beta} \frac{p_i^2}{2m_\beta kT}\right) \prod_{i=1}^{3N_\beta} dp_i \int \cdots \int \prod_{i=1}^{3(N_\alpha+N_\beta)} dq_i$$

$$\times \exp\left[-\frac{v_\alpha(q_1 \ldots q_{3N_\alpha}) + v_\beta(q_{3N_\alpha+1} \ldots q_{3N_\beta}) + v_{\alpha\beta}}{kT}\right]$$

$$= \frac{[Z_{\alpha(\text{trans})}]^{N_\alpha}}{N_\alpha!} \cdot \frac{[Z_{\beta(\text{trans})}]^{N_\beta}}{N_\beta!} \cdot \frac{e^{-F_{\text{config}}/kT}}{V^{N_\alpha+N_\beta}} . \tag{10.2.1}$$

Here v_α consists only of interactions between the α-species, v_β only of interactions between the β-species, while $v_{\alpha\beta}$ consists only of α-β interactions. Thus

$$v_\alpha = \sum_{i>j}^{N_\alpha} \sum_{j=1}^{N_\alpha} \phi_\alpha(r_{ij}),$$

$$v_\beta = \sum_{i>j}^{N_\beta} \sum_{j=1}^{N_\beta} \phi_\beta(r_{ij}), \tag{10.2.2}$$

$$v_{\alpha\beta} = \sum_{i=1}^{N_\beta} \sum_{j=1}^{N_\alpha} \phi_{\alpha\beta}(r_{ij}).$$

Following the procedure we have used in the previous section,

$$e^{-v_\alpha/kT} e^{-v_{\alpha\beta}/kT} e^{-v_\beta/kT} = \left\{\prod_{j=1}^{N_\alpha} \prod_{i>j}^{N_\alpha} [1 - f_\alpha(r_{ij})]\right\} \left\{\prod_{i=1}^{N_\beta} \prod_{j=1}^{N_\alpha} [1 - f_{\alpha\beta}(r_{ij})]\right\}$$

$$\times \left\{\prod_{j=1}^{N_\beta} \prod_{i>j}^{N_\beta} [1 - f_\beta(r_{ij})]\right\} .$$

To terms linear in the f's, we obtain

$$\exp\left(-\frac{v_\alpha + v_\beta + v_{\alpha\beta}}{kT}\right) \doteq 1 - \sum_{j=1}^{N_\alpha} \sum_{i>j}^{N_\alpha} f_\alpha(r_{ij})$$

$$- \sum_{j=1}^{N_\beta} \sum_{i=1}^{N_\alpha} f_{\alpha\beta}(r_{ij}) - \sum_{j=1}^{N_\beta} \sum_{i>j}^{N_\beta} f_\beta(r_{ij}).$$

Continuing the procedure we have already employed,

$$e^{-F_{\text{config}}/kT} \doteq V^{N_\alpha+N_\beta} - V^{N_\alpha+N_\beta-1}[N_\alpha(N_\alpha - 1)B_\alpha(T)$$

$$+ 2N_\alpha N_\beta B_{\alpha\beta}(T) + N_\beta(N_\beta - 1)B_\beta(T)], \qquad (10.2.3)$$

where

$$B_x \equiv 2\pi \int_0^\infty dr\, r^2[1 - e^{-\phi_x(r)/kT}], \qquad x \equiv \alpha, \beta \quad \text{or} \quad \alpha\beta. \qquad (10.2.4)$$

As we have already considered, the extensive character demanded of the Helmholtz function gives us the consistent approximation

$$F \doteq -N_\alpha kT \ln\left[\frac{eZ_{\alpha(\text{trans})}}{N_\alpha}\right] - N_\beta kT \ln\left[\frac{eZ_{\beta(\text{trans})}}{N_\beta}\right]$$

$$+ kT\left(\frac{N_\alpha^2}{V}B_\alpha + \frac{2N_\alpha N_\beta}{V}B_{\alpha\beta} + \frac{N_\beta^2}{V}B_\beta\right). \qquad (10.2.5)$$

The properties of the individual species can be determined easily from Eq. (10.2.5). For example, the chemical potentials

$$\mu_\alpha = \left(\frac{\partial F}{\partial N_\alpha}\right)_{T,V,N_\beta} = \mu_{\alpha(\text{ideal})} + 2kT\left(\frac{N_\alpha}{V}B_\alpha + \frac{N_\beta}{V}B_{\alpha\beta}\right) \qquad (10.2.6)$$

and

$$\mu_\beta = \left(\frac{\partial F}{\partial N_\beta}\right)_{T,V,N_\alpha} = \mu_{\beta(\text{ideal})} + 2kT\left(\frac{N_\beta}{V}B_\beta + \frac{N_\alpha}{V}B_{\alpha\beta}\right), \qquad (10.2.7)$$

where

$$\mu_{\text{ideal}} = -kT\ln\left[\frac{Z_{\text{trans}}}{N}\right]. \qquad (10.2.8)$$

The total pressure of the mixture is, to this approximation,

$$P = -\left(\frac{\partial F}{\partial V}\right)_{T,N_\alpha,N_\beta}$$

$$= \frac{(N_\alpha + N_\beta)kT}{V} + kT\left(\frac{N_\alpha^2}{V^2}B + \frac{2N_\alpha N_\beta}{V^2}B_{\alpha\beta} + \frac{N_\beta^2}{V^2}B_\beta\right)$$

or

$$\frac{P}{kT} = \frac{N}{V} + \left(\frac{N}{V}\right)^2\overline{B}, \qquad (10.2.9)$$

where

$$N = N_\alpha + N_\beta,$$

$$\overline{B} = x_\alpha^2 B_\alpha + 2x_\alpha x_\beta B_{\alpha\beta} + x_\beta^2 B_\beta,$$

$$x_\alpha = \frac{N_\alpha}{N_\alpha + N_\beta}, \quad \text{etc.}$$

We may arrange to express the chemical potential in terms of the reference state corresponding to the ideal gas at the temperature and pressure of the mixture. In that case (noting that the chemical potentials here refer to a *particle*, not mass, basis),

$$\mu_\alpha = \mu_{\alpha(\text{ideal})}(T, P) + kT \ln x_\alpha + kT \ln \frac{PV}{NkT}$$

$$+ \frac{2NkT}{V}(x_\alpha B_\alpha + x_\beta B_{\alpha\beta}),$$

where $\mu_{\alpha(\text{ideal})}(T, P)$ is easily obtained from Eq. (8.1.12). Solving Eq. (10.2.9) we obtain

$$\left(\frac{N}{V}\right) = \frac{\sqrt{1 + (4\overline{B}P/kT)} - 1}{2\overline{B}}. \tag{10.2.10}$$

Hence

$$\mu_\alpha = \mu_\alpha^0(T, P) + kT \ln x_\alpha$$

$$+ kT \ln \left[\frac{2\overline{B}P/kT}{\sqrt{1 + (4\overline{B}P/kT)} - 1}\right]$$

$$+ \left[\frac{\sqrt{1 + (4\overline{B}P/kT)} - 1}{\overline{B}/kT}\right](x_\alpha B_\alpha + x_\beta B_{\alpha\beta}). \tag{10.2.11}$$

Clearly the first term of Eq. (10.2.11) represents the standard free energy based on the ideal gas as a standard state; the second term corresponds to the contribution to the ideal entropy of mixing. The remaining terms are simply related to the activity coefficient. [See Eq. (5.5.1).]

We shall now indicate how a different standard state of reference will alter matters. Consider the state of pure α at the temperature and pressure of the mixture. Then the chemical potential of the pure substance is

$$\mu_\alpha^0(T, P) = \mu_{\alpha(\text{ideal})}(T, P) + kT \ln\left(\frac{PV}{NkT}\right) + \frac{2NkT}{V} B_\alpha. \tag{10.2.12}$$

In these terms, noting by Eq. (10.2.10) that (N/V) depends on composition, pressure, and temperature, we have

$$\mu_\alpha = \mu_\alpha^0(T, P) + kT \ln x_\alpha + kT \ln \left[\frac{\sqrt{1 + (4B_\alpha P/kT)} - 1}{\sqrt{1 + (4\bar{B}P/kT)} - 1} \cdot \frac{\bar{B}}{B_\alpha}\right]$$

$$+ \left[\frac{\sqrt{1 + (4\bar{B}P/kT)} - 1}{\bar{B}/kT}\right](x_\alpha B_\alpha + x_\beta B_\beta)$$

$$- \left[\frac{\sqrt{1 + (4B_\alpha P/kT)} - 1}{B_\alpha/kT}\right] B_\alpha. \qquad (10.2.13)$$

For circumstances in which $\bar{B}$, B_α, and B_β are identical regardless of composition (thereby implying the same value for $B_{\alpha\beta}$), only the first two quantities of Eq. (10.2.13) do not vanish. Clearly such is not the case in Eq. (10.2.11). Thus, in terms of a standard state based on the nonideal gas, a simpler activity coefficient may be anticipated. Other standard states may be chosen with corresponding simplicity of the activity coefficients. These will not be considered.

10.3 Dilute electrolytic solutions: Debye-Hückel theory. The utility of the classical approximation may be illustrated further in the case of electrolytic solutions. Here, however, the approximations of the previous sections are quite inappropriate. While the interaction potentials between dissimilar ions may be adjusted to satisfy Eqs. (10.1.13), the rapidity with which the potentials of ionic interaction tend toward zero with increasing interionic distance is so small as to give divergent values of integrals as in Eq. (10.1.9). For these reasons, quite another viewpoint must be exploited.

The properties of the interionic potentials just noted simply do not allow their being regarded both as *small and localized*—the conditions under which the previous approximations may be justified. Nevertheless, the starting point in the case of electrolytic solutions is quite the same, namely Eq. (9.5.4). We may begin with a description of the Hamiltonian for an electrically neutral mixture of ions in a solvent, otherwise termed an electrolytic solution. For simplicity we may disregard the internal structures of the several species. Then in the classical approximation, we have in terms of Eq. (9.5.5)

$$H_{\text{class}} = K_{\text{ions}} + K_{\text{solvent}} + \mathcal{v}_{(\text{ion-ion})} + \mathcal{v}_{(\text{ion-solvent})} + \mathcal{v}_{(\text{solvent-solvent})},$$

$$(10.3.1)$$

where K is the total kinetic energy of the species indicated. We need only emphasize the configuration integral. However, in order to facilitate doing so we emphasize an interest in the properties of a single "molecule" of the several ionic species of the mixture. That is, we consider an electrically neutral collection of ions which is minimal in the number of each kind. For an electrolyte which dissociates, for example, as

$$(A^{Z_a})_{\nu^+}(B^{Z_b})_{\nu^-} \rightarrow \nu^+ A^{Z_a} + \nu^- B^{Z_b}, \qquad (10.3.2)$$

we are considering the collection of $\nu^+ A$'s and $\nu^- B$'s. Clearly the ν's are positive and $(\nu^+ Z_a + \nu^- Z_b)$ vanishes.

The potential energy of interaction of the entire system evidently may be represented in terms of such a collection as

$$v(N, S) = v_{ii}(m) + v_{ii}(m, N - 1) + v_{is}(m, S) + v(N - 1, S), \qquad (10.3.3)$$

where m refers to one of the "ionic molecules" just described; $v_{ii}(m)$ refers to the electrical interactions between the members of this collection, while $v_{ii}(m, N - 1)$ refers to the interionic interaction of the collection with the remaining ions of the system; and $v_{is}(m, S)$ refers to ion-solvent interactions. Here N and S refer to the "ionic molecules" and the solvent molecules, respectively, in the mixture. For the purposes at hand, it is convenient to express the configurational integral as

$$e^{-F_{\text{config}}(N,S)/kT} = \int \cdots \int e^{-v(N,S)/kT} \prod_{i=1}^{(N,S)} dq_i$$

$$= \int \cdots \int \left[e^{-v_m/kT} \prod_{i=1}^{(m)} dq_i \right] e^{-v(N-1,S)/kT} \prod_{i=1}^{(N-1,S)} dq_i$$

$$= e^{-F_{\text{config}}(N-1,S)/kT} \overline{\int \cdots \int e^{-v_m/kT} \prod_{i=1}^{(m)} dq_i}, \qquad (10.3.4)$$

where $v_m = v(N, S) - v(N - 1, S)$ in Eq. (10.3.3), and the average in Eq. (10.3.4) is taken over the remainder of the system; the products indicated here include all the pertinent configurational coordinates of the "ionic molecule."

In terms of Eq. (9.5.8), we may express

$$e^{-F_{\text{class}}(N,S)/kT} = \frac{e^{-F_{\text{ideal}}(N,S)/kT}}{(N\nu^+)!(N\nu^-)!S!} \cdot \frac{e^{-F_{\text{config}}(N,S)/kT}}{V^{N(\nu^+ + \nu^-) + S}}, \qquad (10.3.5)$$

where we have introduced the correction for indistinguishable permutations. Since

$$e^{-F_{\text{ideal}}(N,S)/kT} = [Z_{A(\text{trans})}]^{N\nu^+} [Z_{B(\text{trans})}]^{N\nu^-} [Z_{S(\text{trans})}]^S,$$

the translational partition function being given by Eq. (8.2.1), we may obtain with Eq. (10.3.4)

$$e^{-F_{\text{class}}(N,S)/kT} = e^{-F_{\text{class}}(N-1,S)/kT} \cdot Z_A^{\nu^+} Z_B^{\nu^-} \frac{[(N-1)\nu^+]![(N-1)\nu^-]!}{(N\nu^+)!(N\nu^-)!}$$

$$\cdot \frac{\int \cdots \int e^{-\overline{\mathcal{U}_m/kT}} \prod_{i=1}^{(m)} dq_i}{V^{(\nu^+ + \nu^-)}},$$

or for extremely large values of N,

$$\exp\left[-\frac{F_{\text{class}}(N,S) - F_{\text{class}}(N-1,S)}{kT}\right] \sim \frac{Z_A^{\nu^+} Z_B^{\nu^-}}{(N_A)^{\nu^+}(N_B)^{\nu^-}}$$

$$\cdot \frac{\int \cdots \int e^{-\overline{\mathcal{U}_m/kT}} \prod_{i=1}^{(m)} dq_i}{V^{(\nu^+ + \nu^-)}}, \quad (10.3.6)$$

where $N_A = \nu^+ N$ and $N_B = \nu^- N$. Since by dealing with electrically neutral collections we assure that no electrical work is involved when the number of ionic species is accordingly changed, we have in the classical approximation for large N

$$F_{\text{class}}(N,S) - F_{\text{class}}(N-1,S) = \mu_m(N,S), \quad (10.3.7)$$

the chemical potential for the collection of $\nu^+ A$'s and $\nu^- B$'s. It is evident that Eq. (10.3.6), with Eq. (10.2.8), may be expressed as

$$e^{-\mu_m(N,S)/kT} = e^{-\mu_m(\text{ideal})/kT} \cdot \frac{\int \cdots \int e^{-\overline{\mathcal{U}_m/kT}} \prod_{i=1}^{(m)} dq_i}{V^{(\nu^+ + \nu^-)}}. \quad (10.3.8)$$

The integral to be evaluated comprises the activity correction. (See Chapter 5.)

We will carry out the evaluation of the integral only approximately. To do so, we shall expand the exponential in the integral and retain only the first two terms. That is, we shall approximate

$$\frac{\int \cdots \int e^{-\overline{\mathcal{U}_m/kT}} \prod_{i=1}^{(m)} dq_i}{V^{(\nu^+ + \nu^-)}} \sim 1 - \frac{\int \cdots \int \overline{\mathcal{U}_m} \prod_{i=1}^{(m)} dq_i}{kT V^{(\nu^+ + \nu^-)}}$$

$$= 1 - \frac{\overline{\overline{\mathcal{U}_m}}}{kT}. \quad (10.3.9)$$

How $\overline{\overline{v_m}}$ may be estimated has been shown by Debye and Hückel. However, we note from Eq. (10.3.3) that v_m contains a term referring to the ion-solvent interactions of the "ionic molecule." These will not be considered, and their effect will be to provide a contribution to Eq. (10.3.9) which is more or less independent of composition. The ideal chemical potential of Eq. (10.3.8) may suitably be altered by the inclusion of this contribution to reflect a change in the standard state of reference. It is with respect to the remaining terms in v_m that the Debye-Hückel theory applies.

Of the remaining terms in v_m, one set refers to the mutual ionic inter-actions of the "ionic molecule," while the other set refers to the interaction of the neutral "ionic molecule" and the remainder of the ions in the system. It can be seen that averaging $v(m, N - 1)$ over the remainder of the system has the effect of altering the effective interaction between the ions of the "ionic molecule" by converting the interionic interaction with the remainder of the system to one depending only on the coordinates of the ions of the "ionic molecule." As a consequence, we need only to refer to the mutual interaction of the ions of the "ionic molecule," suitably altered by the presence of the others.

Instead of determining the alteration, we may follow Debye and Hückel to estimate the energy of interaction of a charge with its environment. We assume that the system may be approximated by a *continuous distri-bution* of electrical charge in a *continuous solvent* medium. As a consequence, the ensuing theory introduces macroscopic properties of the system into the calculation, whereas these very macroscopic properties should themselves be calculated from the statistical procedures we employ. In terms of this model, we seek an equilibrium distribution of ions about a given one. Having obtained this equilibrium distribution of ions, we may associate the resulting charge distribution with that of the remaining ions of the "ionic molecule" and calculate the interaction energy. Carrying this out in turn for each of the ions and dividing by two to account for the obvious double counting, the electrical contribution to $\overline{\overline{v_m}}$ may be estimated.

We note here an important use to which statistical mechanics may be put: that of providing information about the equilibrium *spatial distribu-tion* of the parts of a system. Such information is not apparently available in the statistical-thermodynamic treatment which refers only to the energy values of the relevant systems. It is, however, available from the classical form of statistical mechanics. We can anticipate that a more compre-hensive quantum-statistical-mechanical formulation will remedy this ap-parent deficiency. Such will be described in Chapter 12. For the present we exploit the classical statistical mechanics.

If we imagine a particular ion as fixed in space, we suppose that the Boltzmann distribution formula (see Exercise 2 of Chapter 9) may be employed to estimate the density of ions in the vicinity of some region at a distance r from the fixed ion. We may establish for very dilute solutions that the number density of the ith sort of ion may be expressed as

$$n_i(r) = n_{i,0}e^{-Z_i\epsilon\psi(r)/kT}, \tag{10.3.10}$$

where Z_i is the valence of the ith ionic species, ϵ is the magnitude of the electronic charge, $\psi(r)$ is the electric potential experienced by the ith ionic species at a distance r from the fixed ionic species, and $n_{i,0}$ is the density of the ith ionic species at a point where $\psi(r)$ vanishes. Clearly we shall require $\psi(r)$ to become negligibly small as r increases indefinitely. The net electric charge density at some point, then, becomes

$$\rho(r) = \sum_{\substack{i \\ \text{all ions}}} Z_i\epsilon n_i(r) = \sum_{\substack{i \\ \text{all ions}}} Z_i\epsilon n_{i,0}e^{-Z_i\epsilon\psi(r)/kT}, \tag{10.3.11}$$

which is determined once $\psi(r)$ is determined.

The determination of $\psi(r)$ is dependent on an important relation in electrostatics, namely *Poisson's* equation, which relates the electric potential at a point to the density of electric charge there as follows:

$$\nabla^2\psi \equiv \frac{\partial^2\psi}{\partial x^2} + \frac{\partial^2\psi}{\partial y^2} + \frac{\partial^2\psi}{\partial z^2} = -\frac{4\pi\rho}{D}, \tag{10.3.12}$$

where D is the dielectric constant of the medium containing the electric charge. Any potential ψ will determine, through Eq. (10.3.12), a charge density. When the charge density generally and independently is related to the potential, one restricts the solution to those ψ's which are consistent to both. The use of Eq. (10.3.11) in Poisson's equation gives rise to the *Poisson-Boltzmann* equation. This equation, however, will not be considered here in any detail. We shall, instead, only examine the solution under circumstances where $\epsilon\psi/kT \ll 1$, justifying an expansion of the exponential. Then,

$$\rho(r) = \sum_{\substack{i \\ \text{all ions}}} Z_i\epsilon n_{i,0}\left[1 - \frac{Z_i^2\epsilon\psi(r)}{kT} + \frac{Z_i^2\epsilon^2\psi^2(r)}{2k^2T^2} + \cdots\right]$$

$$\doteq -\left(\sum_{\substack{i \\ \text{all} \\ \text{ions}}} \frac{n_{i,0}Z_i^2\epsilon^2}{kT}\right)\psi(r), \tag{10.3.13}$$

to lowest order of approximation, since $\Sigma n_{i,0}Z_i\epsilon$ vanishes for electrically neutral solutions being considered here. Defining

$$\kappa^2 = 4\pi \sum_{\substack{i \\ \text{all ions}}} \frac{n_{i,0}Z_i^2\epsilon^2}{DkT}, \tag{10.3.14}$$

we obtain

$$\nabla^2 \psi = \kappa^2 \psi. \qquad (10.3.15)$$

For a spherically symmetric ion of radius a (i.e., distance of closest approach such that the interaction energy is indefinitely large and positive for smaller interionic distances), it may be verified that the solution of Eq. (10.3.15) which vanishes at $r = \infty$ and which makes the total system electrically neutral is

$$\psi(r) = \frac{Z_f \epsilon e^{-\kappa(r-a)}}{(1 + \kappa a)\, Dr}, \qquad r \geq a. \qquad (10.3.16)$$

Here Z_f has been taken as the charge of the fixed ion. We have employed the fact that the *net* electrical charge of the solution is $-Z_f \epsilon$. Now, identifying this net charge with the other ions of the "ionic molecule," the effect of the rest of the system has been to impose a certain equilibrium distribution on them. The interaction between the fixed ion and this net electrical charge in the dielectric medium is

$$4\pi \int_a^\infty dr\, r^2 \rho(r) \left(\frac{Z_f \epsilon}{Dr}\right) = -\frac{\kappa^2 kT Z_f^2 \epsilon^2}{(1 + \kappa a)D} \int_a^\infty dr\, e^{-\kappa(r-a)}$$

$$= -\frac{kT\kappa Z_f^2 \epsilon^2}{(1 + \kappa a)D}.$$

This expression must be summed over the ions of the "ionic molecule," and one-half of the result is the estimated value of $\overline{\overline{v_m}}$. Thus,

$$\frac{\overline{\overline{v_m}}}{kT} \doteq -\frac{\kappa \epsilon^2 \sum_i^{(m)} \nu_i Z_i^2}{2D(1 + \kappa a)},$$

to which approximation the chemical potential

$$\mu_m(N, S) = \mu_m \text{ (ideal)} - \frac{\kappa \epsilon^2 \sum_i^{(m)} \nu_i Z_i^2}{2D(1 + \kappa a)}. \qquad (10.3.17)$$

It is convenient occasionally to represent the properties of the solution in terms of *fictional ionic chemical potentials*. To do so, one defines

$$\mu_m(N, S) = \sum_i^{(m)} \nu_i \mu_i(N, S), \qquad (10.3.18)$$

and since

$$\mu_m \text{ (ideal)} = \sum_i^{(m)} \nu_i \mu_i \text{ (ideal)},$$

we have, formally,

$$\mu_i(N, S) = \mu_i \text{ (ideal)} - \frac{\kappa \epsilon^2 Z_i^2}{2D(1 + \kappa a)}, \qquad (10.3.19)$$

which is the "ionic chemical potential" obtained from the Debye-Hückel theory.

We may emphasize in the present "derivation" of Eq. (10.3.19) that the approximation of the Debye-Hückel theory is employed to estimate the average ionic interaction energy of an electrically neutral group of ions, regarded as a "molecular" entity. In this way the general statistical-mechanical theory is related to the procedures employed in electrolytic solution theory. In the usual treatment this connection is not made, there being alternative ways by which the thermodynamic properties of these mixtures may be estimated. We shall not discuss them, however. We may note that while the treatment has explicitly referred to a single kind of "ionic molecule," nothing prevents the extension of the results to mixtures of ionic species.

10.4 Solids: Debye theory of specific heats. We turn now to a case where the interactions of the various atoms and molecules are so strong as to vitiate any attempt to treat them as separable — the case of a solid. We have already mentioned Einstein's model of a solid (Section 8.5), but we avoided the important feature of the interaction between the localized oscillators. Nevertheless, the high-temperature behavior of the Einstein solid correctly yields the law of Dulong and Petit. From this aspect alone we can conjecture that the important differences between various theories is to be found in their predictions of low-temperature properties of solids.

Now, when we investigate the vibratory motion of N atoms to the extent that they can be regarded as coupled harmonic oscillators, we are able to show that there generally will be $(3N - 6)$ different fundamental vibration frequencies. In such a case a better approximation than the Einstein model would consist of a summation over the relevant fundamental frequencies of the pertinent harmonic-oscillator function. Thus the Helmholtz function would, from Eq. (8.5.3), be given by

$$F = \sum_{j=1}^{3N-6} \frac{h\nu_j}{2} + kT \sum_{j=1}^{3N-6} \ln(1 - e^{-h\nu_j/kT}). \qquad (10.4.1)$$

The origin of energy for this system has been taken as the zero of the potential energy of the system. For all ν_j identical, Eq. (10.4.1) reduces to the Einstein theory, and we see here that the Dulong-Petit law obtains for sufficiently large temperatures regardless of the actual frequencies (so long as they are finite).

The problem at hand can be stated as that of estimating the sum of Eq. (10.4.1) without knowing precisely what the fundamental frequencies are. Here also Debye has provided us with a means for rendering a formidable problem into a tractable one. He does so by introducing the approximation that the fundamental vibration frequencies of a solid may be estimated from those of a *continuous* elastic medium with fixed boundaries. Postponing, for the moment, just how this estimate is made, consider the changes that will be prompted in Eq. (10.4.1) if the fundamental frequencies are close spaced. Then the sum will be conveniently replaced by an integral. Formally, we have to take into account the possible nonlinear spacing between the frequencies. This is done by introducing a *frequency density* such that the number of fundamental frequencies between ν and $\nu + d\nu$ is given by

$$dN_\nu = g(\nu)\, d\nu. \tag{10.4.2}$$

When the frequencies are equally spaced it is clear that $g(\nu)$ then is constant and is thereby easily evaluated. In general, we must require

$$3N = \int_0^{\nu_{max}} g(\nu)\, d\nu, \tag{10.4.3}$$

where we have neglected the number 6 in comparison with $3N$; ν_{max} is the largest fundamental frequency. It is unnecessary to make explicit reference to a lowest frequency. With such a frequency density, we have from Eq. (10.4.1)

$$F = \int_0^{\nu_{max}} d\nu\, g(\nu)\, \frac{h\nu}{2} + kT \int_0^{\nu_{max}} d\nu\, g(\nu) \ln\,(1 - e^{-h\nu/kT}), \tag{10.4.4}$$

with an analogous expression for other statistical-thermodynamic functions.

The approximation of Debye consists of assuming that the vibration of a continuous elastic medium should give a reasonable description of the low-frequency vibrations of a solid and applying the frequency density for a continuous medium to evaluate Eq. (10.4.4). For such a medium, the condition of fixed boundaries requires that the wavelength of any "stationary" wave propagated through the solid bear a definite relation to the size and shape of the solid. For a rectangular parallelepiped, the wavelength λ must satisfy

$$\left(\frac{2}{\lambda}\right)^2 = \left(\frac{l}{a}\right)^2 + \left(\frac{m}{b}\right)^2 + \left(\frac{n}{c}\right)^2, \tag{10.4.5}$$

where l, m, and n are positive integers and a, b, and c are the lengths of the sides of the rectangular parallelepiped. [Eq. (10.4.5) can be seen in simple cases to restrict the wavelength so that *nodes* appear at the boundary, which is the essence of the condition.]

An arbitrary wave motion propagated through the solid may be resolved into three component motions, two of which are transverse in character while the other is longitudinal or compressional. The various component wave motions are characterized by different velocities of propagation, c_t for the two transverse components and c_l for the longitudinal component. The previous restrictions apply to each of the component waves. For, say, the longitudinal mode, the number of wavelengths *greater* than a specified value is, clearly, the number of integral points (l, m, and n) contained within the positive octant of an ellipsoid of principal axes ($4a/\lambda_l$, $4b/\lambda_l$, $4c/\lambda_l$). This number is

$$N_{\lambda_l} = \frac{1}{8} \cdot \frac{4\pi}{3} \cdot \left(\frac{2a}{\lambda_l}\right)\left(\frac{2b}{\lambda_l}\right)\left(\frac{2c}{\lambda_l}\right) = \frac{4\pi}{3}\frac{V}{\lambda_l^3},$$

where V is the volume of the solid. The number of longitudinal frequencies *less* than the frequency corresponding to the previous wavelength is, of course, identical with N_λ. To express it in terms of frequency, we employ the relation

$$\lambda_l \nu_l = c_l,$$

whereupon the number of frequencies less than ν_l is given by

$$N_{\nu_l} = \frac{4\pi V}{3c_l^3} \nu_l^3. \tag{10.4.6}$$

Analogously, the number of transverse frequencies is, apart from a difference in subscript, identical with Eq. (10.4.6). As a result, the total number of frequencies of any component whatever, less than a specified value, is

$$N_\nu = \frac{4\pi V}{3}\nu^3 \left(\frac{1}{c_l^3} + \frac{2}{c_t^3}\right), \tag{10.4.7}$$

from which, using Eq. (10.4.2), we obtain for $N_\nu \leq 3N$,

$$g(\nu) = \left(\frac{12\pi V}{c^3}\right)\nu^2, \tag{10.4.8}$$

where we have defined

$$\frac{3}{c^3} \equiv \left(\frac{1}{c_l^3} + \frac{2}{c_t^3}\right). \tag{10.4.9}$$

To satisfy Eq. (10.4.3) we evidently require

$$\nu_{max} = \left(\frac{3N}{4\pi V}\right)^{1/3} c, \qquad (10.4.10)$$

which clearly depends on the density of the solid.

We may now bring our results into a convenient form. By defining the *Debye temperature*,

$$\Theta \equiv \frac{h\nu_{max}}{k}, \qquad (10.4.11)$$

we have

$$F = \frac{9}{8} Nk\Theta + 9NkT\left(\frac{T}{\Theta}\right)^3 \int_0^{\Theta/T} dx\, x^2 \ln(1 - e^{-x}). \qquad (10.4.12)$$

Since Θ depends on V and c (assuming that the latter is independent of T and V), we obtain for the entropy of the solid

$$S = -\left(\frac{\partial F}{\partial T}\right)_\Theta = 9Nk \ln(1 - e^{-\Theta/T})$$

$$- 36Nk\left(\frac{T}{\Theta}\right)^3 \int_0^{\Theta/T} dx\, x^2 \ln(1 - e^{-x}). \qquad (10.4.13)$$

The heat capacity at constant volume, after some manipulation, is

$$C_V = T\left(\frac{\partial S}{\partial T}\right)_\Theta = 9Nk\left(\frac{T}{\Theta}\right)^3 \int_0^{\Theta/T} dx\, \frac{x^4 e^x}{(e^x - 1)^2}. \qquad (10.4.14)$$

For $T \to 0$, we see that

$$C_V \propto \left(\frac{T}{\Theta}\right)^3,$$

a result generally satisfied extremely well by most solids at low temperatures. The interesting thing about Eq. (10.4.14) is its introduction of a *reduced temperature* such that the temperature variation of the heat capacity of all solids can be represented in universal terms. While Θ may be readily calculated from the elastic properties of the solid [Eqs. (10.4.10) and (10.4.11)], it usually is obtained from the temperature variation of the specific heat. The two sorts of values are, however, in agreement.

10.5 Order-disorder in solids: Bragg-Williams theory. We implied in the previous section that the atoms (or the molecules) of a solid can be regarded as localized subsystems. However, we also indicated earlier (Section 7.5) that it is inherently impossible to regard localization as complete, and some likelihood that subsystems may appear in different regions of the system is to be expected. The present section will deal with a simple system in which such is the case.

We shall be concerned with solids composed of two kinds of atoms. Then, the effects of nonlocalization (or inexact localization) will be dependent on the composition of the solid, as we shall see. The properties we have in mind to examine are those exhibited by an alloy of copper and zinc, although other systems also exhibit these properties. For these mixtures, one finds a range of temperatures in which there are relatively abrupt changes in most of their equilibrium properties. When these mixtures are examined at small temperatures, it is found that they exhibit a "more structured" form than they exhibit at sufficiently large temperatures. This information is adduced from x-ray diffraction data. As a result, one refers to an *ordered* form at small temperatures as contrasted with a *disordered* form at large temperatures.

The prevailing situation may be envisaged as corresponding to a checkerboard with rows and columns consisting of sequences of alternately colored and uncolored squares. On the squares of this checkerboard are placed two kinds of objects: they may be otherwise identical objects of two different colors, or coins which differ only in the face shown, etc. An ordered arrangement would correspond to such a one whereby the colored squares contain only one kind of object, while the uncolored squares contain only the other. For equal numbers of objects of each kind, no significant difference is to be attached to which kind of square is occupied by which kind of object. A complete interchange of the two kinds of objects will not alter the ordered character of the arrangement. In these terms it is possible to recognize that a disordered arrangement results from the permutation of any two different objects from their ordered locations. It seems clear that there will be various disordered arrangements, some patently more ordered than others. Since by a long sequence of permutations it is possible to imagine one ordered arrangement being obtained from the other ordered arrangement, it seems reasonable to expect a *most* disordered form. These qualitative considerations will be made quantitative in the subsequent analysis.

For the application to physical systems, we shall assume that the solids of interest contain two interpenetrating lattices, say α and β, as in the example of a checkerboard. The situation corresponding to the ordered form of the solid is that of one of the lattices containing one kind of atom while the other lattice, which is quite similar to the first, is occupied by the other kind of atom. A disordered form is one in which both lattices will contain both kinds of atoms.

To make any calculations of a statistical sort which pertain to the system of interest, we need to know the allowed energies of the system. As usual, we can only estimate these. To do so we shall consider a model in which the use of classical statistical mechanics is justified insofar as the energy differences associated with different configurations of the atoms are concerned. By this means we are able to express the problem at hand in terms of the configurational integral which already has been considered in previous illustrations. By expressing the Hamiltonian as

$$H = K + v_0 + v_{\text{config}}, \tag{10.5.1}$$

where K is the total kinetic energy of the system, v_0 is a reference value of the atomic interaction energy to which the vibratory motion may be ascribed, and v_{config} is an interaction energy which, in contrast to v_0, is dependent upon the precise configuration of the atoms in the solid. It is extremely small compared with v_0. In these terms, we may represent

$$e^{-F/kT} = e^{-F_{\text{solid}}/kT} e^{-F_{\text{config}}/kT}. \tag{10.5.2}$$

Here

$$e^{-F_{\text{solid}}/kT} = \sum_{i=1}^{\infty} e^{-E_i/kT}, \tag{10.5.3}$$

where E_i is one of the energy values of $H_0 = K + v_0$. Also,

$$e^{-F_{\text{config}}/kT} = \sum_{\substack{\text{all} \\ \text{config}}} e^{-v_{\text{config}}/kT}. \tag{10.5.4}$$

The similarity with, as well as the difference from, Eq. (9.5.9) is to be noted. Clearly F_{solid} will be estimated by the method of the previous section.

We now have the task of giving a quantitative expression for the configurational interaction energy, v_{config}. To do so, we consider first a definition of the degree of order in an *average* sense. This definition will refer to what is termed the *long-range order* of the system. Let there be equal numbers of two kinds of atoms A and B. Then the parameter of order will be defined such that when all A atoms are on one lattice, say the α one, the parameter will have the value unity (or its magnitude will be unity). When equal numbers of A atoms and B atoms appear on any one lattice, the ordering parameter will be taken as equal to zero. It is now a matter of constructing an interpolation function for values which lie in between. The simplest such function appears to be the following: the long-range order parameter is defined as

$$S = \frac{N_A(\alpha) - N_A(\beta)}{N/2} = \frac{N_B(\beta) - N_B(\alpha)}{N/2}, \tag{10.5.5}$$

where $N_A(\alpha)$ are the number of A atoms on the α lattice, etc. Clearly

$$N_A(\alpha) = N_B(\beta). \tag{10.5.6}$$

As a consequence, we obtain

$$N_A(\alpha) = N_B(\beta) = \frac{(1 + S)N}{4},$$

$$N_A(\beta) = N_B(\alpha) = \frac{(1 - S)N}{4}. \qquad (10.5.7)$$

It is evident that any positive integral power of Eq. (10.5.5) will satisfy the criteria we have set for quantifying the order. However, we shall retain the linear definition.

To estimate the configurational energy, we introduce the approximation that only nearest neighbors in the solid need be taken into account. Then

$$\mathfrak{v}_{\text{config}} = N_{AA}E_{AA} + N_{AB}E_{AB} + N_{BB}E_{BB}, \qquad (10.5.8)$$

where the N's stand for average numbers and the E's stand for energies of the indicated pairs. The latter must be assumed known. The numbers of pairs may be estimated in terms of the order parameter. The number of nearest neighbors of any lattice point will evidently be those of the inter-penetrating lattice immediately surrounding the original point. For cubic lattices there are eight such nearest neighbors. We shall, however, leave this number represented by Z. Then, for a given value of S, each A atom on the α lattice will be surrounded by

$$Z \cdot \frac{N_A(\beta)}{N/2}$$

A atoms on the average. The average number of AA pairs is, thus,

$$N_{AA} = N_A(\alpha) \cdot \left[Z \frac{N_A(\beta)}{N/2} \right] = \frac{Z}{8}(1 - S^2)N. \qquad (10.5.9)$$

By symmetry the number of BB pairs is identical, so

$$N_{BB} = \frac{Z}{8}(1 - S^2)N. \qquad (10.5.10)$$

The number of AB pairs is simply

$$N_{AB} = N_A(\alpha)\left[Z \frac{N_B(\beta)}{N/2} \right] + N_B(\alpha)\left[Z \frac{N_A(\beta)}{N/2} \right]$$

$$= \frac{Z}{8}(1 + S)^2 N + \frac{Z}{8}(1 - S)^2 N$$

$$= \frac{Z}{4}(1 + S^2)N. \qquad (10.5.11)$$

We may note that

$$N_{AA} + N_{BB} + N_{AB} = \frac{Z}{2} N,$$

a result that could have been anticipated. The configurational energy now may be expressed as

$$\tau_{\text{config}} = \frac{Z}{8} N[(E_{AA} + E_{BB})(1 - S^2) + 2E_{AB}(1 + S^2)]$$

$$= \frac{Z}{8} N(E_0 - S^2 \Delta E), \tag{10.5.12}$$

where

$$E_0 = E_{AA} + E_{BB} + 2E_{AB}, \qquad \Delta E = E_{AA} + E_{BB} - 2E_{AB}.$$

Now in order to utilize the expression we have obtained for the configurational energy, we must sum Eq. (10.5.4) over *all configurations*. For that purpose we require the number of configurations for each value of S. This number is simply the number of different ways of arranging the atoms on the α-lattice, keeping their respective kinds fixed, multiplied by the corresponding number for the β-lattice. In these permutations S is unaltered. The result is

$$W_S = \left\{ \frac{(N/2)!}{[(1 + S)N/4]! [(1 - S)N/4]!} \right\}^2$$

$$\cong \frac{2^N}{(1 - S^2)^{N/2}} \left(\frac{1 - S}{1 + S} \right)^{NS/2}, \tag{10.5.13}$$

using Stirling's approximation. Now, using Eqs. (10.5.12) and (10.5.13),

$$e^{-F_{\text{config}}/kT} = \sum_S W_S \exp\left(-\frac{ZNE_0}{8kT} \right) \exp\left(+\frac{ZN \Delta E S^2}{8kT} \right).$$

To render this into a tractable form, we convert to an integral. Using the form of the Euler-Maclaurin expansion (Section 8.6), we obtain

$$e^{-F_{\text{config}}/kT} \doteq \exp\left(-\frac{ZNE_0}{8kT} \right) \cdot \frac{N}{4} 2^N \int_{-1}^{+1} dS \left(\frac{1 - S}{1 + S} \right)^{NS/2}$$

$$\times \frac{e^{(ZN \Delta E S^2)/8kT}}{(1 - S^2)^{N/2}}, \tag{10.5.14}$$

where h of Eq. (8.6.7) has been taken as the smallest increment in S which is $(4/N)$.

The evaluation of the integral can be carried out only approximately. It can be written as

$$I \equiv \int_{-1}^{+1} dS \, \exp \{(N/2)[\alpha S^2 - (1+S) \ln (1+S) - (1-S) \ln (1-S)]\},$$

where $\alpha = Z \, \Delta E / 4kT$. We attempt an expansion about the maximum value of the exponent. Calling,

$$f(S) = \alpha S^2 - (1 + S) \ln (1 + S) - (1 - S) \ln (1 - S),$$

we have

$$f'(S) = 2\alpha S - \ln \left(\frac{1 + S}{1 - S} \right), \qquad f''(S) = 2\alpha - \frac{2}{1 - S^2},$$

whereupon, expanding in a power series about the maximum value,

$$f(S) \doteq - [\alpha S_0^2 + \ln (1 - S_0^2)]$$

$$+ (S - S_0)^2 \left(\alpha - \frac{1}{1 - S_0^2} \right) + 0[(S - S_0)^3], \qquad (10.5.15)$$

where

$$2\alpha S_0 = \ln \left(\frac{1 + S_0}{1 - S_0} \right). \qquad (10.5.16)$$

Now, one can show that

$$\left(\alpha - \frac{1}{1 - S_0^2} \right) \leq 0,$$

so for very large N the integrand is extremely small for $S \neq S_0$. As a result, the integral can be approximated reliably by extending the limits to $\pm \infty$. Then

$$I \doteq \frac{\sqrt{\pi}}{\sqrt{\frac{N}{2} \left(\frac{1}{1 - S_0^2} - \alpha \right)}} \cdot \exp \left\{ - \frac{N}{2} [\alpha S_0^2 + \ln (1 - S_0^2)] \right\} \cdot$$

With this approximation the contribution to the Helmholtz function becomes, retaining only the extensive portion for $N \to \infty$,

$$F_{\text{config}} \sim \frac{NZ}{8} (E_0 + \Delta E S_0^2) + \frac{NkT}{2} \ln (1 - S_0^2) - NkT \ln 2. \qquad (10.5.17)$$

We may note here that the approximation we have taken corresponds to determining the minimum value of $[(\upsilon_{config}/kT) - \ln W_S]$ as a function of S, which is the usual procedure for describing the Bragg-Williams theory of order-disorder phenomena. We have been able here, however, to relate it to the general statistical-mechanical theory. The quantity minimized is, of course, the configurational free energy, the minimum value of which we have given in Eq. (10.5.17).

From Eq. (10.5.17) we may determine the configurational entropy

$$S_{config} = -\frac{\partial F_{config}}{\partial T} = Nk \ln 2 - \frac{Nk}{2} \ln (1 - S_0^2)$$

$$-\left(\frac{NZ \, \Delta E}{4} - \frac{NkT}{1 - S_0^2}\right) S_0 \frac{\partial S_0}{\partial T}.$$

From Eq. (10.5.16),

$$\left(\frac{NZ \, \Delta E}{4} - \frac{NkT}{1 - S_0^2}\right) \frac{\partial S_0}{\partial T} = \frac{NZ \, \Delta E}{4T} S_0, \qquad (10.5.18)$$

so that

$$S_{config} = Nk \ln 2 - \frac{Nk}{2} \ln (1 - S_0^2) - \frac{NZ \, \Delta E}{4T} S_0^2. \quad (10.5.19)$$

Hence

$$E_{config} = \frac{NZ}{8} (E_0 - \Delta E S_0^2),$$

in agreement with Eq. (10.5.12). The $Nk \ln 2$ in the entropy is noteworthy, corresponding to the entropy of mixing of the two kinds of atoms. It is the value attained by S_{config} when S_0 vanishes, again in agreement with expectations.

A study of the temperature variation of the thermodynamic function requires a study first to be made of the temperature-dependence of the ordering parameter. From Eq. (10.5.16) we see that

$$\alpha = \frac{1}{2S_0} \ln \left(\frac{1 + S_0}{1 - S_0}\right) \geq 0.$$

Otherwise the procedure would not have led to a minimum value of the configurational free energy. But this means that

$$E_{AB} \leq \frac{E_{AA} + E_{BB}}{2},$$

or that there must be a greater attraction (or lesser repulsion) for unlike kinds of atoms than the average attraction (or repulsion) for like pairs of atoms. With this condition, it is apparent that S_0 becomes unity when T vanishes. On the other hand, the minimum value of α is achieved when S_0 vanishes. For this value we obtain a *critical temperature*

$$\alpha_C = \frac{Z \, \Delta E}{4kT_C} = 1,$$

or

$$T_C = \frac{Z \, \Delta E}{4k}, \qquad (10.5.20)$$

above which S_0 vanishes. Immediately below T_C, we can establish from Eq. (10.5.16) that

$$\lim_{T \to T_C^-} S_0 \left(\frac{dS_0}{dT} \right) = -\frac{3}{2T_C^-}, \qquad (10.5.21)$$

which permits the heat capacity at a temperature immediately below the critical temperature to be evaluated. We find

$$\lim_{T \to T_C^-} C_{V,\text{config}} = \frac{3Nk}{2}, \qquad \text{while} \qquad \lim_{T \to T_C^+} C_{V,\text{config}} = 0. \qquad (10.5.22)$$

There is, as a consequence, a discontinuity in the heat capacity of systems exhibiting order-disorder transformations.

For extremely small temperatures, we can verify that

$$\lim_{T \to 0} \tfrac{1}{2} \ln (1 - S_0) = \lim_{T \to 0} \left[\frac{Z \, \Delta E}{4kT} S_0 - \tfrac{1}{2} \ln (1 + S_0) \right],$$

so that the entropy, from Eq. (10.5.19), becomes

$$\lim_{T \to 0} S_{\text{config}} = 0.$$

10.6 Summary. In the present chapter we have been concerned with illustrating the utility of statistical mechanics in constructing statistical-thermodynamic functions for systems of interacting particles. We have selected systems which range from slightly nonideal gases, where the interactions may be regarded as small, to solids where they are so strong as to prevent any meaningful reference being made to the individual particles.

In each of the illustrations considered, a uniform, straightforward approach is available for determining the statistical-thermodynamic functions. In these illustrations, the configurational integral of classical statistical mechanics is considered. Thereby, an important aspect of statistical-*mechanical* theory *vs.* statistical-*thermodynamic* theory becomes manifest. The former permits one to refer to the equilibrium spatial distribution of systems, while the latter is not naturally equipped to do so. Although we have exploited the classical form, it is to be anticipated that quantum statistical mechanics will furnish the requisite information regarding spatial distributions.

EXERCISES

1. Consider the classical grand canonical ensemble for a system of slightly interacting particles and obtain Eq. (10.1.12) as an approximation.

2. Obtain an expression for the activity coefficient of a component in a binary mixture of slightly nonideal gases. Base the standard state of reference on the ideal gas. Determine also the activity coefficient based on a standard state of the pure component.

3. From the second virial coefficient of a mixture of slightly nonideal gases, estimate the relations to be satisfied for combining the van der Waals constants in a mixture of such gases.

4. Determine the entropy of mixing of binary mixtures of slightly nonideal gases.

5. Evaluate the contribution to the Helmholtz function made by the interionic interaction of an electrolytic solution.

6. Determine the contribution made by the interionic attraction to the entropy of mixing of an electrolytic solution.

7. Show that Eq. (10.3.16) is a solution of Eq. (10.3.15) which makes the (physical) solution electrically neutral.

8. Calculate the chemical potential of the solvent for an electrolytic solution satisfying the Debye-Hückel approximation.

9. Determine the contribution made by the interionic attraction to the equation of state of an electrolytic solution.

10. Determine the enthalpy of mixing of a mixture of slightly nonideal gases.

11. Examine the conditions imposed on the interaction potentials for the second virial coefficient to be finite.

12. Employ the procedure of Section 10.3 to obtain directly the chemical potential of a component in a mixture of nonideal gases.

13. Develop the theory of order-disorder phenomena for the case of variable binary composition. To do so, define the ordering parameter

$$S = \frac{N_A(\alpha) - N_A(\beta)}{x_A N},$$

where x_A is the fraction of A atoms, $N_A/(N_A + N_B)$.

14. Determine the chemical potential of A atoms in a system exhibiting order-disorder properties.

15. Determine the vapor pressure of a Debye solid, assuming the vapor to be an ideal gas.

16. Determine the equation of state for a Debye solid, and obtain the thermal coefficient of expansion and the bulk modulus as a function of temperature.

17. Determine the thermodynamic properties of a two-dimensional solid, as approximated by Debye's theory.

18. Verify Eq. (10.4.14).

19. Show that Eq. (10.4.14) gives Dulong and Petit's law for indefinitely large temperatures.

20. The properties of a "box of radiation" may be deduced from the Debye procedure by ascribing only two normal modes of vibration to the "ether." Determine the Planck distribution formula giving the energy-frequency density for radiation. Determine the equation of state of radiation. Note that for radiation, one assumes that ν_{max} is unlimited in magnitude, so that the equations of Section 10.4 must be modified accordingly.

21. Verify the statement made in the text that

$$\frac{Z \, \Delta E}{4kT} \leq \frac{1}{1 - S_0^2}.$$

CHAPTER 11

INTRODUCTION TO WAVE MECHANICS

11.1 The scope of wave mechanics. The preceding chapters have dealt with the means by which the equilibrium macroscopic properties of a physical system can be inferred from a knowledge of the properties of its microscopic constituents. In bridging the extremes of size, we have exploited a statistical viewpoint. To utilize the statistical formulas which have been obtained, we must know the possible values of the energy of a system. This kind of knowledge requires a more-or-less complete consideration of the *mechanics* of the system. To illustrate: if we are to determine the possible energy values which may be associated with the rotational motion of a diatomic molecule, we must have a detailed knowledge of (1) what quantities are both necessary and sufficient to specify its orientation in space, (2) how these quantities may change with the passage of time, and (3) what physical principles are available for determining the latter. The succeeding chapters are directed toward an answer to questions of this sort.

While our essential aim will be to indicate how the properties of microscopic systems may be determined, we shall also be concerned with emphasizing the role that a statistical viewpoint assumes in the realm of the microphysical world. At first one might suppose that all microscopic systems could be described completely in terms of the basic particles of which they are constituted and that such descriptions could be made precise without introducing the uncertainties associated with a statistical viewpoint. Such an assumption, however, is not in accord with the facts. We shall not dwell here unduly on this point, except to emphasize that the properties of the world of microscopic dimensions are known to us rather indirectly. As we have discussed earlier, the application to microscopic systems of notions developed from observations upon macroscopic systems has a *conceptual* idealization associated with it. Some may view it as remarkable that some of our notions thus appear not to apply to the microphysical world. But a judgment can be made only on the basis of experimental evidence. Although the correct viewpoint cannot be established with certainty by experimental evidence, the incorrect viewpoint can be rejected thereby.

By way of anticipation, we can say that we shall find that the description which has proved successful in dealing with the microphysical world is thoroughly permeated with a statistical viewpoint. However, the techniques which pertain to its applicability differ somewhat from those we have already considered. This difference will not detract from the basic similarity there seems to be between the microscopic and the macroscopic worlds. To deal with the ideas which have proved to be so essential in describing the motion of molecular systems, it will be convenient to employ some of the notions, as well as the language, of *wave motion*. As a consequence, the subject we shall be considering is termed *wave mechanics*. We shall use this term interchangeably with *quantum mechanics;* the reasons for the latter term will appear presently.

While we impart to our description of physical systems a basic wave character, in distinct contrast to the particle viewpoint we have been emphasizing, we must not exaggerate it. We still intend that meaning shall be attached to statements referring to material particles. As a result, we shall find at times that we tread a very narrow path between the extreme particle-viewpoint on one side and the extreme wave-viewpoint on the other side; at other times it will be more convenient to abandon the path entirely.

Now, we also may note that in satisfying the need which has been indicated for the possible energy values of a system, we achieve even more. We attain the position of being able to describe the *dynamics* of microscopic systems. This, in turn, will enable us ultimately to describe the nonequilibrium properties of macroscopic systems. However, this aspect will not be developed in any great detail. In ultimate terms, it becomes possible to fuse the quantum-mechanical with the statistical-mechanical to provide a uniform theoretical description of physical phenomena. We shall, however, only indicate briefly how this may be effected.

11.2 Survey of wave properties. An obvious example of a wave motion is that exhibited by a previously smooth surface of water when a pebble, or other object, is dropped onto it. A less obvious example, simpler in some respects to describe, is a forced vibration of a violin string. When the force is such as to produce certain sustained vibrations, the wave motion of the violin string becomes especially simple to describe. In such circumstances one can establish that each portion of the string is moving (1) with a recurrent, periodic motion, and (2) with an amplitude of vibration which is fixed in time.

In the simplest situations such a *stationary* wave motion may be represented mathematically by an equation which relates the displacement of the string in a direction perpendicular to the normal resting or time-average position of the string to the location along the string and the time. To illustrate, if y represents the displacement at position x, measured along the resting string, and at time t, the two aforementioned conditions permit the expression

$$y(x, t) = y_0(x)f(\nu t + a), \qquad (11.2.1)$$

where $y_0(x)$ is the amplitude, or maximum displacement, at x, ν is the (constant) frequency of vibration, and $f(z)$ is a periodic function such that

$$f(z + 1) = f(z); \qquad (11.2.2)$$

the quantity a is referred to as a *phase* constant. Hence,

$$y\left(x, t + \frac{n}{\nu}\right) = y(x, t),$$

where n is an integer. More complicated expressions may be necessary to describe a stationary wave motion. Thus

$$y(x, t) = y_1(x)f_1(\nu t + a_1) + y_2(x)f_2(\nu t + a_2) \qquad (11.2.3)$$

will evidently be periodic if both f_1 and f_2 satisfy Eq. (11.2.2). Yet Eq. (11.2.3) differs markedly from Eq. (11.2.1). In general, we may extend the description for a stationary wave motion to

$$y(x, t) = \sum_{n=1}^{\infty} y_n(x)f_n(\nu t + a_n), \qquad (11.2.4)$$

where each f_n satisfies Eq. (11.2.2). Questions of convergence need to be answered before this last equation can be used effectively.

The *principle of superposition* of waves is embodied in Eq. (11.2.4). Thereby, a displacement generally is to be regarded as composed of stationary waves of the form given in Eq. (11.2.1). In this sense a periodic displacement may be viewed as due to different waves $y_n(x)$ which have been "started" at different times (a_n/ν). The principle just stated is clearly an assumption; it is suggested by the observations that many wave motions can be directed through the same region of space without difficulty and frequently with no interference with one another. The principle is, furthermore, assumed to hold generally for all wave motions, of which stationary wave motions are a special kind.

Equation (11.2.4) poses a challenge. Suppose the left side of this equation were known. How could we determine the representation given on the right side of this equation? Is the latter unique? These are questions we ultimately shall want to answer. For the moment, however, we direct our attention to the simpler, yet related, question: how many *component* waves comprise a given wave motion? There are trivial cases in which all f's are the same, which permit the answer to be obtained by a simple counting. However, more information generally must be made available to answer even this simple question.

To that end, we will suppose that the *set* of waves represented by Eq. (11.2.4) is known to us for *all possible values* of the several a_n's. That is, we shall regard each wave motion as represented by

$$y(x, t) \equiv y(x, t, a_1, a_2, \ldots),$$
(11.2.5)

where the a's are capable of assuming all values in a certain range. Clearly we have an enormously large number of wave motions. In fact, we may properly regard this set in the sense of an ensemble considered previously. In these terms we may establish certain properties of the ensemble. For instance, consider a sum of all members of an ensemble of N-component waves,

$$\overline{F(x, t)} = \sum_{a_1} \sum_{a_2} \cdots \sum_{a_N} y(x, t, a_1 \ldots a_N)$$

$$= \sum_{a_1} \sum_{a_2} \cdots \sum_{a_N} \sum_{n=1}^{N} y_n(x) f_n(\nu t + a_n).$$

If now, because of the periodicity of the f's, we restrict the range of values of each a,

$$0 \le a_n \le 1,$$
(11.2.6)

and assume that all intermediate values are equally likely among the ensemble of waves, the sums can be replaced by integrals and

$$\overline{F(x, t)} = \sum_{n=1}^{N} y_n(x) \int_0^1 da_n f_n(\nu t + a_n)$$

$$= \sum_{n=1}^{N} y_n(x) \int_{\nu t}^{\nu t+1} dz \, f_n(z).$$
(11.2.7)

The latter integral is simply the average value of $f_n(z)$ over one period, which corresponds to the reference value from which the displacements are measured. It evidently has the value zero as a consequence. Hence the superposition of all waves of an ensemble of N-component waves is, itself, a wave of zero amplitude. Such a wave evidently corresponds to an annihilation of all the constituent waves of the ensemble. Stated differently, the result just obtained corresponds to the *phase average* of a wave. It hinges upon the periodic character of the f's *and* the convention that displacements are measured from the time-average value of the displacement. It also requires that the component waves be distributed uniformly with respect to their phases, a condition sometimes referred to as one of "random phases." We have

$$\overline{F(x, t)} = 0. \tag{11.2.8}$$

To obtain a nonzero result, let us consider the sum of the squares of all component waves of the ensemble,

$$
\begin{aligned}
\overline{[F(x, t)]^2} &= \sum_{a_1} \sum_{a_2} \cdots \sum_{a_N} y^2(x, t, a_1, \ldots a_N) \\
&= \sum_{a_1} \sum_{a_2} \cdots \sum_{a_N} \sum_{n=1}^{N} \sum_{m=1}^{N} y_n(x) y_m(x) f_n(\nu t + a_n) f_m(\nu t + a_m),
\end{aligned}
$$

making use of Eq. (11.2.4). As previously, the axiom of random phases leads to

$$
\overline{[F(x, t)]^2} = \tfrac{1}{2} \sum_{\substack{n=1 \\ n \neq m}}^{N} \sum_{m=1}^{N} y_n(x) y_m(x) \int_0^1 da_n \int_0^1 da_m f_n(\nu t + a_n) f_m(\nu t + a_m)
$$

$$
+ \sum_{n=1}^{N} y_n^2(x) \int_0^1 da_n f_n^2(\nu t + a_n). \tag{11.2.9}
$$

By the argument employed previously, the double sum vanishes since

$$
\int_0^1 da_n f_n(\nu t + a_n) f_m(\nu t + a_m) = 0 \qquad \text{if } n \neq m.
$$

Hence

$$
\overline{[F(x, t)]^2} = \sum_{n=1}^{N} y_n^2(x) \int_{\nu t}^{\nu t+1} dz\, f_n^2(z).
$$

Now no loss of generality is entailed if we take the integral to be *normalized* to unity. For, if

$$
\int_{\nu t}^{\nu t+1} dz\, f_n^2(z) = C_n^2, \tag{11.2.10}
$$

we evidently may take a new time-dependent function (which is periodic)

$$
\phi_n(\nu t + a_n) = \frac{1}{C_n} f_n(\nu t + a), \tag{11.2.11}
$$

with

$$
\eta_n(x) = C_n y_n(x),
$$

so that

$$y(x, t) = \sum_{n=1}^{N} \eta_n(x)\phi_n(\nu t + a_n) \tag{11.2.12}$$

and

$$\overline{[F(x, t)]^2} = \sum_{n=1}^{N} \eta_n^2(x).$$

In the special case where all η_n's are the same,

$$\overline{[F(x, t)]^2} = N\eta^2(x), \tag{11.2.13}$$

giving a phase average proportional to the number of component waves. (Note that the ϕ_n's are regarded as distinct from one another.)

A comparison of Eqs. (11.2.8) and (11.2.13) relates the differences between the phase average of the *amplitude* of a *waveform* and its *intensity*. Identical results are to be expected when a waveform is periodic in space as when it is periodic in time. Restricting our attention to one-dimensional waves for the sake of simplicity, we may take

$$\eta_n(x) = A_n\psi_n(kx + b_n), \tag{11.2.14}$$

where

$$\psi_n(z + 1) = \psi_n(z), \tag{11.2.15}$$

$$\int_{kx}^{kx+1} dz\, \psi_n^2(z) = 1, \tag{11.2.16}$$

and k is referred to as the *wave number* of the wave and is the reciprocal of its wavelength,

$$\lambda = \frac{1}{k}; \tag{11.2.17}$$

A_n is an arbitrary constant; b_n is a phase constant for the spatially periodic wave. We may observe that if

$$y(x, t) \equiv y(x, t; a_1, \ldots; b_1, \ldots) = \sum_{n=1}^{\infty} A_n\psi_n(kx + b_n)\phi_n(\nu t + a_n),$$

$$\tag{11.2.18}$$

then

$$A_n = \int_0^1 da_n \int_0^1 db_n \psi_n(kx + b_n)\phi_n(\nu t + a_n)y(x, t) \tag{11.2.19}$$

and

$$\int_0^1 \cdots \int_0^1 \prod_{n=1}^{\infty} da_n \prod_{m=1}^{\infty} db_m y^2(x, t) = \sum_{n=1}^{\infty} A_n^2. \tag{11.2.20}$$

It is clear that the previous results are entirely formal, and the question of convergence must be considered in any practical application. In many cases of practical interest we shall consider such waveforms for which

$$\sum_{n=1}^{\infty} A_n^2 = 1. \tag{11.2.21}$$

In these cases A_n is referred to as a *probability amplitude* and A_n^2 is referred to as a *probability* that the relevant waveform contains the component $\psi_n(kx + b_n)\phi_n(\nu t + a_n)$. (We note here that the A_n's have been regarded as real numbers, but that later applications will be made in which they are complex; in such cases, A_n^2 will appear as the square of the magnitude of A_n.)

It now is evident that our original question dealing with the number of component waves comprising a given wave motion is answered in a general way: if we have an ensemble of normalized component waves which are uniformly distributed in their phases, the phase average of the intensity of a waveform will give the sum of the squares of the coefficients in the superposition of the normalized component waves. Just what form the component waves may take is arbitrary, provided the periodicity and normalization conditions are met. Further *physical* restrictions must be imposed to restrict their form, and how this will be accomplished will be considered presently.

11.3 Interference phenomena. The most interesting properties associated with waves are to be found among those classified as *interference* phenomena. Indeed, if any phenomena may be held to be characteristic of waves, they are precisely those of interference. For a purely formal description of these phenomena it will suffice to consider the simplest situations involving only two component waves. Then, a superposition of two one-dimensional waves which differ also in their phase constants may be expressed as

$$y(x, t) = A_1\psi_1(k_1x + b_1)\phi_1(\nu_1t + a_1) + A_2\psi_2(k_2x + b_2)\phi_2(\nu_2t + a_2)$$
$$= \tfrac{1}{2}(A_1\psi_1 + A_2\psi_2)(\phi_1 + \phi_2) + \tfrac{1}{2}(A_1\psi_1 - A_2\psi_2)(\phi_1 - \phi_2).$$

$$\tag{11.3.1}$$

Now, a simpler situation occurs when the temporal variation of each wave is identical. Then

$$y(x, t) = (A_1\psi_1 + A_2\psi_2)\phi(\nu t + a). \tag{11.3.2}$$

Because of the periodic property of the ψ's there generally may be anticipated regions for which the amplitude $y(x, t)$ vanishes when neither ψ vanishes. This condition will occur when

$$A_1\psi_1(k_1x + b_1) = -A_2\psi_2(k_2x + b_2), \qquad (11.3.3)$$

which, clearly, is less stringent a condition than one requiring both ψ's to vanish. The explicit solution of Eq. (11.3.3) will require an explicit statement of the form of the ψ's.

Related to the spatial interference phenomenon is the phenomenon of "beats." From Eq. (11.3.1), the condition that

$$A_1\psi_1(k_1x + b_1) = A_2\psi_2(k_2x + b_2)$$

for all x yields

$$y(x, t) = A\psi(kx + b)[\phi_1(\nu_1t + a_1) + \phi_2(\nu_2t + a_2)]. \qquad (11.3.4)$$

As previously, $y(x, t)$ may have zeros when neither of the component waves vanishes. Again, an explicit form is required to determine the explicit nature of the zeros.

In either case of interference, we note that the phenomenon arises by virtue of a superposition of component waves, by which means the *amplitudes* of the component waves are added algebraically; thereby, the various component waves are able to annihilate one another at various positions and times.

11.4 Simple periodic waves. An explicit expression for the properties of wave motion requires explicit forms for the spatial and temporal components of waves. The choice which is made here is dictated largely by convenience and tradition. However, no undue loss of generality ensues thereby, for the principle of superposition assures us that any actual wave may be regarded as a composite of any suitable set of component waves. (The restrictions which must be imposed upon sets of component waves to establish their suitability will be discussed later.)

A common set of periodic functions are those associated with the ordinary trigonometric functions: *sine* and *cosine*. These may be recognized as the mutually perpendicular projections of a circular motion. As a consequence of this simple physical genesis, these trigonometric functions are seen to be periodic in 2π radians. Moreover, an arbitrary linear combination of both sine and cosine (with fixed coefficients) also is periodic in 2π radians. As a result, we may take

$$f_m(z) = A_m \cos 2\pi mz + B_m \sin 2\pi mz \qquad (11.4.1)$$

as typical of the periodic functions we wish to employ. In these terms

Eqs. (11.2.12) and (11.2.14) could be expressed as

$$y(x, t) = \sum_{m=0}^{\infty} A_m \cos 2\pi mkx \cos 2\pi m\nu t$$

$$+ \sum_{m=0}^{\infty} B_m \sin 2\pi mkx \cos 2\pi m\nu t, \qquad (11.4.2)$$

which is referred to as a *Fourier* series. The phase constants have been dropped from Eq. (11.4.2) for simplicity. We may confirm that

$$\int_0^1 da_n \cos 2\pi(m\nu t + a_m) \cos 2\pi(n\nu t + a_n) = 0, \qquad n \neq m, \quad (11.4.3)$$

and

$$\int_0^1 da_n [\cos 2\pi(n\nu t + a_n)]^2 = \tfrac{1}{2}, \qquad n \neq 0. \qquad (11.4.4)$$

Hence, in terms of the functions introduced earlier,

$$\phi_m = \frac{1}{\sqrt{2}} \cos 2\pi(m\nu t + a_m),$$

$$\psi_m = \frac{1}{\sqrt{2}} \cos 2\pi(mkx + b_m),$$

or the analogous sine function. We may note, for later purposes, that

$$\int_0^{1/\nu} dt \cos 2\pi(m\nu t + a_m) \cos 2\pi(n\nu t + a_n) = 0, \qquad n \neq m, \quad (11.4.5)$$

while

$$\int_0^{1/\nu} dt [\cos 2\pi(m\nu t + a_m)]^2 = \frac{1}{2\nu}, \qquad m \neq 0, \qquad (11.4.6)$$

which are similar to Eqs. (11.4.3) and (11.4.4); however, they differ markedly in requiring an integration over the *time* and *not* the *phase* of the periodic function. Analogous results obtain for the spatially periodic functions. Equations (11.4.5) and (11.4.6) are illustrative of what are termed *orthogonality* and *normalization* relations among component waves.

Turning now to the interference phenomena considered in the previous section, Eq. (11.3.3) becomes (restricting our attention to the cosine function) for equal amplitude waves

$$\frac{1}{\sqrt{2}} \cos 2\pi(mkx + b_m) = -\frac{1}{\sqrt{2}} \cos 2\pi(nkx + b_n), \qquad (11.4.7)$$

whence

$$2\pi(mkx + b_m) = 2\pi(nkx + b_n) + \pi + 2\pi p, \qquad (11.4.8)$$

p being an integer. In the simplest situation, $m = n$ but $b_m \neq b_n$. We may observe that the phase constants assume the role of determining the "origin" of the wave. Thus, if the respective "sources" of the waves are given by

$$b_m = -mkx_m, \qquad b_n = -mkx_n,$$

we obtain

$$mk(x_m - x_n) = \tfrac{1}{2} + p.$$

Or, introducing the wavelength λ_m by Eq. (11.2.17), we obtain

$$(x - x_m) = (x - x_n) + \left(\frac{2p + 1}{2}\right)\lambda_m. \qquad (11.4.9)$$

Equation (11.4.9) states that annihilation of two otherwise identical waves will occur wherever the distance from the composite wave to each of the "sources" differs by an odd multiple of one-half the wavelength. As given by Eq. (11.4.9), this result readily is obtained for three-dimensional waves.

The beat phenomenon is made explicit in terms of the functions which have been introduced. From Eq. (11.3.4), we obtain

$$y(x, t) = A\psi(kx + b)[\cos 2\pi(\nu_1 t + a_1) + \cos 2\pi(\nu_2 t + a_2)].$$

Since

$$\cos x + \cos y = 2\cos\frac{x + y}{2}\cos\frac{x - y}{2},$$

we obtain

$$y(x, t) = 2A\psi(kx + b)\cos 2\pi\left[\left(\frac{\nu_1 + \nu_2}{2}\right)t + \left(\frac{a_1 + a_2}{2}\right)\right]$$

$$\times \cos 2\pi\left[\left(\frac{\nu_1 - \nu_2}{2}\right)t + \left(\frac{a_1 - a_2}{2}\right)\right]. \qquad (11.4.10)$$

This expression becomes particularly interesting when the frequencies are nearly the same. In that case we obtain a wave of frequency $(\nu_1 + \nu_2)/2$, which is multiplied by a time-dependent factor that varies periodically with a frequency of $(\nu_1 - \nu_2)/2$. The result is a wave with an amplitude varying with time at a frequency smaller than that of the interfering waves. This behavior is referred to as a *modulation* of the original wave motion.

11.5 Matter waves. With the foregoing preliminary description of wave properties, we are in a position to consider those which are exhibited by material objects. It should be kept in mind that the wave properties can be related to the two quantities of frequency and wavelength, and it is to these quantities that we must turn.

An indication of the role of frequency in matter waves was contained in the original discovery of Planck, whose studies on the equilibrium distribution of radiation oscillators gave results in accord with the facts only if the energy of an oscillator were proportional to the frequency of oscillation and, in fact, were some multiple of a lowest (nonzero) value. (See Exercise 20 of Chapter 10.) However, it remained for Einstein to clarify the relation between the frequency of radiation and its energy. In his analysis of the photoelectric effect, Einstein pointed out that the kinetic energy of those electrons which were ejected from an illuminated metal plate depended on the frequency of the illuminating radiation rather than on its intensity. Moreover, the kinetic energy of the ejected electrons varied linearly with the frequency of the absorbed radiation. As a consequence, energy could be conserved in the over-all process if the energy of the radiation were proportional to its frequency, a result already noted by Planck.

In schematic terms, we have for the photoelectric effect

Electron (in metal) + radiation absorbed → electron (ejected in vacuum),

for which conservation of energy requires

ϵ (ejected electron) $= \epsilon$ (radiation absorbed) $+ \epsilon$ (electron in metal)

$$= h\nu + \text{constant} \qquad (11.5.1)$$

as a summary of the experimental findings. Here h is Planck's constant. This particular relationship suggests a general connection between all forms of energy and the frequency of associated radiation

$$\epsilon = h\nu. \qquad (11.5.2)$$

As used by Bohr, Eq. (11.5.2) relates the difference of the energies of a material system to the frequency of the radiation absorbed or emitted.

The role played by wavelength in matter waves was pointed out by de Broglie, who made the important suggestion that a free particle could have a wavelength associated with it,

$$\lambda = \frac{h}{p}, \qquad (11.5.3)$$

where h is Planck's constant and p is the *momentum* of the particle. This suggestion received brilliant confirmation in the experiments of Davisson and Germer and of Thomson, who obtained *interference patterns* from beams of electrons scattered from the surface of various metallic crystals.

The next advance was promptly provided by Schroedinger, who proceeded to combine the properties of frequency and wavelength into a wave theory of matter. If we postpone the question of what a matter wave *is*, and content ourselves for the moment with a purely formal approach, we may associate a *free* material particle with the simple waveform

$$y(x, t) = A \cos\left(\frac{2\pi p x}{h}\right) \cos\left(\frac{2\pi \epsilon t}{h}\right), \tag{11.5.4}$$

where we have used Eqs. (11.5.2) and (11.5.3). Clearly, other forms may be chosen. Until we have a means for introducing *physical principles* into the subject there will always be some arbitrariness in the choice of the *wave function*. Notice that, in an attempt to minimize the arbitrariness,

$$\frac{\partial^2 y(x, t)}{\partial x^2} = -\left(\frac{2\pi}{h}\right)^2 p^2 y(x, t),$$

so that

$$-\frac{\hbar^2}{2m} \frac{\partial^2 y(x, t)}{\partial x^2} = \frac{p^2}{2m} y(x, t), \tag{11.5.5}$$

where $\hbar = (h/2\pi)$. Equation (11.5.5) reveals how the kinetic energy of the particle may be obtained from the relevant wave function. In formal terms, this equation may be expressed as

$$\frac{1}{2m}(p)^2 y(x, t) = \frac{1}{2m}\left(\frac{\hbar}{i}\frac{\partial}{\partial x}\right)\left(\frac{\hbar}{i}\frac{\partial}{\partial x}\right) y(x, t) = \frac{1}{2m}\left(\frac{\hbar}{i}\frac{\partial}{\partial x}\right)^2 y(x, t),$$

which suggests the *identification* made by Schroedinger,

$$\left(\frac{\hbar}{i}\frac{\partial}{\partial x}\right) \leftrightarrow \mathbf{p}, \tag{11.5.6}$$

to which we shall return presently. A most important suggestion was then made by Schroedinger that Eq. (11.5.5) be augmented for *nonfree* particles (i.e., those involved in a potential) to

$$\frac{1}{2m}\left(\frac{\hbar}{i}\frac{\partial}{\partial x}\right)^2 y(x, t) = [\epsilon - V(x)]y(x, t),$$

where ϵ is the total energy and $V(x)$ is the potential energy of the particle. Rearrangement yields the *first Schroedinger equation:*

$$\left[\frac{1}{2m}\left(\frac{\hbar}{i}\frac{\partial}{\partial x}\right)^2 + V(x)\right]y(x,t) = \epsilon y(x,t). \tag{11.5.7}$$

With the identification of Eq. (11.5.6) as the *momentum operator*, the left side of Eq. (11.5.7) becomes

$$\left[\frac{(\mathbf{p})^2}{2m} + V(x)\right]y(x,t) = \epsilon y(x,t),$$

or

$$\mathbf{H}y(x,t) = \epsilon y(x,t), \tag{11.5.8}$$

where **H** is the operator corresponding to the Hamiltonian of the particle. It is presumed, of course, that the wave function is to be determined as a solution of Eqs. (11.5.7) or (11.5.8).

However, since both sides of Eq. (11.5.8) involve the time only in the wave function, it is evident that the temporal dependence of the latter is not thereby determined. As a consequence, we proceed to construct the *second Schroedinger equation.* Clearly,

$$\frac{\partial^2 y(x,t)}{\partial t^2} = -\frac{1}{\hbar^2}\epsilon^2 y(x,t) = -\left(\frac{\mathbf{H}}{\hbar}\right)\left(\frac{\mathbf{H}}{\hbar}\right)y(x,t) = -\left(\frac{\mathbf{H}}{\hbar}\right)^2 y(x,t).$$

This may be written as

$$0 = \left(\hbar^2\frac{\partial^2}{\partial t^2} + \mathbf{H}^2\right)y(x,t) = \left(\mathbf{H} + i\hbar\frac{\partial}{\partial t}\right)\left(\mathbf{H} - i\hbar\frac{\partial}{\partial t}\right)y(x,t),$$

which *suggests* the condition

$$\mathbf{H}y(x,t) = i\hbar\frac{\partial}{\partial t}y(x,t) \tag{11.5.9}$$

as determining the temporal behavior of an otherwise arbitrary wave function. This is the second, or time-dependent, Schroedinger equation. It will be *assumed* to hold for all physical systems, including those for which the Hamiltonian may depend upon the time.

By way of recapitulation, we note that the equations here have been arrived at in a manner which is quite heuristic. Therefore, they have no *a priori* justification and must be assumed. However, the means by which they have been obtained serves to emphasize the role that *operators* play in the exploitation of the equations. In the present context, the operators are somewhat more explicit expressions of procedures which already have been employed. [See, for example, Eq. (9.2.1) as well as

other portions of Chapter 9.] As a result, the procedures of wave mechanics bear a resemblance to the statistical procedures which already
have been elaborated.

11.6 Operators and observables. To emphasize the statistical features
of wave mechanics we note, first of all, that a wave function is able to
yield certain information about a system, as we have seen. For example,
with a wave function which satisfies Eq. (11.5.8), we obtain

$$\epsilon = \frac{\int dx\, y(x, t)\mathbf{H}y(x, t)}{\int dx\, [y(x, t)]^2} \, ,$$

which is *formally* similar to the expressions employed in statistical mechanics. The important distinction to be emphasized here is that operations in the wave-mechanical sense are carried out, not on what might
be regarded as the *distribution*, but rather on its square root. Stated in
terms of a wave description, operations are carried out on the *amplitudes*
for wave mechanics, and on *intensities* (of a formal sort) for statistical
mechanics. As we have seen, this difference will give rise to considerable
differences in the results which may be obtained.

In this light, one aspect in the formulation of a theory is that which
deals with the *operators* and the *operands* of that theory. We shall examine
this aspect of wave mechanics, introducing the requisite axioms in as
motivated a manner as seems desirable.

First of all, in analogy with the previous equations we shall assume that
every physical observable has a corresponding operator which enables
us to determine an *expectation value* for the system when it has a specified
wave function describing its behavior. Thus, if a certain physical property of a system is associated with the operator $\boldsymbol{\alpha}$ and the system is
described by a wave function $\psi(x, t)$, the expectation value of the property in question is *defined* as

$$E_\psi(\boldsymbol{\alpha}) = \frac{\int dx\, \psi^*(x, t)\boldsymbol{\alpha}\psi(x, t)}{\int dx\, \psi^*(x, t)\psi(x, t)} \, , \qquad (11.6.1)$$

where, in the interest of subsequent generality we have allowed $\psi(x, t)$
to be complex and ψ^* is the complex conjugate of ψ. We note that the
range of integration is unspecified for the present; however, Eq. (11.6.1)
can have meaning only if both integrals are finite in value. We shall
return to this question later. For the present, we may emphasize that
the expectation value of an operator is the value one may expect for the
average of the measured values of the corresponding physical properties

when the system is described by the indicated wave function. In view of the character of microphysical measurements, the introduction of an ensemble of systems having the same wave function seems natural, and it is with respect to such an ensemble that the expectation value has significance.

Now, for certain wave function descriptions ϕ_i we may hope to find

$$E_{\phi_i}(\alpha^n) = [E_{\phi_i}(\alpha)]^n$$

for all values of nonnegative integral n. This condition evidently is satisfied by a function ϕ_i such that

$$\alpha\phi_i = \alpha_i\phi_i, \tag{11.6.2}$$

where α_i is a constant numerical value. While we shall not demonstrate it, Eq. (11.6.2) also is necessary for the previous relation to hold. Equation (11.6.2) is referred to as an *eigenvalue* relation, of which the first Schroedinger equation, Eq. (11.5.8), is an outstanding example. In terms of the relation between the expectation values and the measured values, we see that the *eigenvalues* α_i of the operator α represent the possible *precisely measurable* values of the corresponding physical property. We refer to ϕ_i as the corresponding *eigenfunction*. The totality of its eigenvalues is referred to as the *spectrum* of the operator. Hence, we assume that there are precisely measurable properties of a physical system and that their corresponding operators then will satisfy an eigenvalue relation. In this connection, the construction of the first Schroedinger equation has led to a means for determining the possible precise values of the energy for systems of interest. For statistical-mechanical purposes we need go very little further.

However, for definiteness, we state certain assumptions we shall make regarding the operators with which we shall be concerned. We state, in fact, certain relations defining the *algebra of linear operators*. It is assumed that a *distributive law* holds. Thus, for all operators and operands which we consider,

$$\alpha(\psi_1 + \psi_2) = \alpha\psi_1 + \alpha\psi_2 \tag{11.6.3}$$

and

$$(\alpha + \beta)\psi = \alpha\psi + \beta\psi. \tag{11.6.4}$$

An *associative law* is assumed for all the operators we shall consider:

$$\alpha[\beta(\gamma\psi)] = \alpha[(\beta\gamma)\psi] = (\alpha\beta\gamma)\psi. \tag{11.6.5}$$

For any arbitrary constant c, all operators we consider will satisfy

$$\alpha(c\psi) = c(\alpha\psi). \tag{11.6.6}$$

In general, however, the operators we consider may *not commute*, and then

$$\alpha\beta\psi \neq \beta\alpha\psi, \qquad (11.6.7)$$

emphasizing that the order of operation is important. Because the operands are intended to be arbitrary in the previous equations, they may be suppressed entirely, which will enable us to deal with *operator equations* and *operator relations*.

To make some connection with physical reality, we introduce the requirement that physical observables must have operators with *real* expectation values, regardless of the wave function describing the system. From Eq. (11.6.1) we obtain the requirement that

$$\int dx\, \psi^*(x, t)[\alpha\psi(x, t)] = \int dx\, \psi(x, t)[\alpha\psi(x, t)]^*. \qquad (11.6.8)$$

This expression is illustrative of a more general one,

$$\int dx\, \psi_1^*(x, t)[\alpha\psi_2(x, t)] = \int dx\, \psi_1(x, t)[\alpha\psi_2(x, t)]^*, \qquad (11.6.9)$$

which we shall *assume*. Operators which satisfy Eq. (11.6.9) are termed *Hermitian;* they evidently have real eigenvalues. [We must not forget that Eq. (11.6.9) can have meaning only if the integrals are finite. As a result, the ψ's must be suitably restricted.] However, we must point out that reality of the eigenvalues of an operator is not restricted to Hermitian operators. Nevertheless, in the cases with which we shall be concerned the physical observables will have demonstrably Hermitian operators.

At the risk of repetition, we assume that physical systems are described by wave functions determined by Schroedinger's time-dependent equation, Eq. (11.5.9), (in one dimension)

$$\left[-\frac{\hbar^2}{2m}\frac{\partial^2}{\partial x^2} + V(x) \right]\Psi(x, t) = i\hbar\frac{\partial}{\partial t}\Psi(x, t), \qquad (11.6.10)$$

whereupon the expectation values of *all* physical observables is determined with the solution of this equation. In this manner the operand for physical systems is defined.

There remains the important problem of determining the corresponding operators of various physical observables. Some start has been made in that direction, but further developments will be considered in the next chapter.

Finally, for the purposes of the present section, we reiterate the principle of superposition: any wave function may be regarded as a linear combination of a suitable restricted set of component waves; the restriction of suitability refers rather more to the generality of the set of component waves than to the limitations, it being necessary that there be a sufficient number of component waves to render a faithful composite of the intended wave function. For our purposes it will suffice to anticipate that the entire set of solutions of an eigenvalue relation will provide us with a sufficiently large set of functions in terms of which a faithful representation of a given wave function may be had.

11.7 Summary. The need of the possible energy values of a microscopic system necessitated an inquiry into the mechanics of physical systems. For microphysical systems, the mechanics found a form suggested by wave motion, and is termed *wave mechanics*. The basis of this mechanics was examined from a statistical viewpoint.

If a material microphysical system is accorded a wave-function description, it is necessary to establish how information can be obtained about the system. This question is examined, and the consideration of ensembles of waves, or of systems having the various wave functions attributed to the ensemble, reveals how information related to measurements may be obtained from a wave-function description. The principle of superposition, whereby any wave motion is regarded as a linear combination of certain component wave motions, is introduced, and the phenomena of interference which arise thereby are examined. The formal results are given explicit expression in terms of trigonometric functions.

The trigonometric functions are used, with the results of Planck, Einstein, Bohr, and de Broglie relating frequency with energy and wavelength with momentum, to construct wave functions for material particles. Then, following Schroedinger, the equations to be satisfied by physical systems are constructed in an heuristic manner. The examination of physical observables and corresponding wave-mechanical operators is carried out. The precisely measurable values of a physical property are related to an eigenvalue problem. The axioms needed for a discussion of wave mechanics are introduced and related, when feasible, to the physical requirements of the situation.

EXERCISES

1. Verify Eq. (11.2.9).
2. Verify Eq. (11.2.19).
3. Verify Eq. (11.2.20).
4. A particularly useful set of values for the coefficients of Eq. (11.4.1) are $A_m = 1$ and $B_m = i = \sqrt{-1}$. Show that these values lead to

$$f_m(z) = e^{2\pi m i z},$$

which is periodic in 2π.

5. Verify Eqs. (11.4.3) and (11.4.4).
6. Verify Eqs. (11.4.5) and (11.4.6). [Note the difference from the equations in the preceding problem.]
7. Verify that Eq. (11.4.7) leads to Eq. (11.4.8).
8. Extend Eq. (11.4.9) to three dimensions, using a *wave vector* $\mathbf{k}$ such that

$$\mathbf{k} \cdot \mathbf{x} = k_x x + k_y y + k_z z$$

and the wavelength

$$\lambda = 1/\sqrt{k_x^2 + k_y^2 + k_z^2}.$$

9. Take a periodic square wave,

$$t(z) = +1, \qquad 2n < z < 2n + 1,$$
$$= -1, \qquad 2n + 1 < z < 2n + 2,$$

n being a positive integer, and obtain explicit results for the interference phenomena discussed in Section 11.3. Compare with the results of Section 11.4.

10. Indicate how the wavelength of a particle may be determined experimentally without a knowledge of its mass or speed being involved. What would the wavelength of 10 identical such particles be? of 100?

11. The "derivation" given in Section 11.5 does not lead to Eq. (11.5.9) if $\mathbf{H}$ depends on the time explicitly. Show what terms remain. On the other hand, using the form for the periodic function given in Exercise 4, show that Eq. (11.5.9) obtains directly.

12. Verify that the eigenvalue relation, Eq. (11.6.2), leads to the relation immediately preceding.

13. Verify that real expectation values require Eq. (11.6.8).

14. Demonstrate, for wave functions which vanish at the limits of integration, that the momentum operator of Eq. (11.5.6) is an Hermitian operator.

15. Demonstrate, for the wave functions of Exercise 14, that the Hamiltonian operator is Hermitian.

16. Show that Hermitian operators necessarily have real eigenvalues.

17. Show that the eigenfunctions of a given Hermitian operator are spatially orthogonal in the general sense of Eq. (11.4.5) when they satisfy a condition entirely analogous to Eq. (11.4.6) *and* they correspond to *different* eigenvalues.

18. Try to formulate the quantum mechanical analog of Eq. (6.2.6), being explicit in the definitions of all quantities. When done properly, the result comprises what is meant by a function of an operator.

19. Assuming that the Hamiltonian operator is Hermitian, show that a time-dependent Schroedinger equation similar to Eq. (11.5.9), but with i replaced by $-i$, also must be satisfied. As a result, determine the relations existing between the respective solutions of these two equations.

CHAPTER 12

STATIONARY SOLUTIONS OF SCHROEDINGER'S EQUATION

12.1 The stationary state. Inasmuch as the procedure to be employed in determining the expectation values of the operators of physical observables involves the wave function determined by the Schroedinger time-dependent equation, we may refer to the solution of the latter as the *state function*. This designation conveys the notion that the physical state of the relevant system is then characterized. While such is the intention, the connection with the statistical viewpoint is emphasized when one realizes that the wave function is an *operand*, as is a statistical distribution. The original idea of characterizing the states of a physical system by the set of values of its physical properties is modified here to include the operational aspect both in the realm of the physical measurements and in the theory.

In what follows in succeeding chapters as well as in this one, we mainly shall give explicit attention to so-called one-dimensional systems. In so doing, we hope to achieve a clarity which is not dimmed by excessive devotion to matters of mathematical detail. Nevertheless, most of the results we shall obtain are capable of being generalized for systems with motion in more than one dimension. When it is simple to do so, we shall frequently indicate this either in the discussion or in exercises.

We now may ask if there are any states, in the sense described, for which all physical observables have stationary values. From our earlier statistical considerations we may anticipate that the energy of the system will be involved with such states. We consider only those states of a system determined by Eq. (11.6.10) for which $\int dx \Psi^*(x, t)\Psi(x, t)$ has a finite value. Then the value of the integral is constant in time, for

$$\frac{\partial}{\partial t} \int dx \Psi^*(x, t)\Psi(x, t)$$

$$= \int dx \left\{ \left[\frac{\partial}{\partial t} \Psi^*(x, t) \right] \Psi(x, t) + \Psi^*(x, t) \left[\frac{\partial}{\partial t} \Psi(x, t) \right] \right\}$$

$$= \int dx \left\{ \frac{[\mathbf{H}\Psi(x, t)]^*}{-ih} \Psi(x, t) + \Psi^*(x, t) \frac{[\mathbf{H}\Psi(x, t)]}{ih} \right\},$$

by Eqs. (11.5.8) and (11.6.10). Since $\mathbf{H}$ is Hermitian (Exercise 15, Chapter 11), we have

$$\frac{\partial}{\partial t} \int dx \Psi^*(x, t)\Psi(x, t) = 0, \tag{12.1.1}$$

so that the integral is constant. As a result, no undue loss of generality is involved if we suppose that $\Psi(x, t)$ is normalized to unity,

$$\int dx \Psi^*(x, t)\Psi(x, t) = 1.$$

Now we inquire into the conditions for which

$$\frac{\partial}{\partial t} E_\Psi(\boldsymbol{\alpha}) = \frac{\partial}{\partial t} \int dx \Psi^*(x, t)\boldsymbol{\alpha}\Psi(x, t) = 0, \qquad (12.1.2)$$

where $\boldsymbol{\alpha}$ is a time-independent Hermitian operator but otherwise is arbitrary. We can verify directly that the expectation value of such an operator is constant in time when $\Psi(x, t)$ is an eigenfunction of the Hamiltonian, satisfying Eq. (11.5.8). In other words, for those states of a system corresponding to precise values of its energy, the expectation values of all physical observables are constant in time. The necessary condition for such constancy turns out to be exactly the same, but the proof is a little involved.

To establish the necessary condition, we may express Eq. (12.1.2) as

$$\int dx \{[\mathbf{H}\Psi(x, t)]^*[\boldsymbol{\alpha}\Psi(x, t)] - [\boldsymbol{\alpha}\Psi(x, t)]^*[\mathbf{H}\Psi(x, t)]\} = 0, \qquad (12.1.3)$$

where use has been made of the Hermitian property of $\boldsymbol{\alpha}$; in particular,

$$\int dx \{\Psi^*(x, t)[\boldsymbol{\alpha}\Psi(x, t)] - [\boldsymbol{\alpha}\Psi(x, t)]^*\Psi(x, t)\} = 0. \qquad (12.1.4)$$

Now, $\boldsymbol{\alpha}$ is an otherwise arbitrary operator which satisfies Eqs. (12.1.3) and (12.1.4). As a result $[\boldsymbol{\alpha}\Psi(x, t)]$ has real and imaginary parts which may be regarded as arbitrary. Hence, using Lagrange's method of undetermined multipliers, we obtain

$$\int dx \{[(\mathbf{H} - \epsilon)\Psi(x, t)]^*[\boldsymbol{\alpha}\Psi(x, t)] - [\boldsymbol{\alpha}\Psi(x, t)]^*[(H - \epsilon)\Psi(x, t)]\} = 0,$$
$$(12.1.5)$$

where ϵ is a real number. Rearrangement of Eq. (12.1.5) yields

$$\int dx \{[(H - \epsilon)\Psi(x, t)]^* + [(H - \epsilon)\Psi(x, t)]\}$$
$$\times \{[\boldsymbol{\alpha}\Psi(x, t)] + [\boldsymbol{\alpha}\Psi(x, t)]^*\}$$
$$+ \int dx \{[(H - \epsilon)\Psi(x, t)]^* - [(H - \epsilon)\Psi(x, t)]\}$$
$$\times \{[\boldsymbol{\alpha}\Psi(x, t)] - [\boldsymbol{\alpha}\Psi(x, t)]^*\} = 0$$

so that ultimately we obtain

$$(H - \epsilon)\Psi(x, t) = 0, \qquad (12.1.6)$$

as a necessary condition, or $\Psi(x, t)$ is an eigenfunction of the Hamiltonian. Clearly, then,

$$i\hbar \frac{\partial \Psi(x, t)}{\partial t} = \epsilon\Psi(x, t),$$

so that the stationary state has the wave function

$$\Psi(x, t) = \Psi(x, 0)e^{-i\epsilon t/\hbar}, \qquad (12.1.7)$$

where ϵ is now the eigenvalue determined by

$$\mathbf{H}\Psi(x, 0) = \epsilon\Psi(x, 0). \qquad (12.1.8)$$

While we have used the phrase "stationary state" in relation to the temporal variation of expectation values, there is another usage we wish to consider. We have had occasion to refer to the stationary values of the energy and the entropy for systems in statistical thermodynamic equilibrium, when the distribution was altered. (See Section 9.1.) In the present instance we shall consider that state (i.e., as determined by the wave function) for which the expectation value of the energy is unaltered, while the wave function is normalized to unity but otherwise is subject to arbitrary changes. In other words, we consider the variational problem

$$\delta \left[\frac{\int dx \Psi^*(x) \mathbf{H}\Psi(x)}{\int dx \Psi^*(x)\Psi(x)} \right] = 0, \qquad (12.1.9)$$

subject to

$$\delta \int dx \Psi^*(x)\Psi(x) = 0. \qquad (12.1.10)$$

Clearly,

$$\int dx \, \{\delta\Psi^*(x)[\mathbf{H}\Psi(x)] + \Psi^*(x)[\mathbf{H} \, \delta\Psi(x)]\} = 0,$$

and

$$\int dx \, [\delta\Psi^*(x)\Psi(x) + \Psi^*(x) \, \delta\Psi(x)] = 0.$$

Because of the Hermitian property of the Hamiltonian, we can obtain

$$\int dx \, \{\delta\Psi^*(x)[(H - \epsilon)\Psi(x)] + \delta\Psi(x)[(H - \epsilon)\Psi(x)]^*\} = 0, \quad (12.1.11)$$

by taking a linear combination of the two previous equations. Since the real and imaginary parts of $\delta\Psi(x)$ are capable of arbitrary variation, we obtain by the method of Lagrangian multipliers, as previously,

$$(H - \epsilon)\Psi(x) = 0, \qquad (12.1.12)$$

as well as its complex conjugate. As a result, the stationary state (in the sense that arbitrary variations of the normalized wave functions will leave the expectation value of the energy stationary) is that which satisfies the time-independent Schroedinger equation, as in the case where "stationary" refers to temporal behavior of all other properties.

We have yet to establish in what sense the stationary value of the energy is a minimum, but this will be deferred to a later chapter.

In concluding this section, we note the formal parallel existing between the stationary state in quantum mechanics and equilibrium in statistical mechanics, as expressed in Eqs. (12.1.9), (12.1.10) and (7.2.4). However, a correspondence involving the first of the latter is lacking. Since we have just considered a *single* state, there exists no analogy with the entropy. However, in the statistical-mechanical sense a single state would correspond to zero entropy with no corresponding constraint.

12.2 Operators for physical observables. Before considering the stationary states of various systems, we may prepare for a determination of the properties of the systems in such states by considering the operators for physical observables.

In our heuristic "derivation" of Schroedinger's equations, we already have introduced the operator for momentum, Eq. (11.5.6),

$$\mathbf{p} \leftrightarrow \frac{\hbar}{i} \frac{\partial}{\partial x} ; \qquad (12.2.1)$$

this identification is due to Schroedinger and has the counterpart that the operator for position is taken as

$$\mathbf{x} \leftrightarrow x. \qquad (12.2.2)$$

Equations (12.2.1) and (12.2.2) form the basis of what is termed a "Schroedinger representation" of operators. Other representations are possible, but these are not readily apparent from our present viewpoint. Indeed, it is necessary to provide a general procedure for constructing operators corresponding to physical observables in order to obtain alternative representations of operators.

While we mainly shall utilize the Schroedinger representation, it will be of interest nevertheless to indicate briefly a basic relation which must be satisfied. From Eqs. (12.2.1) and (12.2.2) it is easily established that for an arbitrary function, $f(x)$

$$(\mathbf{xp} - \mathbf{px})f(x) = i\hbar f(x)$$

or

$$\mathbf{xp} - \mathbf{px} = i\hbar, \qquad (12.2.3)$$

which is referred to as a *quantum condition* or *commutation relation* between the operators for position and momentum. This relation, introduced originally by Heisenberg, serves as a basic starting point for quantum mechanics. We shall consider later the celebrated *uncertainty principle* due to Heisenberg, which follows as a direct consequence of Eq. (12.2.3). Our present interest is in noting that if we identify

$$\mathbf{p} \leftrightarrow p, \qquad (12.2.4)$$

then Eq. (12.3.3) has a solution (not unique, however)

$$\mathbf{x} = i\hbar \frac{\partial}{\partial p} \qquad (12.2.5)$$

for the position operator. In this form, it is tacitly assumed that the operand is a function of the value of the momentum of the system. This representation is termed the *momentum representation* of operators.

For the simplest situations with which we shall be concerned the construction of operators simply calls for determining the ordinary, or classical, mechanical quantity as a function of position and momentum, and replacing these quantities by operators which satisfy Eq. (12.2.3). When these quantities appear in a distinct manner, as in the Hamiltonian, no difficulty arises. However, when products of position and momentum variables occur in the classical mechanical expression, the ambiguity associated with the order of the operators must be removed. Moreover, when nonalgebraic functions of the operators arise, even greater difficulties are apparent. There also are operators which have no classical analogs and so cannot be constructed from the aforementioned operators. We shall not deal with these matters except to note that one generally may anticipate as a result that a very small number of different kinds of operators will be employed in wave mechanics. Those with which we shall deal will be very few in number and relatively free from any ambiguity.

We take the opportunity here to mention the procedures available for constructing operators for many-dimensional systems. First of all, we note that the motion of a single particle in three dimensions can be regarded as the composite of three (orthogonal) independent motions. In this sense the "construction" of Schroedinger's equation must take each motion into account. In fact, one identifies in the Schroedinger representation for three-dimensional motion the *coordinate* operators

$$\mathbf{x} \leftrightarrow x, \qquad \mathbf{y} \leftrightarrow y, \qquad \mathbf{z} \leftrightarrow z, \qquad (12.2.6)$$

and their *conjugate momentum* operators (following the nomenclature of classical mechanics)

$$\mathbf{p}_x \leftrightarrow \frac{\hbar}{i} \frac{\partial}{\partial x}, \qquad \mathbf{p}_y \leftrightarrow \frac{\hbar}{i} \frac{\partial}{\partial y}, \qquad \mathbf{p}_z \leftrightarrow \frac{\hbar}{i} \frac{\partial}{\partial z}. \qquad (12.2.7)$$

In these terms the Hamiltonian operator would be given by

$$\mathbf{H} \leftrightarrow -\frac{\hbar^2}{2m} \left(\frac{\partial^2}{\partial x^2} + \frac{\partial^2}{\partial y^2} + \frac{\partial^2}{\partial z^2} \right) + V(x, y, z), \qquad (12.2.8)$$

an obvious extension of Eq. (11.5.7).

The commutation relation, Eq. (12.2.3), now may be augmented for each component of motion. However, we observe that

$$\mathbf{p}_x \mathbf{p}_y - \mathbf{p}_y \mathbf{p}_x = 0, \qquad \mathbf{xy} - \mathbf{yx} = 0, \qquad \mathbf{p}_z \mathbf{x} - \mathbf{xp}_z = 0,$$

as well as additional relations involving the operators referring to *different* (orthogonal) components of motion. Hence the quantum conditions, as expressed in Eq. (12.2.3), refer only to *conjugate* position and momentum variables.

There is one operator which we need to consider in addition to those given. This operator may be termed a *location operator*. Let this operator be a function of position such that if the system is in the location specified, the value of the function is unity, and zero otherwise. That is, let

$$\Lambda(x_1, x, x_2) = 1, \qquad x_1 \leq x \leq x_2,$$
$$= 0, \qquad x < x_1,\ x > x_2, \qquad (12.2.9)$$

as a location operator for the "location" $|x_1 - x_2|$. The expectation value of this operator is *identified* as the probability that the system will have the indicated location. This seems a reasonable interpretation to ascribe to this quantity. But then

$$\lim_{|x_1 - x_2| \to 0} E_\Psi(\Lambda) = \lim_{|x_1 - x_2| \to 0} [\Psi^*(x, t)\Psi(x, t)] |x_1 - x_2|, \qquad (12.2.10)$$

where $x_1 \leq x \leq x_2$ and we have assumed that the wave functions are normalized to unity. As a result, $[\Psi^*(x, t)\Psi(x, t)]$ may be identified as the *probability density* (in x) of the system being located at x. This important role of the wave function was first suggested by Born. We shall have occasion to employ this meaning as a means for describing the behavior of physical systems. By Eq. (12.1.7), the probability density is constant as a function of time for the stationary state.

By virtue of Born's assumption the spatial distribution of a physical system is given in terms of its wave functions. As considered previously, the spatial distribution was related to the *classical* statistical-mechanical description accorded systems. We now are free of this restriction. It is possible to reformulate a complete quantum statistical-mechanical theory in which spatial distributions appear in a more natural manner. However, we shall not consider this possibility except to note its existence.

The result that the probability density is constant in time has an interesting consequence. From Schroedinger's time-dependent equation, we obtain

$$\frac{\partial}{\partial t} \Psi^*(x, t)\Psi(x, t)$$

$$= \frac{1}{i\hbar} [\Psi^*(x, t)\mathbf{H}\Psi(x, t) - \Psi(x, t)\mathbf{H}\Psi^*(x, t)]$$

$$= \frac{1}{i\hbar} \cdot \left(-\frac{\hbar^2}{2m}\right)\left[\Psi^*(x, t)\frac{\partial^2}{\partial x^2}\Psi(x, t) - \Psi(x, t)\frac{\partial^2}{\partial x^2}\Psi^*(x, t)\right]$$

$$= \frac{i\hbar}{2m}\frac{\partial}{\partial x}\left[\Psi^*(x, t)\frac{\partial\Psi(x, t)}{\partial x} - \Psi(x, t)\frac{\partial\Psi^*(x, t)}{\partial x}\right].$$

Hence, we may write the *continuity equation* for probability

$$\frac{\partial}{\partial t}|\Psi(x, t)|^2 + \frac{\partial}{\partial x}J = 0, \tag{12.2.11}$$

where

$$J = \frac{\hbar}{2mi}\left[\Psi^*(x, t)\frac{\partial\Psi(x, t)}{\partial x} - \Psi(x, t)\frac{\partial\Psi^*(x, t)}{\partial x}\right] \tag{12.2.12}$$

is termed the *probability (density) current*. Since $\int_{x_1}^{x_2}|\Psi(x, t)|^2 dx$ is interpreted as the probability of finding the particle in the region indicated, its time derivative is the difference in the values of J at the boundaries of the region, suggesting the role with which it has been identified. For stationary states J is constant as a function of position. [The extension to more dimensions is made simply by summing Eq. (12.2.11) over all components.]

With the operators of the present section we are able to make a start in determining the properties of some simple systems. We only require some means for assuring that the wave functions correspond to physically meaningful states even though they formally may satisfy Schroedinger's equations.

12.3 Physical states and wave functions. Mainly because of the interpretation of the wave function as a "probability density" amplitude, due to Born, we now are in a position to confine our attention to a restricted class of wave functions. Because of the probability connotations, it follows that a wave function having more than a single value (as a function of position and time) will generally give rise to more than a single probability density. This situation we shall reject as being "unphysical."

We shall also restrict our considerations to those functions which are *continuous*, corresponding to continuous probability densities; this requirement will not assure continuous derivatives.

However, we emphasize that the wave functions of physical interest satisfy Schroedinger's equations, and these involve the second derivatives of the wave functions. In particular, the stationary states will involve

$$-\frac{\hbar^2}{2m}\frac{d^2\Psi(x, 0)}{dx^2} = [\epsilon - V(x)]\Psi(x, 0).$$

As a result, with $\Psi(x, 0)$ assumed continuous, the second derivative can have discontinuities only where $V(x)$ has them. When $V(x)$ is restricted to finite discontinuities, so will be the second derivative of the wave function. But then the first derivative will be continuous. Even when $V(x)$ has singularities, it is possible that the integral of $V(x)$ in the neighborhood of the singularity is a finite quantity. Under these conditions, the first derivative of the wave function also will be continuous. We shall assume, in fact, that the potentials with which we shall be concerned permit our restricting the wave functions of physical interest to those which have continuous first derivatives.

We also shall require physically sensible wave functions to give a finite value of the integral $\int_a^b dx\Psi^*(x, t)\Psi(x, t)$ when $(b - a)$ is finite. Thereby, only such singularities in $\Psi(x, t)$ are allowed that permit the stated integral to exist. Clearly, this limits $\Psi(x, t)$ to point singularities; in particular, the wave function cannot assume an asymptotic $(x \rightarrow \pm\infty)$ value which is unbounded in magnitude.

We may anticipate here that there are two sorts of wave functions. The first sort corresponds to functions which are *quadratically integrable* or, as we have previously described them, functions for which $\int dx\Psi^*(x, t)\Psi(x, t)$ always is finite. These generally arise from operators which have a *discrete spectrum* of eigenvalues. The second sort gives rise to normalization integrals which do not have finite values and arises from operators which have a *continuous spectrum* of eigenvalues. (Both of these statements will be illustrated here, but not proved.) The second kind of wave function requires an alteration, but no abandonment, of our probability viewpoint. Since the functions are not normalizable, it becomes impossible to speak of probability in an absolute sense. However, we may retain the sense of Born's suggestion by referring to the square of the magnitude of such wave functions as the *relative* probability density. As it turns out, such is sufficient for us to describe the systems having continuous spectra of eigenvalues of the Hamiltonian operator. We shall consider such systems in detail in Chapter 13.

With these preliminary considerations, we now are in a position to consider the stationary states of physical systems. We note that the solution of a Schroedinger time-independent equation will give the eigenvalues for the energy, which quantities are needed for the statistical-thermodynamic description of the relevant physical system. However, to make the techniques involved clear, we shall consider only simple systems which are, or may be made equivalent with, single-particle systems. In fact, we shall emphasize one-dimensional systems. In that case, the formal mathematical theory which pertains to the Schroedinger equation is furnished by what is termed *Sturm-Liouville* theory. We shall not, however, make explicit use of the theory since the intention here is to emphasize the explicit results obtained from several Schroedinger equations.

12.4 The free particle. To indicate the methods used in describing physical systems with the aid of wave mechanics, we consider several simple systems, beginning with what appears to be the simplest—the "free" particle. Such a system corresponds to motion under the influence of a constant potential energy. The Schroedinger time-independent equation evidently is

$$-\frac{h^2}{2m}\frac{d^2\phi_k(x)}{dx^2} + V\phi_k(x) = \epsilon_k\phi(x), \qquad (12.4.1)$$

where the subscript k has been added to emphasize the connection of ϵ_k with $\phi_k(x)$. Since V is constant, we evidently obtain the general solution to Eq. (12.4.1):

$$\phi_k(x) = A_k \exp\left[\frac{i}{h}\sqrt{2m(\epsilon_k - V)}\,x\right] + B_k \exp\left[-\frac{i}{h}\sqrt{2m(\epsilon_k - V)}\,x\right],$$

$$(12.4.2)$$

which has well-behaved solutions as $x \to \pm\infty$ if and only if

$$(\epsilon_k - V) \geq 0. \qquad (12.4.3)$$

Classically,

$$\frac{p^2}{2m} = (\epsilon - V), \qquad (12.4.4)$$

so that Eq. (12.4.3) corresponds to real values for the momentum of the particle and, hence, positive values of its kinetic energy. Any nonnegative value will do. As a result, we see that the energy spectrum of a free particle is continuous.

We note that the wave functions in the present case do not vanish at infinity. Moreover, they generally form a linear superposition of eigenfunctions of momentum, as we now see. The eigenvalue relation satisfied by the momentum operator may be expressed as

$$\frac{\hbar}{i} \frac{\partial \psi_p(x)}{\partial x} = p\psi_p(x),$$

where p is the eigenvalue of momentum. This equation has the solution

$$\psi_p(x) = Ce^{(i/\hbar)px},$$

where p must be restricted to real values if $\psi(x)$ is to be well-behaved in the sense we have discussed. Comparison of this equation with Eqs. (12.4.2) and (12.4.4) confirms the assertion made earlier. In fact, we may write

$$\phi_k(x) = A_k\psi_{(p_k)}(x) + B_k\psi_{(-p_k)}(x)$$

to emphasize that the eigenfunction of kinetic energy [which is really all we have been considering in Eq. (12.4.1)] is to be regarded generally as a linear combination of momentum eigenfunctions which correspond to motion in opposite directions (*viz.*, p_k and $-p_k$).

The probability density for an eigenfunction of kinetic energy is seen to be

$$|\phi_k(x)|^2 = |A_k|^2 + |B_k|^2$$
$$+ (A_kB_k^* + A_k^*B_k) \cos\left(\frac{2px}{\hbar}\right)$$
$$+ i(A_kB_k^* - A_k^*B_k) \sin\left(\frac{2px}{\hbar}\right). \tag{12.4.5}$$

The last two terms give rise to interference phenomena, discussed in the last chapter, which produce variations in intensity. Clearly, such will be absent only if either A_k or B_k vanishes. Hence, if one requires a uniform probability density for the particle, the particle also must be in an eigenstate of momentum.

Now, if one were to consider the quantity $\int_a^b dx |\phi_k(x)|^2$ for a large but finite value of $|b - a|$, one readily verifies that the trigonometric functions contribute a maximum value to the integral which does not increase with increasing values of $|a - b|$. Hence, asymptotically,

$$\int_a^b dx|\phi_k(x)|^2 \sim (|A_k|^2 + |B_k|^2)|b - a|, \quad (12.4.6)$$

which prompts the *interpretation* that $|A_k|^2$ is the *relative probability* that the system has a momentum of $(+p_k)$, and $|B_k|^2$ is the *relative probability* that the system has the momentum $(-p_k)$. This interpretation may be justified by determining the expectation values for momentum and energy. Because the wave functions are not normalizable, care must be taken to deal with meaningful quantities. We shall take, then,

$$E_{\phi_k}\left(\frac{\mathbf{p}^2}{2m}\right) = \lim_{\substack{a \to -\infty \\ b \to +\infty}} \frac{\displaystyle\int_a^b dx\phi_k^*(x)\left[-\frac{\hbar^2}{2m}\frac{\partial^2\phi_k}{\partial x^2}(x)\right]}{\displaystyle\int_a^b dx|\phi_k(x)|^2}. \quad (12.4.7)$$

Using Eqs. (12.4.2), (12.4.4), (12.4.5), and (12.4.6), we obtain the expected result

$$E_{\phi_k}\left(\frac{\mathbf{p}^2}{2m}\right) = \frac{p_k^2}{2m}.$$

By comparison, we can obtain

$$E_{\phi_k}(\mathbf{p}) = \lim_{\substack{a \to -\infty \\ b \to +\infty}} \frac{\displaystyle\int_a^b dx\phi_k^*(x)\left[\frac{\hbar}{i}\frac{\partial\phi_k(x)}{\partial x}\right]}{\displaystyle\int_a^b dx|\phi_k(x)|^2} = \frac{|A_k|^2 - |B_k|^2}{|A_k|^2 + |B_k|^2}\, p_k. \quad (12.4.8)$$

Clearly the expectation value for the momentum is the *net* result of motion in opposite directions. Comparing with the expectation value for the kinetic energy, we make the interpretation to which reference already has been made. No restrictions are apparent for A_k and B_k.

The interpretation we have accorded the last equation can be reinforced by a consideration of the *probability current*. From Eq. (12.2.12) we obtain from Eq. (12.4.2)

$$J_k = \frac{p_k}{m}(|A_k|^2 - |B_k|^2) = v_k(|A_k|^2 - |B_k|^2), \quad (12.4.9)$$

or that the current of probability is simply proportional to the difference in probabilities for the motion in opposite directions; v_k is the speed of the particle and, as seems reasonable, the current is proportional to the speed of the particle.

12.5 The particle in a linear box. The profound effect on the energy spectrum produced by localizing the particle can be seen in the next system we consider. We assume a potential-energy function of the form

$$V(x) = V_0, \qquad 0 < x < a,$$
$$= +\infty, \qquad x \le 0, \; x \ge a. \tag{12.5.1}$$

To ensure that the particle is confined to the box we require that the eigenfunctions of the energy vanish outside of the box.

Now, the Schroedinger equation for this system is the same as for the free particle, in the region of finite potential energy. Hence we may take the eigenfunctions to be of the general form expressed in Eq. (12.4.2). However, we require in the present case that

$$\phi_k(0) = \phi_k(a) = 0, \tag{12.5.2}$$

as demanded by considerations of continuity. But then it is necessary that

$$A_k = -B_k,$$

so that

$$\phi_k(x) = 2iA_k \sin\left[\sqrt{2m(\epsilon_k - V_0)} \, \frac{x}{\hbar}\right],$$

where A_k is to be determined. By the second boundary condition we must require that

$$\sqrt{2m(\epsilon_k - V_0)} \, \frac{a}{\hbar} = n\pi, \tag{12.5.3}$$

where n is a positive (i.e., nonzero) integer. Hence we obtain the condition that

$$\epsilon_k = \frac{n^2 h^2}{8ma^2} + V_0, \tag{12.5.4}$$

so that the energy spectrum of the particle in a box is discrete. We already have encountered the three-dimensional extension of this expression in Chapter 7.

Imposing the condition that the wave functions be normalized to unity, we obtain (now labeling them by n instead of k)

$$\phi_n(x) = \sqrt{2/a} \sin \frac{n\pi x}{a}, \qquad 0 < x < a,$$
$$= 0 \quad \text{otherwise}; \qquad n = 1, 2, 3, \dots. \tag{12.5.5}$$

(The wave functions are given to within a factor of proportionality which has a magnitude of unity. Such a factor evidently has the form e^{iu}, where

u is an arbitrary real number. The factor frequently is referred to as an arbitrary *phase factor*.) It is interesting to observe that these wave functions exhibit nodes, which correspond to a zero probability density of finding the particle there. We can understand these nodes from the wave picture we have adopted, whereby interference phenomena may occur. Nevertheless, some similarity with a particle viewpoint is manifest, for, if we compute the expectation value of the momentum, we would obtain

$$E_{\phi_n}(\mathbf{p}) = 0, \tag{12.5.6}$$

which also is what we may expect from the time-average value of the momentum of a classically describable particle in a box.

The wave functions form an *orthonormal* set,

$$\int_0^a dx \, \phi_n^*(x)\phi_m(x) = \delta_{nm}, \tag{12.5.7}$$

where the Kronecker delta,

$$\delta_{nm} - 1, \quad n = m,$$
$$= 0, \quad n \neq m.$$

As a result, any function satisfying the same boundary conditions as the ϕ's, which by the superposition principle may be expressed as a linear combination of the ϕ's, has easily determined coefficients. Thus, if

$$\psi(x) = \sum_{n=1}^{\infty} C_n \phi_n(x), \tag{12.5.8}$$

then

$$C_m = \sum_{n=1}^{\infty} C_n \, \delta_{nm} = \sum_{n=1}^{\infty} C_n \int_0^a dx \, \phi_m^*(x)\phi_n(x)$$

$$= \int_0^a dx \, \phi_m^*(x)\psi(x). \tag{12.5.9}$$

These relations are analogous to those discussed in Section 11.2.

12.6 The linear harmonic oscillator: Schroedinger representation. In the linear harmonic oscillator we encounter a system which serves as the basis for generally approximating the properties of systems under the influence of a potential energy having a minimum value at some point. In the classical mechanical description of such systems, the states of lowest energy would correspond to motion in the immediate vicinity of the minimum.

For definiteness, the linear harmonic oscillator corresponds to a Hooke's law restoring force, which is proportional to the displacement of the particle measured from the minimum position (termed the *equilibrium position*) and in a sense opposite to the sense of the displacement. This relation gives rise to the potential energy as a function of displacement (the origin being the equilibrium position),

$$V(x) = \tfrac{1}{2}kx^2,$$ (12.6.1)

where k is the so-called "force-constant." We see that, apart from an irrelevant constant, any potential-energy function which has a minimum value at some point can be approximated by Eq. (12.6.1) for small values of the displacement. Schroedinger's equation for the present system is

$$-\frac{\hbar^2}{2m}\frac{d^2\psi_n(x)}{dx^2} + \tfrac{1}{2}kx^2\psi_n(x) = \epsilon_n\psi_n(x),$$ (12.6.2)

with x unlimited in value.

To simplify the symbolic aspects of the problem, we introduce a change of variable,

$$x = \left(\frac{\hbar^2}{km}\right)^{\frac{1}{4}} y,$$ (12.6.3)

which upon substitution into Eq. (12.6.2) yields

$$-\frac{d^2\psi_n(y)}{dy^2} + y^2\psi_n(y) = \lambda_n\psi_n(y),$$ (12.6.4)

where

$$\epsilon_n = \frac{\hbar}{2}\sqrt{k/m}\,\lambda_n = \frac{h\nu}{2}\lambda_n,$$ (12.6.5)

where

$$\nu = \frac{1}{2\pi}\sqrt{k/m}$$ (12.6.6)

is the oscillation frequency of the classically described harmonic oscillator.

The differential equation (12.6.4) is easily solved with the aid of Sommerfeld's *polynomial method*. To illustrate this method, we attempt first to have the solutions of the differential equation properly behaved in regions where the Hamiltonian operator manifests divergent behavior. In the present instance, the term quadratic in the variable introduces such difficulty. As a result, we can approximate the equation by

$$\frac{d^2\psi_n(y)}{dy^2} \sim y^2\psi_n(y), \qquad y \to \pm\infty.$$

To satisfy this equation in an asymptotic sense, we note that

$$\frac{d^2}{dy^2} e^{-y^2/2} = (y^2 - 1)e^{-y^2/2}.$$

Hence we take

$$\psi_n(y) = \phi_n(y)e^{-y^2/2}, \tag{12.6.7}$$

whereupon Eq. (12.6.4) leads to the equation

$$\frac{d^2\phi_n(y)}{dy^2} - 2y\frac{d\phi_n(y)}{dy} + (\lambda_n - 1)\phi_n(y) = 0. \tag{12.6.8}$$

This differential equation is known as Hermite's differential equation. We are interested only in those solutions of this equation which leave Eq. (12.6.7) finite as $y \to \pm\infty$.

To solve Eq. (12.6.8) we attempt a series solution:

$$\phi_n(y) = \sum_{k=0}^{\infty} a_{n,k}\, y^k,$$

as a result of which

$$\sum_{k=0}^{\infty} k(k-1)a_{n,k}\, y^{k-2} - 2\sum_{k=0}^{\infty} ka_{n,k}\, y^k + (\lambda_n - 1)\sum_{k=0}^{\infty} a_{n,k}\, y^k = 0,$$

or

$$\sum_{k=0}^{\infty} y^k\{(k+2)(k+1)a_{n,k+2} - [2k - (\lambda_n - 1)]a_{n,k}\} = 0.$$

For this to be valid for all k, evidently we obtain the *recurrence relation* among the coefficients,

$$a_{n,k+2} = \frac{2k - (\lambda_n - 1)}{(k+2)(k+1)} a_{n,k}. \tag{12.6.9}$$

The general solution of Eq. (12.6.8) is thus determined in terms of, say, the first two coefficients of the series. In fact, it may be seen to consist of the linear combination of an *odd* series and an *even* series in the variable. We shall consider each such series separately. The even series consists of

$$a_{n,0}\left[1 + \sum_{m=1}^{\infty} \prod_{j=0}^{m-1} \frac{4j - (\lambda_n - 1)}{(2j+2)(2j+1)} y^{2m}\right]$$

$$= a_{n,0}\left\{1 + \sum_{m=1}^{\infty} \frac{\prod_{j=0}^{m-1}[4j - (\lambda_n - 1)]}{(2m)!} y^{2m}\right\}.$$

This series generally diverges asymptotically, as we shall see; by itself the divergence is not serious so long as Eq. (12.6.7) remains finite. However, even this condition generally is not satisfied.

To examine the asymptotic properties of the even series, it proves convenient to consider the ratios of successive terms of large power. For nonvanishing values of Eq. (12.6.9), we obtain for $M \gg 1$

$$\frac{a_{n,M+1} y^{2(M+1)}}{a_{n,M} y^{2M}} = \frac{4(M + 1) - (\lambda_n - 1)}{4M - (\lambda_n - 1)} \cdot \frac{(2M)!}{(2M + 2)!} y^2$$

$$\sim \frac{y^2}{(2M + 2)(2M + 1)},$$

which is identically the ratio of large successive terms in the series expansion of e^{+y^2}. Thus, Eq. (12.6.7) would yield a divergent wave function for arbitrary values of λ_n. On the other hand, proper behavior is assured if and only if Eq. (12.6.9) vanishes for some value of k (and thereafter). This may be assured if $a_{n,0}$ is set equal to zero, whereupon $H_n(y)$ is ostensibly represented by an odd function. However, we may anticipate that the odd series generally exhibits the same divergent properties as the even series. (This will not be examined here, but is left as an exercise for the reader.) Under these circumstances, a nonzero wave function which is properly behaved at infinity is assured if Eq. (12.6.9) vanishes for a value of k determined by λ_n. Thereupon all succeeding terms of the series vanish and the $\phi_n(y)$ are polynomials. In other words, the wave functions of the linear harmonic oscillator are well behaved if and only if

$$\lambda_n = 2n + 1, \quad n = 0, 1, 2, \quad (12.6.10)$$

or λ_n is an odd positive integer. Hence the energy values of this system form a discrete spectrum, by Eq. (12.6.5),

$$\epsilon_n = (n + \tfrac{1}{2})h\nu. \quad (12.6.11)$$

We see here, as in the particle-in-a-box system, the influence of the boundary conditions upon the eigenvalues of the energy. These energy values have been employed in Chapter 8.

The polynomials generated by the indicated value of λ_n are either odd or even in the variable, as may be verified. They may be generated in a simple manner if we notice that

$$H_n(y) = (-1)^n e^{y^2} \frac{d^n}{dy^n} e^{-y^2}, \quad n = 0, 1, \ldots, \quad (12.6.12)$$

will satisfy Eq. (12.6.8) with Eq. (12.6.10). In this form the solutions are referred to as *Hermite polynomials*. These functions also may be generated from the formal identity

$$e^{-t^2+2ty} = \sum_{n=0}^{\infty} \frac{t^n}{n!} H_n(y), \qquad (12.6.13)$$

the left side frequently being referred to as a *generating function* for the Hermite polynomials. In terms of these polynomials, the wave functions of the linear harmonic oscillator are referred to as *Hermite functions*. By Eq. (12.6.7), they are (apart from an arbitrary phase factor)

$$\psi_n(y) = C_n H_n(y) e^{-y^2/2}, \qquad (12.6.14)$$

where the condition, together with Eq. (12.6.3), that

$$\int_{-\infty}^{+\infty} dx H_n^2(y) e^{-y^2} = 1 \qquad (12.6.15)$$

yields

$$C_n^2 = \left[2^n n! \, \pi^{1/2} \frac{\hbar^{1/2}}{(km)^{1/4}} \right]^{-1}.$$

Different Hermite functions are orthogonal to one another, which property facilitates the expansion of an arbitrary function in terms of them.

The harmonic-oscillator wave functions illustrate an important aspect of the wave-mechanical description as compared with the classical mechanical description. For large but finite values of y, the probability density is a nonzero quantity. But for such values of y, the classical value of the kinetic energy is given by

$$\frac{h\nu}{2} (\lambda_n - y^2) = \epsilon_n - \tfrac{1}{2}kx^2 < 0, \qquad y \gg 1,$$

a situation which has no classical counterpart. In other words, a wave-mechanical description permits a particle apparently to be in a region of *negative kinetic energy*. However, we should note that such a statement is untenable in a precise sense since it is a moot question that the kinetic energy can be so specified. The anomaly persists only by virtue of an insistence upon the classical expression for the kinetic energy.

12.7 The linear harmonic oscillator: momentum representation. The linear harmonic oscillator affords an excellent opportunity to illustrate the use of the momentum representation. Making use of Eqs. (12.2.4) and (12.2.5), we obtain for the Hamiltonian

$$\mathbf{H} = \frac{p^2}{2m} + V\left(i\hbar \frac{\partial}{\partial p}\right),$$ (12.7.1)

as a result of which Schroedinger's equation is

$$\frac{p^2}{2m}f_n(p) - \frac{\hbar^2 k}{2}\frac{d^2 f_n(p)}{dp^2} = \epsilon_n f_n(p).$$ (12.7.2)

The similarity with Eq. (12.6.2) is reinforced by introducing the change in variable

$$p = (\hbar^2 km)^{1/4} y.$$ (12.7.3)

Then we obtain

$$-\frac{d^2 f_n(y)}{dy^2} + y^2 f_n(y) = \lambda_n f_n(y),$$ (12.7.4)

where λ_n is related to ϵ_n as in Eqs. (12.6.5) and (12.6.6). Clearly this equation is identical with Eq. (12.6.4). As a result, it will have the same solutions as that equation (only a change in the significance of the variable is involved).

To utilize these wave functions we need to introduce the analog of the location operator of Eq. (12.2.9). In effect, we simply assume the Born interpretation in the momentum component: $|f_n(p)|^2$ is proportional to the probability density in momentum. As a result, the functions of the preceding section may be employed with a suitable transcription of the variables.

The main interest in the present case is the relation between the wave functions in the two representations, which can be elaborated rather simply. We start by searching for a linear superposition of momentum eigenfunctions to give a solution of Eq. (12.6.2). (The relevance of such a solution to the present case will appear presently.) Because the eigenvalues of momentum form a continuous spectrum, we express

$$\psi_n(x) = \frac{1}{\sqrt{h}}\int_{-\infty}^{+\infty} dp\, e^{ipx/\hbar} f_n(p),$$ (12.7.5)

where $f_n(p)$ is not necessarily a solution of Eq. (12.7.4) for the present. [We shall see, however, that it is such when $\psi_n(x)$ satisfies Eq. (12.6.2).] Application of the Hamiltonian operator in the Schroedinger representation yields

$$\mathbf{H}\psi_n(x) = \frac{1}{\sqrt{h}}\int_{-\infty}^{+\infty} dp\, f_n(p)\left[\frac{p^2}{2m} + V(x)\right]e^{ipx/\hbar}.$$

Representing

$$V(x) = \sum_{n=0}^{\infty} C_n x^n,$$

$$\int_{-\infty}^{+\infty} dp\, f_n(p)\, V(x) e^{ipx/\hbar} = \int_{-\infty}^{+\infty} dp\, f_n(p)\, V\left(\frac{\hbar}{i}\frac{\partial}{\partial p}\right) e^{ipx/\hbar}.$$

However,

$$\int_{-\infty}^{+\infty} dp\, f_n(p) \left(\frac{\hbar}{i}\frac{\partial}{\partial p}\right)^m e^{ipx/\hbar} = \left(\frac{\hbar}{i}\right)^m \left[f_n(p) \left(\frac{\partial}{\partial p}\right)^{m-1} e^{ipx/\hbar} \Big|_{-\infty}^{+\infty} \right.$$

$$\left. - \int_{-\infty}^{+\infty} dp\, \frac{\partial f_n(p)}{\partial p} \cdot \left(\frac{\partial}{\partial p}\right)^{m-1} e^{ipx/\hbar} \right],$$

carrying out an integration by parts. Assuming that $f_n(p)$ and all derivatives vanish asymptotically, we obtain ultimately

$$\int_{-\infty}^{+\infty} dp\, f_n(p)\, V(x) e^{ipx/\hbar} = \int_{-\infty}^{+\infty} dp\, e^{ipx/\hbar} V\left(i\hbar\frac{\partial}{\partial p}\right) f_n(p), \quad (12.7.6)$$

whereupon,

$$\frac{1}{\sqrt{h}} \int_{-\infty}^{+\infty} dp\, e^{ipx/\hbar} \left[\frac{p^2}{2m} + V\left(i\hbar\frac{\partial}{\partial p}\right) - \epsilon_n\right] f_n(p) = 0, \quad (12.7.7)$$

which clearly is satisfied if Eq. (12.7.2) is satisfied. [We do not consider the necessary condition, but state that Eqs. (12.7.2) and (12.7.7) are equivalent.] In these terms the eigenfunctions in the Schroedinger representation simply are a superposition of eigenfunctions of momentum, the weighting coefficient being an eigenfunction of the Hamiltonian in the momentum representation.

We consider the quantity

$$\frac{1}{\sqrt{h}} \int_{-\infty}^{+\infty} dx\, \psi_n(x) e^{ip'x/\hbar} = \frac{1}{h} \int_{-\infty}^{+\infty} dx \int_{-\infty}^{+\infty} dp\, f_n(p) e^{ix(p-p')/\hbar} \quad (12.7.8)$$

$$= \frac{1}{h} \int_{-\infty}^{+\infty} dp\, f_n(p) \lim_{A\to\infty} \int_{-A}^{+A} dx\, e^{ix(p-p')\hbar}$$

$$= \frac{1}{\pi} \int_{-\infty}^{+\infty} dp\, f_n(p) \lim_{A\to\infty} \frac{\sin\,(p-p')A/\hbar}{(p-p')}$$

$$= \lim_{A\to\infty} \int_{-\infty}^{+\infty} dp\, f_n(p) \cdot \frac{1}{\pi}\frac{\sin\,(p-p')A/\hbar}{(p-p')}.$$

$$(12.7.9)$$

Since

$$\lim_{(p-p')\to 0} \frac{\sin (p - p')A/h}{(p - p')} = \frac{A}{h},$$

while

$$\int_{-\infty}^{+\infty} dy \frac{\sin yA/h}{y} = \pi,$$

it is evident that the bulk of the integration in Eq. (12.7.9) will come for $p = p'$. As a result, we may let $p = p' + (zh/A)$, so that

$$\frac{1}{\sqrt{h}} \int_{-\infty}^{+\infty} dx\, \psi_n(x) e^{-ip'x/h} = \lim_{A\to\infty} \frac{1}{\pi} \int_{-\infty}^{+\infty} dz\, f_n\left(p' + \frac{zh}{A}\right) \frac{\sin z}{z}$$

$$= f_n(p'), \tag{12.7.10}$$

which is to be compared with Eq. (12.7.5). Equations (12.7.5) and (12.7.10) relate the eigenfunctions in the Schroedinger (or position) representation with those in the momentum representation as *Fourier transforms* of one another. (We see here that inclusion of the factor $1/\sqrt{h}$ produces a symmetrical relation.) We shall demonstrate this relation for the harmonic oscillator explicitly. Generally, we have the *Fourier inversion theorem* from Eqs. (12.7.8) and (12.7.10)

$$f(p') = \frac{1}{2\pi}\left[\frac{1}{h} \int_{-\infty}^{+\infty} dx \int_{-\infty}^{+\infty} dp f(p) e^{ix(p-p')/h}\right]. \tag{12.7.11}$$

From Eqs. (12.6.3), (12.6.13), and (12.6.14) we obtain

$$\frac{1}{\sqrt{h}} \int_{-\infty}^{+\infty} dx \sum_{n=0}^{\infty} \frac{t^n}{n!} H_n(y) e^{-y^2/2} e^{-ipx/h}$$

$$= (4\pi^2 km)^{-1/4} \int_{-\infty}^{+\infty} dy\, e^{-t^2+2ty} e^{-y^2/2} e^{-i(h^2 km)^{-1/4} py}$$

$$= (4\pi^2 km)^{-1/4} e^{-t^2} \exp\{\tfrac{1}{2}[2t - i(h^2 km)^{-1/4} p]^2\}$$

$$\times \int_{-\infty}^{+\infty} dy \exp\{-\tfrac{1}{2}[y - 2t + i(h^2 km)^{-1/4} p]^2\}$$

$$= (km)^{-1/4} \exp\left[-\left(\frac{t}{i}\right)^2 + 2\left(\frac{t}{i}\right)(h^2 km)^{-1/4} p\right]$$

$$\times \exp\left[-\frac{(h^2 km)^{-1/2}}{2} p^2\right]$$

$$= (km)^{-1/4} \sum_{n=0}^{\infty} \frac{(t/i)^n}{n!} H_n[(h^2 km)^{-1/4} p] \exp\{-\tfrac{1}{2}[(h^2 km)^{-1/4} p]^2\}.$$

Hence, equating equal powers of t, we obtain

$$\frac{1}{\sqrt{h}} \int_{-\infty}^{+\infty} dx \psi_n \left[\left(\frac{\hbar^2}{km} \right)^{1/4} x \right] e^{-ipx/\hbar}$$

$$= \frac{e^{-n\pi i/2} H_n[(\hbar^2 km)^{-1/4} p] e^{-1/2[(\hbar^2 km)^{-1/4} p]^2}}{[2^n n! \pi^{1/2} (\hbar^2 km)^{1/4}]^{1/2}}, \quad (12.7.12)$$

which apart from a phase factor can be recognized as identical with $f_n(p)$, the normalized eigenfunction in the momentum representation.

12.8 The rigid linear rotor. The previous examples have illustrated both continuous and discrete spectra of eigenvalues. In the latter cases, however, only nondegenerate eigenvalues have arisen. For that reason we consider rotational motion, where the eigenvalues of the energy generally are degenerate. Also, our consideration of rotational motion enables us to consider nontrivial situations of multi-dimensional motion.

We consider a straight, rigid, massless rod of length R, at each end of which is a point mass. We restrict our attention to the situation in which the center of mass of the system is fixed in position. (While we shall not demonstrate it, the Schroedinger equation of a collection of particles generally can be separated into two equations, one relating to the motion of the center of mass of the system and the other to motion relative to the center of mass. We are considering a special instance of the latter.) Because of the rigidity of the system, the motion of one end clearly correlates with the motion of the other. In the case chosen, if m_1 and m_2 represent the two masses, the center of mass will be located at a distance

$$\left(\frac{m_2}{m_1 + m_2} \right) R$$

from the mass m_1. The velocity of each mass about the center of mass will vary inversely as its distance from the center. The velocity is a vector perpendicular to the rod (i.e., the axis of the rotor) with a magnitude equal to the circumferential speed at the point in question. As a result, the kinetic energy of the rotor is

$$\text{K.E.} = \frac{m_1 v_1^2 + m_2 v_2^2}{2} = \frac{m_1}{2} \left(\frac{m_2}{m_1 + m_2} \right)^2 R^2 \omega^2 + \frac{m_2}{2} \left(\frac{m_1}{m_1 + m_2} \right)^2 R^2 \omega^2,$$

where v_1 and v_2 are the speeds associated with the masses m_1 and m_2 and ω is the angular speed of rotation (measured in radians per unit time) of the rotor. Introducing the moment of inertia

$$I = m_1 \left(\frac{m_2}{m_1 + m_2} \right)^2 R^2 + m_2 \left(\frac{m_1}{m_1 + m_2} \right)^2 R^2, \qquad (12.8.1)$$

we obtain

$$\text{K.E.} = \tfrac{1}{2} I \omega^2.$$

We can easily employ the definition of momentum in the present instance and obtain for the square of the *angular momentum*

$$P_\omega^2 = |m_1 \mathbf{v}_1 + m_2 \mathbf{v}_2|^2$$

$$= 4 \left(\frac{m_1 m_2}{m_1 + m_2} \right)^2 R^2 \omega^2$$

$$= (I \omega)^2.$$

Hence, the kinetic energy of the rotor may be expressed as

$$\text{K.E.} = \frac{1}{2I} P_\omega^2. \qquad (12.8.2)$$

As a result, it can be seen that the motion of the rigid rotor about its center of mass may be regarded as the *equivalent* of the motion of a *single* particle constrained to move on a sphere. The important difference here is that the effective mass of the system is the *reduced mass* of the system,

$$\mu = \frac{m_1 m_2}{m_1 + m_2}. \qquad (12.8.3)$$

In this sense, we now examine the Hamiltonian operator for two-dimensional motion

$$\mathbf{H} = - \frac{\hbar^2}{2\mu} \left(\frac{\partial^2}{\partial x^2} + \frac{\partial^2}{\partial y^2} \right). \qquad (12.8.4)$$

This corresponds to the restriction that the rotor is confined to a plane. It is convenient to transform to polar coordinates. Thus, if

$$x = R \cos \theta,$$
$$y = R \sin \theta, \qquad (12.8.5)$$

we obtain

$$\left(\frac{\partial}{\partial x} \right)_y = \left(\frac{\partial R}{\partial x} \right)_y \left(\frac{\partial}{\partial R} \right)_\theta + \left(\frac{\partial \theta}{\partial x} \right)_y \left(\frac{\partial}{\partial \theta} \right)_R,$$

$$\left(\frac{\partial}{\partial y} \right)_x = \left(\frac{\partial R}{\partial y} \right)_x \left(\frac{\partial}{\partial R} \right)_\theta + \left(\frac{\partial \theta}{\partial y} \right)_x \left(\frac{\partial}{\partial \theta} \right)_R.$$

From Eqs. (12.8.5), we may obtain

$$\left(\frac{\partial R}{\partial x}\right)_y = \cos\theta; \qquad \left(\frac{\partial R}{\partial y}\right)_x = \sin\theta;$$

$$\left(\frac{\partial\theta}{\partial x}\right)_y = -\frac{\sin\theta}{R}; \qquad \left(\frac{\partial\theta}{\partial y}\right)_x = \frac{\cos\theta}{R}.$$

Hence we finally may obtain

$$\mathbf{H} = -\frac{\hbar^2}{2\mu}\left(\frac{\partial^2}{\partial R^2} + \frac{1}{R^2}\frac{\partial^2}{\partial\theta^2}\right). \tag{12.8.6}$$

Because we are here considering a *rigid* rotor there will be no dependence of the wave function upon R. The (planar) rigid linear rotor has, then, the Schroedinger equation

$$-\frac{\hbar^2}{2I}\frac{d^2\psi_k(\theta)}{d\theta^2} = \epsilon_k\psi_k(\theta), \qquad 0 \le \theta \le 2\pi, \tag{12.8.7}$$

which is subject to the boundary condition

$$\psi_k(\theta \pm 2\pi) = \psi_k(\theta). \tag{12.8.8}$$

Equations (12.8.7) and (12.8.8) have the well-behaved normalized solutions

$$\psi_k(\theta) = \frac{1}{\sqrt{2\pi}}e^{ik\theta}, \qquad k = 0, \pm1, \pm2, \ldots, \tag{12.8.9}$$

and the energy values

$$\epsilon_k = \frac{\hbar^2}{2I}k^2, \tag{12.8.10}$$

which are clearly doubly degenerate (except for $k = 0$).

A more realistic rotational motion of the rigid rotor would not confine it to a plane. In that case, the motion of the equivalent single particle takes place upon a sphere instead of in a circle. The Hamiltonian for such a system is

$$\mathbf{H} = -\frac{\hbar^2}{2\mu}\left(\frac{\partial^2}{\partial x^2} + \frac{\partial^2}{\partial y^2} + \frac{\partial^2}{\partial z^2}\right). \tag{12.8.11}$$

The differential operator in this equation is well known as the *Laplacian*. To describe the motion of the particle upon a sphere it is convenient to imagine a (right-handed) cartesian axis system with its origin at the center of the sphere. Letting the z-axis be referred to as the polar axis, the angle made between the radius vector to some point on the sphere and the z-axis will be designated by θ. The projection of the radius vector upon the xy-plane will make an angle ϕ with the x-axis. In these terms, the cartesian coordinates are expressible in terms of spherical polar coordinates,

$$z = R \cos \theta,$$
$$y = R \sin \theta \sin \phi, \qquad (12.8.12)$$
$$z = R \sin \theta \cos \phi,$$

it being evident that $\theta = \pi/2$ is the planar case. Note that

$$0 \le \theta \le \pi, \qquad 0 \le \phi \le 2\pi.$$

Now, in a manner entirely similar to that which has been used for the planar rigid rotor, we may establish that

$$\mathbf{H} = -\frac{\hbar^2}{2\mu} \left\{ \frac{1}{R^2} \frac{\partial}{\partial R} \left(R^2 \frac{\partial}{\partial R} \right) + \frac{1}{R^2} \left[\frac{1}{\sin \theta} \frac{\partial}{\partial \theta} \left(\sin \theta \frac{\partial}{\partial \theta} \right) + \frac{1}{\sin^2 \theta} \frac{\partial^2}{\partial \phi^2} \right] \right\}.$$

Since the wave function is independent of R, we obtain for the rigid linear rotor in three dimensions the Schroedinger equation

$$-\frac{\hbar^2}{2I} \left[\frac{1}{\sin \theta} \frac{\partial}{\partial \theta} \sin \theta \frac{\partial \psi_{KM}(\theta, \phi)}{\partial \theta} + \frac{1}{\sin^2 \theta} \frac{\partial^2 \psi_{KM}(\theta, \phi)}{\partial \phi^2} \right]$$
$$= \epsilon_{KM} \psi_{KM}(\theta, \phi), \quad (12.8.13)$$

the double index being introduced in anticipation of the ultimate result. We have the boundary conditions

$$\psi_{KM}(\theta, \phi \pm 2\pi) = \psi_{KM}(\theta, \phi). \qquad (12.8.14)$$

If we seek to solve Eq. (12.8.13) by a *separation of variables*, we set

$$\psi_{KM}(\theta, \phi) = \Theta_{KM}(\theta) \Phi_{KM}(\phi) \qquad (12.8.15)$$

and obtain from Eq. (12.8.13), setting

$$\epsilon_{KM} = \frac{\hbar^2}{2I} \lambda_{KM},$$

$$\left[\frac{1}{\Theta_{KM}(\theta)} \cdot \sin \theta \frac{d}{d\theta} \sin \theta \frac{d\Theta_{KM}(\theta)}{d\theta} + \lambda_{KM} \sin^2 \theta \right]$$
$$+ \left[\frac{1}{\Phi_{KM}(\phi)} \cdot \frac{d^2 \Phi_{KM}(\phi)}{d\phi^2} \right] = 0.$$

As a result, the terms in the first brackets must equal a constant independent of (θ, ϕ); the same is true for the second bracketed term. We ultimately can show that the Φ_{KM}'s may be taken to be of the form

$$\Phi_{KM}(\phi) = \Phi_M(\phi) = \frac{1}{\sqrt{2\pi}} e^{iM\phi}, \qquad M = 0, \pm 1, \pm 2, \ldots, \qquad (12.8.16)$$

which leads to the differential equation for $\Theta_{KM}(\theta)$:

$$\frac{1}{\sin\theta} \frac{d}{d\theta} \sin\theta \frac{d\Theta_{KM}(\theta)}{d\theta} - \frac{M^2}{\sin^2\theta} \Theta_{KM}(\theta) + \lambda_{KM}\Theta_{KM}(\theta) = 0. \quad (12.8.17)$$

Introducing $u = \cos\theta$, with $-1 \le u \le +1$, we obtain

$$(1 - u^2)\frac{d^2\Theta_{KM}(u)}{du^2} - 2u\frac{d\Theta_{KM}(u)}{du} + \left(\lambda_{KM} - \frac{M^2}{1 - u^2}\right)\Theta_{KM}(u) = 0.$$

$$(12.8.18)$$

This equation is well known as Legendre's equation.

We are interested in the well-behaved solutions of Eq. (12.8.18). Immediately, we observe that singularities generally will be associated with the values of the functions and their derivatives at $u = \pm 1$. We can minimize this difficulty by substituting

$$\Theta_{KM}(u) = (1 - u^2)^{|M|/2} R_{KM}(u), \qquad (12.8.19)$$

whereupon

$$(1 - u^2)\frac{d^2 R_{KM}}{du^2} - 2(|M| + 1)u\frac{dR_{KM}}{du}$$
$$+ (\lambda_{KM} - |M| - M^2)R_{KM} = 0.$$

[Clearly the exponent in Eq. (12.8.19) could have been left arbitrary and then adjusted to eliminate the singularity in Eq. (12.8.18).] Now, setting

$$R_{KM}(u) = \sum_{n=0}^{\infty} b_n u^n,$$

we obtain, ultimately, the recurrence relation

$$b_{n+2} = \frac{(|M| + n)(|M| + n + 1) - \lambda_{KM}}{(n + 1)(n + 2)} b_n. \qquad (12.8.20)$$

As in Section 12.6, this recurrence relation will give rise to a divergent value of the function at $u = \pm 1$, for the ratio of successive terms is (noting the series to be odd or even)

$$\lim_{N \to \infty} \frac{b_{N+2}}{b_N} = 1.$$

As a result, we require that Eq. (12.8.20) shall vanish for some fixed value of n. Thus we require that

$$\lambda_{KM} = K(K + 1), \quad K = 0, 1, \ldots, \quad (12.8.21)$$

and, since n is a nonnegative integer,

$$K \equiv |M| + n \geq |M|. \quad (12.8.22)$$

With Eq. (12.8.21) we obtain

$$\epsilon_{KM} = \frac{\hbar^2}{2I} K(K + 1), \quad (12.8.23)$$

with a multiplicity, according to Eq. (12.8.22) of $(2K + 1)$. These results also have been used in Chapter 8.

As in the preceding two sections, the functions $R_{KM}(u)$ are polynomials. We may verify that

$$\frac{d^{|M|}}{du^{|M|}} R_{K0}(u) = R_{KM}(u). \quad (12.8.24)$$

Hence only the solutions for $M = 0$ need be examined in detail. In a certain form, these solutions are referred to as *Legendre polynomials* and are given the symbol

$$P_K(u) \equiv R_{K0}(u).$$

The Legendre polynomials are generated by

$$(1 - 2uh + h^2)^{-1} = \sum_{n=0}^{\infty} h^n P_n(u); \quad (12.8.25)$$

also,

$$P_K(u) = \frac{1}{2^K K!} \frac{d^K}{du^K} (u^2 - 1)^K. \quad (12.8.26)$$

In these terms, the normalized eigenfunctions of Eq. (12.8.13) may be expressed as

$$\psi_{KM}(\theta, \phi) = \frac{C_{KM}}{\sqrt{2\pi}} (1 - \cos^2 \theta)^{|M|/2} P_K^{|M|} (\cos \theta) e^{iM\phi}, \quad (12.8.27)$$

where the normalizing constant (apart from an arbitrary phase factor) is

$$C_{KM} = \sqrt{\frac{2}{2K+1} \cdot \frac{(K+M)!}{(K-M)!}}. \qquad (12.8.28)$$

The $P_K^{|M|}(u)$ are referred to as *associated Legendre functions*. [Apart from the change in notation, they are the $R_{KM}(u)$ considered in Eq. (12.8.24).]

12.9 The uncertainty principle. Each of the systems which has been considered can be employed to evaluate various expectation values. Particular interest centers on the quantum fluctuation, or uncertainty, in position and momentum. In complete analogy with the statistical-mechanical quantities (see Chapter 9) the fluctuations in position

$$E_\psi(\Delta x)^2 \equiv E_\psi\{x - [E_\psi(x)]\}^2 = E_\psi(x^2) - [E_\psi(x)]^2, \qquad (12.9.1)$$

with similar expressions for the momentum as well as other physical variables.

The result, due to Heisenberg, will be obtained now for conjugate position and momentum variables. From Eq. (12.2.3) we have

$$\int dx \, \psi^*(x)(\mathbf{xp} - \mathbf{px})\psi(x) = i\hbar, \qquad (12.9.2)$$

where we have assumed $\psi(x)$ to be normalized to unity. (The restriction to one dimension is made for simplicity and is easily extended to three dimensions.)

Now, because the operators are hermitian, we may take

$$\hbar = \frac{1}{i} \int dx[(\mathbf{x}\psi)^*(\mathbf{p}\psi) - (\mathbf{p}\psi)^*(\mathbf{x}\psi)]. \qquad (12.9.3)$$

To simplify this expression, consider the quantity

$$\int dx[f(x)^* - i\lambda g^*(x)][f(x) + i\lambda g(x)] \geq 0,$$

where $f(x)$ and $g(x)$ are arbitrary functions and λ is a real number. The last integral has its minimum value (as a function of λ) when

$$\frac{\partial}{\partial \lambda} \int dx[f^*f - i\lambda(g^*f - f^*g) + \lambda^2 g^*g] = 0,$$

or when

$$\lambda = \frac{\int dx(f^*g - g^*f)}{2i \int dx g^*g},$$

which evidently is real. With this value of λ we obtain

$$\left(\int dx f^* f\right)\left(\int dx g^* g\right) \geq \tfrac{1}{4}\left[\frac{1}{i}\int dx (f^* g - g^* f)\right]^2. \qquad (12.9.4)$$

Hence, comparing with Eq. (12.9.3), after some rearranging,

$$\left[\int dx \psi^*(x)\mathbf{x}^2\psi(x)\right]\left[\int dx \psi^*(x)\mathbf{p}^2\psi(x)\right] \geq \frac{\hbar^2}{4}. \qquad (12.9.5)$$

Now, since

$$(\mathbf{x} - C_1)(\mathbf{p} - C_2) - (\mathbf{p} - C_2)(\mathbf{x} - C_1) = i\hbar,$$

where C_1 and C_2 are arbitrary real constants, we evidently may utilize Eq. (12.9.1) and obtain

$$[E_\psi(\Delta x)^2][E_\psi(\Delta p)^2] \geq \frac{\hbar^2}{4}, \qquad (12.9.6)$$

the celebrated uncertainty relation of Heisenberg. From this relation it evidently is impossible to find a state ψ for which the position *and* the conjugate momentum have precise expectation values. Herein lies a vast difference between the classical-mechanical and quantum-mechanical viewpoints.

12.10 Summary. The present chapter has considered the stationary states of several simple physical systems.

To begin with, the stationary state has been defined as one for which the expectation values for all physical observables have fixed, time-independent values. An alternative criterion, whereby the expectation value of the energy is an extremum with respect to arbitrary changes in the wave function, also has been considered. In either case, the wave functions of the stationary states are eigenfunctions of the Hamiltonian.

The operators for physical observables are considered briefly, and the Heisenberg commutation relation between conjugate position and momentum variables is inferred from the Schroedinger representation of operators. The Born interpretation of the wave function as a probability-density amplitude is motivated by a consideration of location operators. The latter interpretation is particularly useful in arriving at restrictions placed upon physically significant wave functions. As a result, only a limited class of functions need be considered.

The means by which Schroedinger's time-independent equation may be solved are illustrated in connection with the following systems: the free particle, the particle in a box, the linear harmonic oscillator in both the Schroedinger and momentum representation, and the linear rigid rotor.

The eigenvalues of these systems pertain to values of statistical-mechanical interest. Nevertheless, the wave-mechanical nature of the solutions of the relevant Schroedinger equations also is of pertinence. The role played by the principle of superposition is illustrated, and the effect that boundary conditions have upon the determination of the eigenvalues is emphasized.

Various sets of orthonormal functions are derived and some of their mathematical properties are displayed.

The uncertainty relation of Heisenberg is derived, in general terms, and relates the quantum-mechanical fluctuations in the position and conjugate momentum in such a way as to make it impossible to find a single state for which these quantities will have precise expectation values.

EXERCISES

1. Verify that Eq. (12.1.2) leads to Eq. (12.1.3).

2. Supply the details for concluding that Eq. (12.1.5) implies Eq. (12.1.6).

3. Supply the details for concluding that Eq. (12.1.12) follows from Eq. (12.1.11).

4. Construct the three-dimensional analog of Eq. (12.2.9), and hence obtain Born's original interpretation of the probability density.

5. Obtain the time-dependent eigenfunction of the energy for a free particle in three dimensions.

6. Verify Eq. (12.4.6).

7. Verify Eq. (12.4.8).

8. Show that the expectation value of x^2 does not exist for the free particle. (Work in one dimension, for simplicity.)

9. Establish that the functions in Eq. (12.5.5) satisfy Eq. (12.5.7).

10. Verify that the functions of Eqs. (12.6.14) and (12.6.15) satisfy Eq. (12.5.7).

11. Verify that the functions of Eqs. (12.8.27) and (12.8.28) satisfy Eq. (12.5.7).

12. Determine the uncertainty in position for all energy eigenstates of a particle in a linear box; determine also the corresponding uncertainty in conjugate momentum. Hence explicitly test Eq. (12.9.4).

13. Repeat Exercise 12, with the energy eigenfunctions for the linear harmonic oscillator.

14. Derive Eq. (12.8.20).

15. Use the generating function, Eq. (12.6.13), to evaluate integrals of the form

$$x_{mn} = \int_{-\infty}^{+\infty} dx \, \psi_m^*(y) x \psi_n(y),$$

where the ψ's are given by Eq. (12.6.14) and (12.6.3).

16. A linear harmonic oscillator has its energy, Eq. (12.6.1), modified by an additional term, $+bx$, due to a constant force acting on the particle. Determine the eigenvalues of the energy of this system. Relate the eigenfunctions to those for which $b = 0$.

17. Prove, for the linear harmonic oscillator, that for any eigenstate of the energy

$$E_{\psi_n}[V(x)] = E_{\psi_n}\left(\frac{\mathbf{p}^2}{2m}\right).$$

18. Verify that Eq. (12.6.12) will satisfy Eq. (12.6.8) with Eq. (12.6.10).

19. Formulate the problem of the particle in a three-dimensional box and solve the appropriate Schroedinger equation in cartesian coordinates.

20. Repeat Exercise 19 for the three-dimensional harmonic oscillator.

21. Utilizing the results of Section 12.8, formulate the problem of a particle in a spherical box.

22. Utilizing the results of Section 12.8, formulate the problem of the spherically symmetric, or isotropic, harmonic oscillator. *Note:* take as an extension of Eq. (12.6.1)

$$V(x, y, z) = \tfrac{1}{2}k(x^2 + y^2 + z^2).$$

23. Establish the recurrence relations

$$H_{n+1}(x) - 2xH_n(x) + 2nH_{n-1}(x) = 0,$$

$$\frac{dH_n(x)}{dx} = 2nH_{n-1}(x).$$

24. Establish the recurrence relations

$$(K + 1)P_{K+1}(u) - (2K + 1)uP_K(u) + KP_{K-1}(u) = 0,$$

$$\frac{dP_K(u)}{du} = (K + 1)\frac{uP_K(u) - P_{K+1}(u)}{1 - u^2}.$$

25. Consider the "semifree" particle in which the particle certainly is *not* to be found in any portion of space for which (x, y, z) are negative. Obtain the energy eigenvalues and eigenfunctions. Relate the latter to the eigenfunctions of momentum.

26. Express the function

$$f(x) = x, \qquad 0 \le x \le \frac{a}{2},$$

$$= a - x, \qquad \frac{a}{2} \le x \le a,$$

as a linear combination of particle-in-a-box energy eigenfunctions (i.e., in a Fourier series).

27. Show that the momentum representation of the linear harmonic oscillator leads to the conclusion that the system may have *negative* values of the classical potential energy,

$$\epsilon_n - \frac{p^2}{2m} < 0,$$

in spite of the fact that Eq. (12.6.1) is nonnegative.

28. Determine the probability density in p for a particle in a linear box for each energy eigenstate.

29. Express the first three Legendre polynomials as linear combinations of the functions of Eq. (12.8.9).

30. Show that two Hermitian operators may have common eigenfunctions only if they commute. Hence discuss why the free particle but not the particle in a box may have simultaneous eigenfunctions of kinetic energy and momentum.

31. Set up the problem of the particle in a linear box so that

$$V(x) = V_0, \quad -\frac{a}{2} < x < +\frac{a}{2},$$

$$= +\infty, \quad |x| \geq \frac{a}{2}.$$

Solve the Schroedinger equation in this coordinate system, and show that results identical with those of the text are obtained.

32. Reconcile the probability interpretation of Section 12.4 with the idea that the system is in a stationary state. It will be useful to relate the interpretation to the process of measurement upon an ensemble of systems.

33. Suggest how statistical mechanics may be formulated to introduce a spatial distribution directly from a quantum-mechanical viewpoint. Make use of Born's interpretation and regard the probability density as a property of the system. Test the suggestion for a free particle and compare with the results of Chapter 9.

34. Consider a statistical-mechanical distribution corresponding to a single value of the energy of a system and relate such a distribution to Eq. (12.1.8).

35. Work out the statistical mechanics of a system of noninteracting linear harmonic oscillators in the classical approximation as in Exercise 11, Chapter 9, and verify the validity of the relation given in Exercise 17 of this chapter.

CHAPTER 13

ILLUSTRATIONS OF NONCLASSICAL BEHAVIOR

13.1 Rectangular barriers and wells. While the statistical-thermodynamic description of physical systems requires a knowledge only of their energy values, a fuller description of microphysical systems is required for dealing with nonequilibrium phenomena. At the same time, a fuller description can be of great utility in providing good approximations to the equilibrium properties when exact expressions are excessively difficult to obtain.

For these reasons, in addition to an intrinsic interest which these matters have, the present chapter is concerned with a class of systems in which the distinctly wave-mechanical aspects are made prominent. In particular, certain nonequilibrium phenomena may be illustrated by the systems considered here. Thus, while we shall not give a detailed description, the phenomenon of thermionic emission of electrons from metals may be treated as a one-dimensional barrier problem. The general phenomena of intermolecular scattering may be treated as a three-dimensional extension of the systems considered here. The problem of molecular binding is illustrated.

The present section is devoted to the relatively simple cases of one-dimensional rectangular potential barriers or wells. The latter can be characterized by a potential-energy function (which is arbitrarily located in a symmetric way in respect to the origin of position)

$$V(x) = 0, \qquad x \le -l, \qquad (13.1.1)$$

$$= V_0, \quad -l < x < +l, \qquad (13.1.2)$$

$$= 0, \quad +l \le x. \qquad (13.1.3)$$

Here V_0 is constant, positive for barriers and negative for wells; the scale of energy has its origin as the asymptotic value of the potential energy. Subsequently we shall consider a system of more than a single barrier or well.

In terms of the foregoing potential-energy function, we have Schroedinger's equation for a particle of mass m:

$$-\frac{\hbar^2}{2m} \frac{d^2\phi_k(x)}{dx^2} + V(x)\phi_k(x) = \epsilon_k \phi_k(x), \qquad (13.1.4)$$

the general solution of which we have obtained in Eq. (12.4.2) for each of the regions in Eqs. (13.1.1) through (13.1.3).

To simplify the notational details, we shall drop the subscript k and define (taking always the *positive* root, real or imaginary)

$$\alpha \equiv \sqrt{2m(\epsilon - V_0)/\hbar^2} \, ,$$
$$\beta \equiv \sqrt{2m\epsilon/\hbar^2} \, , \tag{13.1.5}$$

whereupon the solution to Eq. (13.1.4) consists of

$$\phi_1(x) = A_1 e^{i\beta x} + B_1 e^{-i\beta x}, \qquad x \leq -l,$$
$$\phi_2(x) = A_2 e^{i\alpha x} + B_2 e^{-i\alpha x}, \qquad -l < x < +l, \tag{13.1.6}$$
$$\phi_3(x) = A_3 e^{i\beta x} + B_3 e^{-i\beta x}, \qquad +l \leq x.$$

Clearly, the A's and B's are not all independent. Continuity of the wave function and the first derivative at the discontinuities in the potential (Section 12.3) will give four relations among the six coefficients. The magnitude of the wave function may be fixed as either $x \rightarrow +\infty$ or $x \rightarrow -\infty$ (but not both) with no attending loss of generality since we shall deal with relative probabilities in such circumstances. As a result, there will be one arbitrary constant at most.

The continuity conditions are

$$A_1 e^{-i\beta l} + B_1 e^{i\beta l} = A_2 e^{-i\alpha l} + B_2 e^{i\alpha l},$$
$$A_2 e^{i\alpha l} + B_2 e^{-i\alpha l} = A_3 e^{i\beta l} + B_3 e^{-i\beta l},$$
$$\beta(A_1 e^{-i\beta l} - B_1 e^{i\beta l}) = \alpha(A_2 e^{-i\alpha l} - B_2 e^{i\alpha l}), \tag{13.1.7}$$
$$\alpha(A_2 e^{i\alpha l} - B_2 e^{-i\alpha l}) = \beta(A_3 e^{i\beta l} - B_3 e^{-i\beta l}).$$

In addition, for well-behavedness we shall require that

$$A_1 = B_3 = 0, \quad \text{for } \epsilon < 0; \tag{13.1.8}$$

otherwise we shall make explicit restrictions upon the relative values of A_1 and B_1 or A_3 and B_3.

We consider first the solution for $\epsilon = 0$. Then, since $\beta = 0$, Eqs. (13.1.7) yield

$$A_2 e^{-i\alpha l} - B_2 e^{i\alpha l} = 0,$$
$$A_2 e^{i\alpha l} - B_2 e^{-i\alpha l} = 0.$$

Hence, for $\phi_2(x)$ *not to vanish identically* in the region [in the other case all of Eqs. (13.1.6) vanish], it is necessary that

$$e^{-2i\alpha l} = e^{+2i\alpha l}, \tag{13.1.9}$$

which can be satisfied only if α is real. Hence, only for $V_0 < 0$ can $\epsilon = 0$. Moreover, it is apparent that

$$e^{2i\alpha l} = \pm 1 = e^{in\pi},$$

or

$$2\alpha l = n\pi, \qquad n \text{ a nonnegative integer.}$$

As a consequence, not all potential wells can exhibit a stationary state of zero energy, but only those for which

$$V_0 = -\frac{h^2 n^2}{8m(2l)^2},$$

which may be compared with the eigenvalues of the kinetic energy of a particle in a box [Eq. (12.5.4)]. In other words, a state of zero energy is possible for a potential well if and only if the depth of the well is such as to equal in magnitude any one of the energy eigenvalues of the particle in a linear box of the same width. This behavior is at variance with the behavior of a classically described system.

We consider next the solution of Eqs. (13.1.7) for $\epsilon < 0$; we have to invoke Eq. (13.1.8). Then, one can obtain

$$(\alpha + \beta)A_2 e^{-i\alpha l} - (\alpha - \beta)B_2 e^{i\alpha l} = 0,$$

$$(\alpha - \beta)A_2 e^{i\alpha l} - (\alpha + \beta)B_2 e^{-i\alpha l} = 0.$$

Again, for $\phi_2(x)$ not to vanish identically [which is necessary for Eqs. (13.1.6) not to vanish identically in the present case], we must have

$$\begin{vmatrix} (\alpha + \beta)e^{-i\alpha l} & -(\alpha - \beta)e^{i\alpha l} \\ (\alpha - \beta)e^{i\alpha l} & -(\alpha + \beta)e^{-i\alpha l} \end{vmatrix} = 0,$$

or

$$(\alpha + \beta)^2 e^{-2i\alpha l} = (\alpha - \beta)^2 e^{2i\alpha l},$$

or

$$\left(\frac{\alpha + \beta}{\alpha - \beta}\right)^2 = e^{4i\alpha l}. \tag{13.1.10}$$

For imaginary α [taking the positive root, by the convention of Eqs. (13.1.5)], Eq. (13.1.10) would be inconsistent. Hence, α must be real, or

$$V_0 \leq \epsilon < 0, \tag{13.1.11}$$

so that only potential wells will give "bound" states, a result which is not unexpected. Moreover, the energy of such states is not less than the minimum value of the energy of the well.

By Eq. (13.1.11), α is real and β is imaginary. By equating the real and imaginary parts of that equation, we obtain

$$\tan 2\alpha l = \frac{2\alpha |\beta|}{\alpha^2 - |\beta|^2},$$

or

$$\tan\left[2l\sqrt{\frac{2m}{\hbar^2}(\epsilon - V_0)}\right] = \frac{2\sqrt{\epsilon(V_0 - \epsilon)}}{2\epsilon - V_0}, \tag{13.1.12}$$

which transcendental equation generally must be solved numerically for the discrete energy levels of the potential well.

Under the present circumstances, Eq. (13.1.10) yields

$$\frac{\alpha + \beta}{\alpha - \beta} e^{-2i\alpha l} = \pm 1,$$

so that

$$A_2 = \pm B_2. \tag{13.1.13}$$

Thereupon, Eqs. (13.1.7) yield [with Eq. (13.1.8)]

$$A_3 = \pm B_1. \tag{13.1.14}$$

We consider finally the solution of Eqs. (13.1.7) for $\epsilon > 0$. We may obtain

$$2\beta A_1 e^{-i\beta l} = \quad (\alpha + \beta)A_2 e^{-i\alpha l} - (\alpha - \beta)B_2 e^{i\alpha l},$$

$$2\beta B_1 e^{i\beta l} = -(\alpha - \beta)A_2 e^{-i\alpha l} + (\alpha + \beta)B_2 e^{i\alpha l},$$

$$2\beta A_3 e^{i\beta l} = \quad (\alpha + \beta)A_2 e^{i\alpha l} - (\alpha - \beta)B_2 e^{-i\alpha l},$$

$$2\beta B_3 e^{-i\beta l} = -(\alpha - \beta)A_2 e^{i\alpha l} + (\alpha + \beta)B_2 e^{-i\alpha l}.$$

Since $\epsilon > 0$, β is real. We now inquire into the possibility that there is zero (relative) probability of finding the particle to the right of the barrier or well. This requires that $A_3 = B_3 = 0$. But then it follows for *all* α that all coefficients vanish, or the wave function is identically zero. Hence, if and only if there is a nonzero probability of finding the particle on one side of the barrier or well, there is also a nonzero probability of finding it on the other side. This result holds for *all* nonnegative total energy *and* all barriers and wells. The systems containing a potential well would give the same result from a classical description, but not the systems containing a barrier. For the latter, imaginary values of α would correspond to the particle being on only one side of the barrier.

This nonclassical behavior may be described in quantitative terms. For simplicity, we confine our attention to states for which the particle when on the right of the barrier or well only is moving *away* from it. This means we shall take $B_3 = 0$. Under this restriction,

$$(\alpha - \beta)A_2 e^{i\alpha l} = (\alpha + \beta)B_2 e^{-i\alpha l},$$

and

$$\frac{|A_3|^2}{|A_1|^2} = \frac{16|\alpha|^2\beta^2}{|(\alpha + \beta)^2 e^{-2i\alpha l} - (\alpha - \beta)^2 e^{2i\alpha l}|^2}, \quad (13.1.15)$$

while

$$\frac{|B_1|^2}{|A_1|^2} = \frac{(\alpha^2 - \beta^2)^2 |e^{+2i\alpha l} - e^{-2i\alpha l}|^2}{|(\alpha + \beta)^2 e^{-2i\alpha l} - (\alpha - \beta)^2 e^{2i\alpha l}|^2}. \quad (13.1.16)$$

Equation (13.1.15) is termed the *transmission coefficient*, T_ϵ, for the barrier or well, and Eq. (13.1.16) is termed the corresponding *reflection coefficient*, R_ϵ.

The case when α is real corresponds to all potential wells (for $\epsilon > 0$) and barriers with heights less than the total energy. For this case, we obtain

$$T_\epsilon = \left\{ 1 + \frac{V_0^2}{4\epsilon(\epsilon - V_0)} \sin^2 \left[2l \sqrt{\frac{2m}{\hbar^2}(\epsilon - V_0)} \right] \right\}^{-1}, \quad (13.1.17)$$

while when α is imaginary, the barrier height exceeds the total energy, and we obtain

$$T_\epsilon = \left\{ 1 + \frac{V_0^2}{4\epsilon(V_0 - \epsilon)} \sinh^2 \left[2l \sqrt{\frac{2m}{\hbar^2}(V_0 - \epsilon)} \right] \right\}^{-1}. \quad (13.1.18)$$

In both cases, it is easy to verify that

$$R_\epsilon + T_\epsilon = 1, \quad (13.1.19)$$

as might have been anticipated.

The nonclassical behavior alluded to is now displayed. Thus, for potential wells Eq. (13.1.17) reveals that T_ϵ generally is not unity, so that some reflection occurs in the wave-mechanical description. However, we may notice that the reflection coefficient vanishes whenever the energy is such as to make

$$2l \sqrt{\frac{2m}{\hbar^2}(\epsilon - V_0)} = n\pi,$$

or when

$$\epsilon = \frac{n^2 h^2}{8m(2l)^2} + V_0 > 0, \quad (13.1.20)$$

which may be recognized as the energy levels of the "related" particle in a box, Eq. (12.5.4). Thus, complete transmission occurs whenever the energy corresponds to one of the energy values of the "related" particle in a box. This behavior has its qualitative counterpart in the so-called *Ramsauer effect* in which the scattering of low-energy electrons by atoms is remarkably small for certain ranges of values of their relative kinetic energy. Also, for barriers we see from Eq. (13.1.18) that T_ϵ is not zero, so that some transmission occurs even for energies less than the barrier height. This phenomenon is frequently referred to as *quantum-mechanical tunnelling*.

We may emphasize that the considerations of the present section have focused attention on the wave functions for particularly simple systems of a barrier or a well; the energy has offered no real problem to determine since Schroedinger's equation is soluble for such systems in elementary terms.

13.2 Model of molecular binding. The use of rectangular barriers and wells permits the construction of model systems to illustrate many phenomena which are complicated to describe in terms of realistic Schroedinger equations. One such model will be considered here which bears some resemblance to chemical binding, as will be seen.

We consider, for simplicity, the potential-energy function

$$
\begin{aligned}
V(x) &= +\infty, & x &\leq -l, \\
&= 0, & -l &< x < -a, \\
&= V_0 > 0, & -a &\leq x \leq +a, \\
&= 0, & +a &< x < +l, \\
&= +\infty, & +l &\leq x.
\end{aligned}
\tag{13.2.1}
$$

With this potential-energy function, the definitions of Eq. (13.1.5) and the formal solutions of Eq. (13.1.6) may be used. (The latter need modification only as to their range.) The boundary conditions are different from Eqs. (13.1.7). We have

$$
\begin{aligned}
\phi_1(x) &= A_1 e^{i\beta x} + B_1 e^{-i\beta x}, & -l &< x < -a, \\
\phi_2(x) &= A_2 e^{i\alpha x} + B_2 e^{-i\alpha x}, & -a &\leq x \leq +a, \\
\phi_3(x) &= A_3 e^{i\beta x} + B_3 e^{-i\beta x}, & +a &< x < +l,
\end{aligned}
\tag{13.2.2}
$$

and zero otherwise. The continuity conditions on $\phi_1(x)$ are

$$A_1 e^{-i\beta l} + B_1 e^{i\beta l} = 0,$$

$$A_1 e^{-i\beta a} + B_1 e^{i\beta a} = A_2 e^{-i\alpha a} + B_2 e^{i\alpha a},$$

$$A_2 e^{i\alpha a} + B_2 e^{-i\alpha a} = A_3 e^{i\beta a} + B_3 e^{-i\beta a}, \qquad (13.2.3)$$

$$A_3 e^{i\beta l} + B_3 e^{-i\beta l} = 0.$$

From the discussion of Section 12.3, we cannot expect the derivatives of $\phi(x)$ to be continuous at $x = \pm l$; however, they must be such at $x = \pm a$. Hence,

$$\beta(A_1 e^{-i\beta a} - B_1 e^{i\beta a}) = \alpha(A_2 e^{-i\alpha a} - B_2 e^{i\alpha a}),$$

$$\alpha(A_2 e^{i\alpha a} - B_2 e^{-i\alpha a}) = \beta(A_3 e^{i\beta a} - B_3 e^{-i\beta a}). \qquad (13.2.4)$$

Equations (13.2.3) and (13.2.4) determine the A's and B's. However, these equations must be linearly dependent for a nonzero wave function. As a result, α and β must be related, giving a restriction upon the values which ϵ may assume. From Section 14.4, we can establish that the eigenfunctions are either symmetric or antisymmetric with respect to inversion through the origin. As a result,

$$A_1 = \pm B_3,$$

$$B_1 = \pm A_3, \qquad (13.2.5)$$

$$A_2 = \pm B_2,$$

the $(+)$ referring to those functions which are unaltered by the transformation while $(-)$ refers to those which change sign.

Considering the symmetric states, we have the relations

$$B_3 e^{-i\beta l} + B_1 e^{i\beta l} = 0,$$

$$B_3 e^{-i\beta a} + B_1 e^{i\beta a} = B_2(e^{-i\alpha a} + e^{i\alpha a}), \qquad (13.2.6)$$

$$\beta(B_3 e^{-i\beta a} - B_1 e^{i\beta a}) = \alpha B_2(e^{-i\alpha a} - e^{i\alpha a}).$$

The B's can differ from zero only if the equations are linearly dependent, or

$$\begin{vmatrix} e^{-i\beta l} & e^{i\beta l} & 0 \\ e^{-i\beta a} & e^{i\beta a} & -2\cos\alpha a \\ \beta e^{-i\beta a} & -\beta e^{i\beta a} & 2i\alpha\sin\alpha a \end{vmatrix} = 0. \qquad (13.2.7)$$

This determinant reduces to

$$\beta \cos \alpha a \cos \beta(a - l) + \alpha \sin \alpha a \sin \beta(a - l) = 0, \quad (13.2.8)$$

for $\epsilon > V_0$. For $\epsilon < V_0$, we obtain

$$\beta \cosh |\alpha| a \cos \beta(a - l) - |\alpha| \sinh |\alpha| a \sin \beta(a - l) = 0. \quad (13.2.9)$$

We consider $V_0 \rightarrow +\infty$, so that $\epsilon < V_0$. Then

$$\frac{\tan \beta(a - l)}{\beta} = \frac{\coth |\alpha| a}{|\alpha|}$$

$$\rightarrow 0, \quad \text{for} \quad |\alpha| \rightarrow \infty. \quad (13.2.10)$$

Under these conditions, $\beta > 0$, $a - l < 0$,

$$\beta(a - l) = -n\pi, \quad n = 1, 2, \ldots, \quad (13.2.11)$$

and

$$\epsilon_n(V_0 = \infty) = \frac{n^2 h^2}{8m(a - l)^2},$$

the result expected for a particle in a box. In general, it is necessary to solve the transcendental equation. From Eq. (13.2.10) we can verify that with $\beta > 0$, $l - a > 0$,

$$(n + \tfrac{1}{2})\pi \leq \beta_n(l - a) \leq (n + 1)\pi, \quad n = 0, 1, \ldots. \quad (13.2.12)$$

In particular, the lowest symmetric state corresponds to $n = 0$, with

$$\pi/2 \leq \beta_0(l - a) \leq \pi.$$

In this interval,

$$\frac{\tan \beta_0(l - a)}{\beta_0(l - a)}$$

is a *monotonic increasing* function of the variable, or from Eq. (13.1.5), a monotonic increasing function of the energy for fixed $(l - a)$. From Eq. (13.2.10),

$$\frac{\tan \beta_0(l - a)}{\beta_0(l - a)} = -\frac{\coth |\alpha_0| a}{|\alpha_0|(l - a)}.$$

Hence, any change of the right side which will decrease its value will decrease the energy of the system. For large V_0, the change in $|\alpha_0|$ due to a change in ϵ will be very small. As a result, one can see that *decreasing a*, for fixed $(l - a)$ will *decrease* the energy. This can be made precise. Differentiation of both sides of the last equation for fixed V_0 and $(l - a)$

with respect to a yields

$$\left(\frac{\partial \epsilon}{\partial a}\right)_{(l-a)} = - \frac{1 - \coth |\alpha_0| a}{\left\{\left(\frac{l-a}{2\epsilon}\right)\left[1 - \frac{\tan \beta_0(l-a)}{\beta_0(l-a)} + \tan^2 \beta_0(l-a)\right]\right.} \cdots$$

$$\cdots \frac{}{\left. - \frac{a}{2(V_0 - \epsilon)}\left[1 - \frac{\coth |\alpha_0| a}{|\alpha_0| a} - \coth^2 |\alpha_0| a\right]\right\}} . \quad (13.2.13)$$

The right side of this equation is demonstrably positive for the lowest energy value. Hence, the energy of the system is a monotonic increasing function of the distance between the wells, or

$$\left(\frac{\partial \epsilon}{\partial a}\right)_{(l-a)} > 0. \quad (13.2.14)$$

This sort of behavior is illustrative of the change in the ground-state energy of a diatomic molecule when the internuclear repulsion is omitted. In other words, the so-called *electronic energy* of the molecule behaves in a manner similar to that which has been described. The effect of nuclear repulsion can be simulated here by such a repulsion imposed upon the wells. However, we shall not consider it.

We may, however, emphasize that the behavior which we have found is not characteristic of a classical description of the same system. For a similar system described by classical mechanics, the particle could be found in either well but the lowest energy would in no way depend on the distance between the wells. The behavior we have observed is to be attributed entirely to the wave-mechanical description we have imposed.

Nevertheless, there is an important connection between the wave-mechanical and the classical-mechanical descriptions that must be kept in mind: in a sense to be exposed in Chapter 15, the wave-mechanical systems satisfy the equations for classical motion associated with Hamilton.

13.3 Summary. The intent of the present chapter has been to emphasize certain of the nonclassical properties which systems manifest.

The expedient of dealing with rectangular barriers and wells permits the Schroedinger equation to be solved for such systems in general terms. The comparison between the behavior of systems thus described and that expected for classically describable systems is easily effected.

The comparison is made in terms of the properties of *transmission* and *reflection* from barriers and wells and the effect of proximity between wells upon the energy of the system.

Exercises

1. Show why Eq. (13.1.8) must be introduced.

2. Show that there are no states for which the energy is less than the minimum value of the energy of a rectangular potential well.

3. Verify Eqs. (13.1.12), (13.1.13), and (13.1.14).

4. Derive Eq. (13.1.18).

5. Verify Eq. (13.1.19) by explicit evaluation of the pertinent quantities.

6. Evaluate transmission coefficient for a *step barrier* with a potential

$$V(x) = 0, \qquad x \leq 0,$$
$$= V_0 > 0, \qquad x > 0.$$

7. Consider the statistical mechanics for a system having the potential *barrier* in Section 13.1. For any temperature, relate the statistical-mechanical distribution-in-position to the wave-mechanical statistical distribution-in-position. (Use the statistical-mechanical theory for classical systems given in Chapter 10.)

8. Taking the energy to be measured in terms of $|V_0|$ and setting

$$\left(\frac{\hbar^2 |V_0|}{32ml^2\pi^2} \right)$$

equal to 10, determine the first three energy levels of a particle in a potential well.

9. Indicate how to obtain an ensemble-averaged value of the transmission coefficient for an equilibrium ensemble of systems having a potential barrier. Consider especially the value of such an average for very large values of V_0 (as compared with kT).

10. Determine the wave functions for the system considered in Section 13.2.

11. Evaluate the expectation value for the kinetic energy in the ground state; evaluate also the expectation value for the potential energy in the ground state. Compare with the eigenvalue of the energy. [For convenience, express the energy in terms of V_0, take

$$\left(\frac{\hbar^2 V_0}{32m\pi^2(l-a)^2} \right)$$

equal to 10 and

$$\left(\frac{a}{l-a} \right) = 1, 2, \infty.]$$

12. Consider the statistical mechanics for a system having the potential energy of Eq. (13.2.1). Use classical statistical theory to determine the ensemble average value of the total energy as a function of the distance between wells. For fixed temperature, compare the result with the quantum-mechanical one and relate to the remarks made in the text.

CHAPTER 14

ALGEBRAIC METHODS FOR STATIONARY STATES

14.1 The variational method. The previous two chapters have been devoted to very simple systems for which exact solutions of Schroedinger's time-independent equation may be obtained. As the idealizations become more realistic, they become more complicated. As a result there are very few problems in quantum mechanics which can be solved exactly. However, a number of approximation methods exist which permit an accurate description of many physical systems, and these will be illustrated in the present chapter.

Perhaps one of the most widely used methods employed in the determination of precise values of the properties of physical systems is the *variational method*, originated by Ritz for solving eigenvalue relations. In the present case, interest will be centered upon the Schroedinger equation. We have already indicated in Chapter 12 that Schroedinger's equation is a necessary consequence that the expectation value of the Hamiltonian remains stationary with respect to arbitrary variations in the normalized wave function. In the usual application, primary interest is devoted to the *lowest eigenvalue* corresponding to the *ground state* of the relevant system. In such cases, the stationary value of the expectation value also is a minimum. However, of greater significance is the fact that the lowest eigenvalue is minimal with respect to *any* arbitrary expectation value of the operator.

To see this, consider the time-independent Schroedinger equation

$$\mathbf{H}\psi_n(x) = \epsilon_n\psi_n(x), \tag{14.1.1}$$

with

$$\int dx\, \psi_n^*(x)\psi_m(x) = \delta_{nm}. \tag{14.1.2}$$

Now, by the superposition principle any arbitrary state may be assumed to be expressible in terms of the energy eigenfunctions. Hence such a state with a wave function $\phi(x)$ may be expressed as

$$\phi(x) = \sum_{n=0}^{\infty} a_n\psi_n(x), \tag{14.1.3}$$

the ψ_n's being solutions of Eqs. (14.1.1) and (14.1.2). No loss of generality is entailed by assuming

$$\int dx \, |\phi(x)|^2 = \int dx \sum_{n,m=0}^{\infty} a_n^* a_m \psi_n^*(x) \psi_m(x)$$

$$= \sum_{n=0} |a_n|^2 = 1. \tag{14.1.4}$$

The use of Eqs. (14.1.1) through (14.1.4) will yield

$$E_\phi(\mathbf{H}) = \int dx \, \phi^*(x) \mathbf{H} \phi(x) = \sum_{n=0} |a_n|^2 \epsilon_n.$$

But by ordering the energy eigenvalues so that

$$\epsilon_0 \leq \epsilon_1 \leq \epsilon_2 \leq \cdots, \tag{14.1.5}$$

it is immediately apparent that

$$E_\phi(\mathbf{H}) \geq \epsilon_0, \tag{14.1.6}$$

so that an *upper bound* to the smallest eigenvalue may be obtained. By evaluating the expectation value with functions that contain adjustable parameters, then *minimizing* the expectation value with respect to changes in these parameters, a "best" approximation of a sort is obtained.

We may obtain a better insight into what is involved if we consider a simple example. Therefore, consider a particle in a box (linear) which lies between $(-a/2)$ and $(+a/2)$ on the x-axis. (See Exercise 31, Chapter 12.) Letting

$$x = \frac{a}{2} y, \tag{14.1.7}$$

we obtain the Schroedinger equation

$$-\frac{2\hbar^2}{ma^2} \frac{d^2}{dy^2} \psi_n(y) = \epsilon_n \psi_n(y), \tag{14.1.8}$$

with the boundary conditions

$$\psi_n(\pm 1) = 0.$$

To illustrate the variational method, we take a rudimentary function which satisfies the boundary condition

$$\phi_1(y) = C(1 - y^2). \tag{14.1.9}$$

It is immediately apparent that C is determined by the normalization condition, Eq. (14.1.4), so no variation in the expectation value of the energy with this wave function is possible. Nevertheless

$$E_{\phi_1}(\mathbf{H}) = \frac{\displaystyle\int_{-1}^{+1} dy\ \phi_1^*(y)\left[-\frac{2\hbar^2}{ma^2}\frac{d^2\phi_1(y)}{dy^2}\right]}{\displaystyle\int_{-1}^{+1} dy\ |\phi_1(y)|^2}$$

$$= \frac{\hbar^2}{(4\pi^2/5)ma^2} \geq \frac{\hbar^2}{8ma^2}, \tag{14.1.10}$$

as can readily be verified. The right side of Eq. (14.1.10) is the smallest eigenvalue of Eq. (14.1.8). In these terms the corresponding "best" function is

$$\phi_1(y) = \sqrt{15/16}\,(1 - y^2).$$

Now, to introduce a function capable of being varied sufficiently, try

$$\phi_2(y) = C_1[\phi_1(y) + C_2(1 - y^4)]. \tag{14.1.11}$$

After some manipulation, we obtain

$$E_{\phi_2}(\mathbf{H}) = \frac{\hbar^2}{(4\pi^2/5)ma^2}\frac{1 + (48/5\sqrt{15})C_2 + (64/35)C_2^2}{1 + (64/7\sqrt{15})C_2 + (64/45)C_2^2}.$$

Clearly, the rational fraction must be minimized. When this is done, we can find that

$$C_2 = -2.280 \quad\text{or}\quad -0.1022,$$

but the *minimum* value occurs with the latter value of C_2. Then we obtain

$$[E_{\phi_2}(\mathbf{H})]_{\min} = \frac{\hbar^2}{7.993ma^2}, \tag{14.1.12}$$

which estimates the lowest eigenvalue with an error of 0.1%. In these terms, the corresponding "best" function is (normalized in y)

$$\phi_2(y) = 0.986(1 - 1.118y^2 + 0.118y^4), \tag{14.1.13}$$

while the eigenfunction is (normalized in y)

$$\psi_1(y) = \cos\frac{\pi y}{2}$$

$$= 1 - 1.233y^2 + 0.254y^4 + 0(y^6). \tag{14.1.14}$$

It is apparent that the eigenvalue is estimated more precisely than is the eigenfunction. (To the approximation which has been given in the series, the latter is not normalized to unity.)

The application of the variational method depends only on the ready evaluation of the expectation values of kinetic-energy and potential-energy operators. It would thus seem to be a most useful approximation method. However, it generally develops that changes in the functions produce only very small changes in the expectation values of the Hamiltonian. Nevertheless, the values so obtained may be relatively poor approximations to the lowest eigenvalue. These difficulties generally become more pronounced when greater accuracy is desired.

14.2 The Rayleigh-Schroedinger series perturbation method. Also of great utility as an approximation method is one which has a much more physically useful viewpoint, although the formal use of the method is quite abstract. Exemplifying the general category of *perturbation methods*, the Rayleigh-Schroedinger method attempts to solve the Schroedinger equation by a series expansion about some approximation to the Hamiltonian which has readily obtainable eigenvalues and eigenfunctions. That is, the Hamiltonian of the system under consideration is viewed as corresponding to that of a system which has been *perturbed* by the inclusion of kinetic- and (most usually) potential-energy terms which are lacking in the *unperturbed* system.

We represent the Hamiltonian for the perturbed system (i.e., the actual system of interest) by

$$\mathbf{H} = \mathbf{H}_0 + \lambda\mathbf{H}_1, \tag{14.2.1}$$

where the unperturbed Hamiltonian $\mathbf{H}_0$ is sufficiently simple so that one can solve

$$\mathbf{H}_0\psi_k^{(0)} = \epsilon_k^{(0)}\psi_k^{(0)}, \tag{14.2.2}$$

$$\int dx \, [\psi_k^{(0)}]^*\psi_j^{(0)} = \delta_{jk}. \tag{14.2.3}$$

Moreover, $\lambda\mathbf{H}_1$ with real λ is *small* (in what sense will be discerned subsequently). We wish to solve Eqs. (14.1.1) and (14.1.2). To do so we need to distinguish two separate cases:

(a) *Nondegenerate cases, whereby each eigenvalue of Eq. (14.2.2) is distinct from every other eigenvalue.*

We imagine that

$$\psi_n(x) = \sum_{p=0}^{\infty} \lambda^p \psi_n^{(p)}(x), \tag{14.2.4}$$

and

$$\epsilon_n = \sum_{p=0}^{\infty} \lambda^p \epsilon_n^{(p)}. \tag{14.2.5}$$

Substitution of these expressions into Eq. (14.1.1) yields

$$(\mathbf{H}_0 + \lambda \mathbf{H}_1)\psi_n = \sum_{p=0}^{\infty} \lambda^p \mathbf{H}_0 \psi_n^{(p)} + \sum_{p=0}^{\infty} \lambda^{p+1} \mathbf{H}_1 \psi_n^{(p)}$$

$$= \left[\sum_{p=0}^{\infty} \lambda^p \epsilon_n^{(p)} \right]\left[\sum_{p=0}^{\infty} \lambda^p \psi_n^{(p)} \right]. \tag{14.2.6}$$

Since Eq. (14.2.6) is presumed to hold for all values of λ, we may combine all terms of the same power of λ and set each coefficient equal to zero. The first few coefficients lead to the equations

$$\lambda^0 \colon \mathbf{H}_0 \psi_n^{(0)} = \epsilon_n^{(0)} \psi_n^{(0)},$$

$$\lambda^1 \colon \mathbf{H}_0 \psi_n^{(1)} + \mathbf{H}_1 \psi_n^{(0)} = \epsilon_n^{(0)} \psi_n^{(1)} + \epsilon_n^{(1)} \psi_n^{(0)}, \tag{14.2.7}$$

$$\lambda^2 \colon \mathbf{H}_0 \psi_n^{(2)} + \mathbf{H}_1 \psi_n^{(1)} = \epsilon_n^{(0)} \psi_n^{(2)} + \epsilon_n^{(1)} \psi_n^{(1)}$$

$$+ \epsilon_n^{(2)} \psi_n^{(0)}, \text{ etc.}$$

These equations may be referred to as *zeroth-*, *first-* and *second-*order equations. The zeroth-order equations correspond to Eq. (14.2.2). We require also that Eq. (14.1.2) be satisfied so that

$$\int dx \sum_{\substack{p=0 \\ s=0}}^{\infty} \lambda^{p+s} [\psi_n^{(p)}]^* [\psi_n^{(s)}] = 1, \tag{14.2.8}$$

so that

$$\lambda^0 \colon \int dx [\psi_n^{(0)}]^* \psi_n^{(0)} = 1,$$

$$\lambda^1 \colon \int dx [\psi_n^{(0)}]^* \psi_n^{(1)} + \int dx [\psi_n^{(1)}]^* \psi_n^{(0)} = 0, \tag{14.2.9}$$

$$\lambda^2 \colon \int dx [\psi_n^{(0)}]^* \psi_n^{(2)} + \int dx [\psi_n^{(1)}]^* \psi_n^{(1)}$$

$$+ \int dx [\psi_n^{(2)}]^* \psi_n^{(0)} = 0, \text{ etc.}$$

The zeroth-order equations correspond to Eq. (14.2.3).

Now, the first-order equations may be solved for $\epsilon_n^{(1)}$. Multiplication of both sides of the first-order equation by $[\psi_n^{(0)}]^*$, followed by integration, yields

$$\int dx \, [\psi_n^{(0)}]^* \mathbf{H}_0 \psi_n^{(1)} + \int dx \, [\psi_n^{(0)}]^* \mathbf{H}_1 \psi_n^{(0)}$$

$$= \epsilon_n^{(0)} \int dx \, [\psi_n^{(0)}]^* \psi_n^{(1)} + \epsilon_n^{(1)}.$$

Because of the fact that $\mathbf{H}_0$ is Hermitian, we obtain

$$\int dx \, [\psi_n^{(0)}]^* \mathbf{H}_0 \psi_n^{(1)} = \int dx \, [\mathbf{H}_0 \psi_n^{(0)}]^* \psi_n^{(1)}$$

$$= \epsilon_n^{(0)} \int dx \, [\psi_n^{(0)}]^* \psi_n^{(1)}.$$

Hence

$$\epsilon_n^{(1)} = \int dx \, [\psi_n^{(0)}]^* \mathbf{H}_1 \psi_n^{(0)}, \tag{14.2.10}$$

so that the first-order correction to the energy is simply the expectation value of the perturbation operator $\mathbf{H}_1$.

The first-order correction to the wave function is obtainable from Eqs. (14.2.7). Multiplication of the first-order equation by $[\psi_m^{(0)}]^*$ and integration yields, making use of the Hermitian property of $\mathbf{H}_0$,

$$\int dx \, [\psi_m^{(0)}]^* \psi_n^{(1)} = \frac{\int dx \, [\psi_m^{(0)}]^* \mathbf{H}_1 \psi_n^{(0)}}{\epsilon_n^{(0)} - \epsilon_m^{(0)}}, \qquad n \neq m. \tag{14.2.11}$$

If we represent

$$\psi_n^{(1)}(x) = \sum_{m=0}^{\infty} C_{nm} \psi_m^{(0)}(x), \tag{14.2.12}$$

Eq. (14.2.12) gives all the C_{nm} for $m \neq n$, since

$$C_{nm} = \int dx \, [\psi_m^{(0)}]^* \psi_n^{(1)}. \tag{14.2.13}$$

From the first-order equation of Eqs. (14.2.9) we see that C_{nn} must be a pure imaginary number. As a result, if we can deal only with real functions for the ψ_n and $\psi_n^{(0)}$, then C_{nn} will be zero. When the eigenvalues are distinct, this can always be assured. Hence $\psi_n^{(1)}(x)$ is determined.

The second-order equation of Eqs. (14.2.7) may now be treated in a manner analogous to that which yielded Eq. (14.2.10). The result obtained for the second-order correction to the energy is

$$\epsilon_n^{(2)} = \sum_{m \neq n} \frac{\left| \int dx \, [\psi_n^{(0)}]^* \mathbf{H}_1 \psi_m^{(0)} \right|^2}{\epsilon_n^{(0)} - \epsilon_m^{(0)}}. \tag{14.2.14}$$

The form for the second-order correction admits of the interesting result that the various unperturbed energy levels repel one another.

Since we do not propose to go beyond the second-order terms in the energy, the second-order terms in the wave function are not needed. They may be left as an exercise for the reader.

(b) *Degenerate cases, whereby several of the eigenvalues of Eq. (14.2.2) have the same value. As a result, Eqs. (14.2.14) generally then diverge.*

We may orient the problem by noting that in the nondegenerate case we required implicitly

$$\lim_{\lambda \to 0} \mathbf{H}\psi_n = \mathbf{H}_0 \left(\lim_{\lambda \to 0} \psi_n\right) = \epsilon_n^{(0)} \left(\lim_{\lambda \to 0} \psi_n\right),$$

which reduces to the appropriate unperturbed eigenfunction when $\epsilon_n^{(0)}$ is nondegenerate. Otherwise, the limit need only be some linear combination of the degenerate unperturbed eigenfunctions. That is, if we designate the M_n degenerate unperturbed eigenfunctions by $\psi_{nj}^{(0)}$, each j value of the same eigenvalue $\epsilon_n^{(0)}$, we require evidently that

$$\lim_{\lambda \to 0} \mathbf{H}\psi_{nk} = \epsilon_n^{(0)} \left[\sum_{j=1}^{M_n} a_{kj}\psi_{nj}^{(0)}\right].$$

This latitude makes a considerable difference in the first-order energy and eliminates the divergence of the second-order energy corrections.

We shall express the wave function, first order in λ,

$$\psi_{nk} \doteq \phi_{nk} + \lambda\psi_{nk}^{(1)},$$

where

$$\phi_{nk} = \sum_j a_{kj}\psi_{nj}^{(0)},$$

and

$$\psi_{nk}^{(1)} = \sum_m \sum_n b_{nk,mn}\psi_{mn}^{(0)},$$

the summation being taken over the necessary values. Substitution of these expressions into Eq. (14.1.1) yields the first-order equation

$$\mathbf{H}_0\psi_{nk}^{(1)} + \mathbf{H}_1\phi_{nk} = \epsilon_n^{(0)}\psi_{nk}^{(1)} + \epsilon_{nk}^{(1)}\phi_{nk}^{(0)}.$$

Multiplication by $[\psi_{ns}^{(0)}]^*$ and integration yield, assuming orthogonality of the $\psi_{nk}^{(0)}$, for *every* s for a given n

$$\sum_j a_{kj} \int dx\, [\psi_{ns}^{(0)}]^*\mathbf{H}_1\psi_{nj}^{(0)} = \epsilon_{nk}^{(1)}a_{ks}, \qquad (14.2.15)$$

or
$$\sum_j a_{kj} \left\{ \int dx \, [\psi_{ns}^{(0)}]^* \mathbf{H}_1 \psi_{nj} - \epsilon_{nk}^{(1)} \delta_{js} \right\} = 0. \qquad (14.2.16)$$

There are M_n equations of the form of Eq. (14.2.16), equal in number to the number of a_{kj}'s with fixed k. Since the equations are linear and homogeneous in the a_{kj}'s, a nontrivial solution (*viz.*, not all a_{kj}'s zero) requires the determinant of the coefficients of the a_{kj}'s to vanish. That is

$$\det \left\{ \int dx \, [\psi_{ns}^{(0)}]^* \mathbf{H}_1 \psi_{nj}^{(0)} - \epsilon_{nk}^{(1)} \delta_{js} \right\} = 0,$$

which can be represented better as follows. Letting

$$\int dx \, [\psi_{ns}^{(0)}]^* \mathbf{H}_1 \psi_{nj}^{(0)} = H_{js},$$

we obtain the determinantal form of the *secular equation*

$$\begin{vmatrix} H_{11} - \epsilon_{nk}^{(1)} & H_{12} & H_{1M_n} \\ H_{21} & H_{22} - \epsilon_{nk}^{(1)} & H_{2M_n} \\ H_{M_n 1} & H_{M_n 2} & H_{M_n M_n} - \epsilon_{nk}^{(1)} \end{vmatrix} = 0,$$

$$(14.2.17)$$

which is an algebraic equation in $\epsilon_{nk}^{(1)}$.

We shall consider the generalization of Eq. (14.2.17) in a later section. However, we note that the present section has converted the problem of solving a differential equation to one of evaluating certain integrals and *then* solving an algebraic equation.

The determination of the a_{kj} can be carried out once the roots [i.e., the $\epsilon_{nk}^{(1)}$] of Eq. (14.2.17) are determined, for then there will be less than M_n equations of the form of Eq. (14.2.16) which are linearly independent. This situation will allow the determination of the relative values of a_{kj} (with fixed k). To complete the determination we need to invoke the condition of orthogonality and normalization, *viz.*,

$$\int dx \, \phi_{nk}^* \phi_{nl} = \sum_j a_{kj}^* a_{lj} = \delta_{kl}. \qquad (14.2.18)$$

The net result of these considerations is to represent the eigenfunctions of the original unperturbed Hamiltonian in a form that permits the second-order correction to the energy to be evaluated. The basis of eigenfunctions are the ϕ_{nk} instead of the $\psi_{nk}^{(0)}$ and

$$\int dx \, \phi_{nk}^* \mathbf{H}_1 \phi_{nl} = \sum_{i,j} a_{ki}^* a_{lj} H_{ji} = \sum_i a_{ki}^* a_{li} \epsilon_{nl}^{(1)}$$

$$= \epsilon_{nl}^{(1)} \delta_{kl}, \qquad (14.2.19)$$

by Eqs. (14.2.15) and (14.2.18). As a result, no terms in the numerator appear in Eq. (14.2.14) for degenerate levels when the ϕ_{nk} are used as the unperturbed wave functions. We shall not exhibit the second-order correction to the energy, however.

It seems worth while to indicate by an explicit elementary example how the perturbation theory of the present section is employed. We consider the case of a rigid planar rotor (Section 12.8) which has been perturbed by an external force so that it acquires a potential energy proportional to the cosine of the angle made by the rotor with the x-axis. The Schroedinger equation for the system is ($0 \leq \theta \leq 2\pi$)

$$-\frac{\hbar^2}{2I} \frac{d^2\phi_k(\theta)}{d\theta^2} + \lambda \cos \theta \phi_k(\theta) = \epsilon_k \phi_k(\theta). \qquad (14.2.20)$$

In these terms, the unperturbed solutions ($\lambda = 0$) are given by Eq. (12.8.9), with the corresponding eigenvalues given by Eq. (12.8.10). We see here that we must deal with degenerate unperturbed eigenvalues. We first evaluate

$$\int_0^{2\pi} d\theta \, \phi_k^*(\theta) \cos \theta \phi_k(\theta) = \frac{1}{4\pi} \int_0^{2\pi} d\theta \, [e^{i(k-k'+1)\theta} + e^{i(k-k'-1)\theta}]$$

$$= \tfrac{1}{2}(\delta_{k',k+1} + \delta_{k',k-1}). \qquad (14.2.21)$$

As a consequence, we see that since the degenerate unperturbed states ($\pm k$) do not cause any difficulty, we may proceed with the theory of the nondegenerate cases. We evidently obtain to second-order

$$\epsilon_k = \frac{\hbar^2}{2I} k^2 + \frac{\lambda^2 I}{\hbar^2} \cdot \frac{1}{4k^2 - 1}, \qquad (14.2.22)$$

by substitution into Eq. (14.2.14). The first-order wave function is given by

$$\phi_k(\theta) = \frac{1}{\sqrt{2\pi}} \left[e^{ik\theta} + \frac{\lambda}{2} e^{i(k-1)\theta} + \frac{\lambda}{2} e^{i(k+1)\theta} \right]. \qquad (14.2.23)$$

The present simple system corresponds to a model for the *Stark effect* for the planar rigid rotor. The perturbation corresponds to the interaction of an electric dipole along the axis of the rotor with a uniform electric field λ. The energy of the perturbed rotor exhibits a quadratic Stark effect.

The effect of a similar but different perturbation may clarify the relation between the degenerate cases. Thus, consider the Schroedinger equation $(0 \leq \theta \leq 2\pi)$

$$-\frac{\hbar^2}{2I} \frac{d^2\phi_k(\theta)}{d\theta^2} + \lambda \cos 2\theta \phi_k(\theta) = \epsilon_k \phi_k(\theta), \qquad (14.2.24)$$

which is a trivial modification of *Mathieu's equation*, and the solutions are well known. Proceeding as previously, we evaluate

$$\int_0^{2\pi} d\theta \, \phi_{k'}^*(\theta) \cos 2\theta \phi_k(\theta) = \tfrac{1}{2}(\delta_{k',k+2} + \delta_{k',k-2}). \qquad (14.2.25)$$

Here we see that the usual second-order correction to the energy would diverge for $k = \pm 1$, $k' = \mp 1$. As a result, we must consider the theory for degenerate unperturbed states involving $k = \pm 1$. We have, in fact, to solve the secular equation

$$\begin{vmatrix} -\epsilon_{\pm 1}^{(1)} & \dfrac{\lambda}{2} \\[2mm] \dfrac{\lambda}{2} & -\epsilon_{\pm 1}^{(1)} \end{vmatrix} = 0, \qquad (14.2.26)$$

or

$$\epsilon_{\pm 1}^{(1)} = \pm \frac{\lambda}{2}. \qquad (14.2.27)$$

To first-order in λ, then,

$$\epsilon_{\pm 1} = \frac{\hbar^2}{2I} \pm \frac{\lambda}{2}, \qquad (14.2.28)$$

so that the perturbation in this case may be said to "split the degeneracy." Only the values for $k = \pm 1$ will be so affected in the present case; other values of k require higher-order corrections to effect the "splitting" of the degenerate unperturbed levels.

From Eqs. (14.2.15), we obtain the coefficients of the new unperturbed wave function. If we take

$$\psi_{-1}(\theta) = a_{-1,-1}\phi_{-1}(\theta) + a_{-1,+1}\phi_{+1}(\theta),$$

$$\psi_{+1}(\theta) = a_{+1,-1}\phi_{-1}(\theta) + a_{+1,+1}\phi_{+1}(\theta),$$

then Eqs. (14.2.15) yield

$$a_{-1,+1}\frac{\lambda}{2} = -\frac{\lambda}{2} a_{-1,-1}, \qquad a_{+1,-1}\frac{\lambda}{2} = \frac{\lambda}{2} a_{+1,+1}, \qquad (14.2.29)$$

so that

$$\psi_{-1}(\theta) = \frac{1}{\sqrt{\pi}} \sin \theta, \qquad \psi_{+1}(\theta) = \frac{1}{\sqrt{\pi}} \cos \theta. \qquad (14.2.30)$$

It is with respect to these functions that the remainder of the perturbation theory must be carried out. However, we shall turn now to a general consideration of the algebraic method.

14.3 Matrix mechanics: stationary states. The trends emphasized in the previous two sections are capable of considerable generalization. As a result, the wave mechanics of Schroedinger assumes a form which, in fact, was introduced prior to Schroedinger's form and for a time appeared to be quite different from it. We are referring to the *matrix mechanics* introduced by Heisenberg and developed considerably by Born and Jordan. However, we shall not follow Heisenberg's original exposition, but will formulate the precise algebraic analog of Schroedinger's equation for stationary states. The algebraic analog of the time-dependent equation will be considered in the next chapter.

We begin with the eigenvalue relation, Eq. (11.6.2)

$$\alpha \phi_i = \alpha_i \phi_i.$$

(It is evident that Schroedinger's equation obtains for the special instance of $\alpha \equiv \mathbf{H}$. We therefore consider the general eigenvalue problem.) Now, we represent each of the eigenfunctions by a *linear transformation* of some set of other functions

$$\phi_i = \sum_{j=1}^{\infty} a_{ij} \psi_j, \qquad \text{all } i, \tag{14.3.1}$$

where the ψ_j form a complete set of orthonormal functions (i.e., the ψ_i are sufficient in number to permit the expansion to be carried out accurately). We obviously are interested only in those coefficients which satisfy Eq. (14.2.18). We now obtain

$$\sum_{j=1}^{\infty} a_{ij} \alpha \psi_j = \alpha_i \sum_{j=1}^{\infty} a_{ij} \psi_j.$$

Multiplication by ψ_k^* and integration yields

$$\sum_{j=1}^{\infty} a_{ij} \alpha_{jk} = \alpha_i a_{ik}, \tag{14.3.2}$$

where

$$\int dx \, \psi_k^* \alpha \psi_j = \alpha_{jk}. \tag{14.3.3}$$

Equation (14.3.2) holds for *every* i and k. As previously, the equations may be written in a more compact form:

$$\sum_{j=1}^{\infty} a_{ij}(\alpha_{jk} - \alpha_i \, \delta_{jk}) = 0, \tag{14.3.4}$$

which comprises an infinite set of linear homogeneous equations for the a_{ij}'s. In a formal way, then, the determinant of the coefficients of the a_{ij}'s must vanish for them not to all vanish; or, we obtain the secular equation

$$\det (\alpha_{jk} - \alpha_i \delta_{jk}) = 0. \tag{14.3.5}$$

The distinction as well as the similarity between Eq. (14.3.5) and that of the previous section is to be noted.

Now the algebraic formulation is most conveniently stated in terms of the matrix $\|\alpha_{jk}\|$:

$$\|\alpha_{jk}\| \equiv \begin{pmatrix} \alpha_{11} & \alpha_{12} & \alpha_{13} \ldots \\ \alpha_{21} & \alpha_{22} & \alpha_{23} \ldots \\ \alpha_{31} & \alpha_{32} & \alpha_{33} \ldots \\ \vdots & \vdots & \vdots \end{pmatrix} . \tag{14.3.6}$$

With the appropriate choice of the ψ_i, we may hope to find the $a_{ij} = \delta_{ij}$. (Such a choice evidently corresponds to the eigenfunctions themselves.) In such a case, clearly,

$$\alpha_{ik} = \alpha_i \delta_{ik}, \tag{14.3.7}$$

or the matrix, Eq. (14.3.6), is then *diagonal*. Thus, the eigenvalue problem is converted to the problem of diagonalizing a matrix. (The formalism described here is suited to a basis which corresponds to eigenvalues forming discrete spectra. The formalism for continuous spectra of eigenvalues may be achieved in several ways; the most directly related manner involves regarding the continuous case as the limit of the appropriate discrete cases. We shall not pursue the continuous formalism, however.)

From this point of view it seems desirable to re-examine the previous equations from a completely matrix viewpoint. To do so, we first consider the algebra of matrices. We shall take a matrix to be defined as a rectangular (including square) array of numbers which generally are complex. To simplify the notation, we shall use the same symbol as the corresponding operator. In fact, we shall see that we are simply dealing with the matrix representation of operators. Thus an $m \times n$ matrix is

$$\|a_{ij}\| \equiv \mathbf{a} = \begin{pmatrix} a_{11} & a_{12} & \ldots & a_{1n} \\ a_{21} & a_{22} & \ldots & a_{2n} \\ \vdots & \vdots & & \vdots \\ a_{m1} & a_{m2} & \ldots & a_{mn} \end{pmatrix} . \tag{14.3.8}$$

In the previous cases, the matrices have been square (but infinite). A particularly important rectangular matrix is the column matrix,

$$\mathbf{x} = \begin{pmatrix} x_1 \\ x_2 \\ \vdots \\ x_m \end{pmatrix}, \tag{14.3.9}$$

which can be regarded as *a vector having m components.*

Now, equality of matrices is meaningful only for those which have the same numbers of rows and the same numbers of columns. For equal matrices,

$$\|a_{ij}\| = \mathbf{a} = \mathbf{b} = \|b_{ij}\|,$$

it is understood that corresponding elements are equal,

$$a_{ij} = b_{ij}, \qquad \text{all } i \text{ and } j. \tag{14.3.10}$$

The addition of two matrices (or more) likewise can have meaning only when the matrices have the same numbers of rows and the same numbers of columns. Then

$$\mathbf{a} + \mathbf{b} = \mathbf{c}$$

means

$$a_{ij} + b_{ij} = c_{ij}, \qquad \text{all } i \text{ and } j. \tag{14.3.11}$$

The product of two matrices is defined as follows. If

$$\mathbf{ab} = \mathbf{c},$$

then

$$(ab)_{ik} = \sum_j a_{ij} b_{jk} = c_{ik}, \tag{14.3.12}$$

the summation extending over all relevant values of j. From the definition of the matrix, the first index corresponds to the *row*, the second to the *column*. Hence the multiplication requires only that the number of columns of the first matrix equals the number of rows of the second. In general, therefore,

$$\mathbf{ab} \neq \mathbf{bc}.$$

There is no meaningful division of matrices, in general.

An important square matrix is the *identity* matrix:

$$\mathbf{I} = \begin{pmatrix} 1 & 0 & 0 & \dots \\ 0 & 1 & 0 & \dots \\ 0 & 0 & 1 & \dots \\ \vdots & \vdots & \vdots & \end{pmatrix}. \tag{14.3.13}$$

Clearly, when meaningful (i.e., **a** an appropriate square matrix),

$$\mathbf{Ia} = \mathbf{a} = \mathbf{aI}. \tag{14.3.14}$$

Multiplication by a constant changes all the elements of a matrix by a constant factor,

$$c\mathbf{a} = c\|a_{ij}\| = \|ca_{ij}\| = \mathbf{a}c. \tag{14.3.15}$$

The *transpose* of a matrix is an interchange of its columns and rows. Thus the transpose of **a** is

$$\tilde{\mathbf{a}} = \|(\tilde{a})_{ij}\| = \|a_{ji}\|. \tag{14.3.16}$$

The *adjoint* of a matrix is the complex conjugate of its transpose. Thus the adjoint of **a** is

$$\mathbf{a}^\dagger = \|(a^\dagger)_{ij}\| = \|(a_{ji})^*\|. \tag{14.3.17}$$

The adjoint of a product is the product of the adjoints in the reverse order:

$$(\mathbf{ab})^\dagger = \|(ab)^*_{ji}\| = \left\|\left(\sum_k (a_{jk})^*(b_{ki})^*\right)\right\|$$

$$= \|(b^\dagger)_{ij}\| \cdot \|(a^\dagger)_{ij}\| = \mathbf{b}^\dagger \mathbf{a}^\dagger. \tag{14.3.18}$$

An identical relation holds for the transpose of a product.

An *Hermitian* matrix is defined as a square matrix which is equal to its adjoint,

$$\mathbf{b} = b^\dagger. \tag{14.3.19}$$

A *unitary* matrix is a square one for which

$$\mathbf{cc}^\dagger = \mathbf{I}. \tag{14.3.20}$$

In these terms $\mathbf{c}^\dagger$ is the *inverse* of **c**. When **c** is a real square matrix, then its transpose and adjoint are the same. If it satisfies Eq. (14.3.20), it is termed an *orthogonal* matrix.

Now, Eq. (14.3.2) can be rendered in a matrix form. Defining a matrix of the a_{ij}'s offers no problem, so that we obtain

$$\mathbf{a}\boldsymbol{\alpha} = \|\alpha_i \, \delta_{ij}\|\mathbf{a}, \tag{14.3.21}$$

where

$$\boldsymbol{\alpha} \equiv \|\alpha_{ij}\|$$

and $\|\alpha_i \, \delta_{ij}\|$ is a diagonal matrix. The matrix representation of Eqs. (14.2.18) is seen to be

$$\mathbf{a}\mathbf{a}^\dagger = \mathbf{I}. \tag{14.3.22}$$

Hence, postmultiplication of Eq. (14.3.21) by $\mathbf{a}^\dagger$ yields

$$\mathbf{a}\boldsymbol{\alpha}\mathbf{a}^\dagger = \|\alpha_i\,\delta_{ij}\|. \tag{14.3.23}$$

Hence the eigenvalue problem reduces to one of finding a unitary matrix [i.e., a *transformation* matrix by Eq. (14.3.1)] which will render the matrix of the operator in a diagonal form. This unitary matrix is the one for which

$$\Phi = \begin{vmatrix} \phi_1 \\ \phi_2 \\ \vdots \end{vmatrix} = \mathbf{a} \begin{vmatrix} \psi_1 \\ \psi_2 \\ \vdots \end{vmatrix} = \mathbf{a}\Psi \tag{14.3.24}$$

is the matrix expression of Eq. (14.3.1). The set of eigenfunctions assumes here the role of components of a vector. However, note that the components here are *functions* and not numbers.

Having achieved an algebraic formulation of the eigenvalue problem, we now make the obvious extension that *all operators* (in the Schroedinger scheme) may be represented by *matrices* (in the Heisenberg scheme). It is assumed that operators corresponding to physical observables will have Hermitian matrices. (The analog of the wave function is the unitary matrix.) The actual numerical values of the elements of such matrices will depend, however, upon the basis of functions employed for their evaluation. Moreover, the values of the matrix elements will depend upon the precise form of the operator involved. It is here that the fusion of the Schroedinger and Heisenberg forms of (stationary) quantum mechanics becomes most useful: the Schroedinger theory facilitates the construction of the operators corresponding to physical observables; the Heisenberg theory facilitates the solution of the eigenvalue problem.

14.4 Symmetry properties of the Hamiltonian. Frequently problems of physical interest have Hamiltonians which are unchanged in form, referred to here as *invariant*, when changes are made in the variables of that operator. For example, if $V(x)$ is an even function of (x), it follows that replacing (x) in the Hamiltonian [e.g., Eq. (11.5.7)] by $(-y)$ leaves the Hamiltonian unaltered except for the change in the symbol referring to the variable. As another illustration, suppose that $V(x)$ is a periodic function of (x) with a period of λ. The substitution of $(y + n\lambda)$ for (x), with n an integer, will leave the Hamiltonian invariant apart from symbol. These illustrations exemplify what generally is referred to as the symmetry properties of the Hamiltonian. How these properties may be exploited in obtaining the solution of quantum-mechanical problems will be indicated in the present section.

At the outset, we emphasize that the symmetry properties of the Hamiltonian reflect an inherent symmetry possessed by the physical system under consideration. Thus, a system having the Hamiltonian of the first illustration corresponds to one which is *physically* identical with one for which the labeling of the coordinate system is inverted (i.e., reflected through the origin). A system having the Hamiltonian of the second illustration is presumed to have the identical physical behavior as any one for which the coordinate system is given an origin at any one of the potential-energy minima of the system. These remarks are intended to illustrate that the symmetry properties of the Hamiltonian determine, so to speak, the symmetry properties of the physical system. Clearly the relationship is a reciprocal one, and the symmetry properties of the physical system frequently are exploited to determine the symmetry properties of the Hamiltonian. Thus, if one is certain that a set of changes of the coordinates of a particular system renders that system into an equivalent indistinguishable system, one confidently may expect the corresponding operation to leave the Hamiltonian invariant as well.

For the mathematical formulation of the implications of the symmetry properties of the Hamiltonian, consider the first illustration in which

$$V(-x) = V(x). \tag{14.4.1}$$

Define the *reflection* operator, $\mathbf{R}$, such that

$$\mathbf{R}f(x) = f(-x). \tag{14.4.2}$$

Moreover, we shall take its effect upon operators to be the same,

$$\mathbf{R}f\left(x, \frac{d}{dx}\right) = f\left(-x, -\frac{d}{dx}\right). \tag{14.4.3}$$

As a result we may establish the important relation

$$\mathbf{R}f\left(x, \frac{d}{dx}\right)g\left(x, \frac{d}{dx}\right) = \left[\mathbf{R}f\left(x, \frac{d}{dx}\right)\right]\left[\mathbf{R}g\left(x, \frac{d}{dx}\right)\right], \tag{14.4.4}$$

where the brackets represent that result obtained from the application of $\mathbf{R}$ only to the operator (or function) included within the brackets. For the Hamiltonian of the first illustration, it is evident that

$$[\mathbf{RH}] = \mathbf{H},$$

so that for an arbitrary function,

$$\mathbf{RH}\phi = \mathbf{HR}\phi,$$

or since ϕ is arbitrary,

$$\mathbf{RH} = \mathbf{HR}. \tag{14.4.5}$$

Hence, Schroedinger's equation for this system yields

$$\mathbf{H}(\mathbf{R}\psi_n) = \epsilon_n(\mathbf{R}\psi_n). \tag{14.4.6}$$

Thus $(\mathbf{R}\psi_n)$ is an eigenfunction of $\mathbf{H}$ if ψ_n is such; moreover, they both have the same eigenvalue.

In the second illustration, we have a *displacement* operator, $\mathbf{\Delta}_n$, such that

$$\mathbf{\Delta}_n f(x) = f(x + n\lambda), \tag{14.4.7}$$

and for the pertinent Hamiltonian,

$$\mathbf{\Delta}_n \mathbf{H} = \mathbf{H}\,\mathbf{\Delta}_n, \tag{14.4.8}$$

as previously, so that $(\mathbf{\Delta}_n\psi_n)$ is an eigenfunction of $\mathbf{H}$ if ψ_n is such. Generally, operators which satisfy Eqs. (14.4.5) or (14.4.8) possess common eigenfunctions (Exercise 30, of Chapter 12). On this basis, the matrix representations of $\mathbf{H}$ and the pertinent commutable operator are both diagonal. In fact, it is relatively easy to show that any number of operators which commute with each other have matrices which may be diagonalized simultaneously. As a result, the symmetry operations assume an important role in solving the energy eigenvalue problem; for, by imposing more restrictions upon the eigenfunctions, less arbitrariness is possible in the latter, as we shall see.

In the interest of brevity, we proceed in a more-or-less abrupt manner to consider a *set* of symmetry operators which have the property that they each commute with the Hamiltonian. In addition, they are presumed to have the following algebraic properties:

(a) They comprise a finite set of operators;

(b) The product of any pair of these operators (including a power of an operator) is a member of that set;

(c) Each of these operators commutes with every member of the set;

(b) Multiplication of these operators satisfies an associative law;

(e) There exists among the set of operators the *inverse* of each member of the set; as a result the identity element is included in the set.

Any set of quantities satisfying the listed properties comprises a *finite Abelian group*. (Note that the requirement that each member of the set commute with the Hamiltonian is not a requisite for the definition of an Abelian group; we are only interested here in such Abelian groups of symmetry operations that commute with the Hamiltonian. The consideration of non-Abelian groups will not be undertaken here.)

While the study of the properties of a finite group can be facilitated by reference to one-dimensional Hamiltonians, the full power and importance of *group theory* becomes apparent for multidimensional systems. Nevertheless, we shall restrict our attention to the physical system described by Mathieu's equation, Eq. (14.2.24), and hope, thereby, to give explicit expression to the ideas of group theory in a simple but non-trivial manner. For this Schroedinger equation it is evident that the transformations

$$I: \theta \to 2\pi + \theta,$$

$$R_1: \theta \to 2\pi - \theta,$$

$$R_2: \theta \to \ \pi - \theta,$$ (14.4.9)

$$R_3: \theta \to \ \pi + \theta,$$

comprise an Abelian group of operators which leave the Hamiltonian of Eq. (14.2.24) invariant. The group properties are conveniently summarized in a multiplication table (the entries correspond to the product of an element listed in the left column postmultiplied by an element of the top row):

	I	R_1	R_2	R_3
I	I	R_1	R_2	R_3
R_1	R_1	I	R_3	R_2
R_2	R_2	R_3	I	R_1
R_3	R_3	R_2	R_1	I

(14.4.10)

From the multiplication table, we see that the sets of elements (I, R_n), (I, R_m, R_n) also form groups, which are termed *subgroups*. In the present case, but not in general, each element is its own inverse. Generally, some power other than the second is required for each element to be raised to for the result to equal the identity. The value of this power is termed the *order of the element*. The number of its elements is the *order of the group*. In the present case, all the elements except the identity are of second order; the order of the group is *four*. If the order of a particular element R is n, then the set of elements (I, R, R^2, R^{n-1}) comprises a *cyclic group* of order n.

Two elements of a group A, C which are related by

$$A = BCB^{-1},$$ (14.4.11)

where B^{-1} is the inverse of some element B of the group, are said to be *conjugate* to one another. As a result, two elements which are conjugate to a third element are conjugate to each other, for if

$$A = BCB^{-1}, \quad D = FCF^{-1}, \quad C = F^{-1}DF,$$

and

$$A = (BF^{-1})D(FB^{-1}).$$

Now, since

$$(BF^{-1})(FB^{-1}) = (FB^{-1})(BF^{-1}) = I,$$

so that

$$(BF^{-1})^{-1} = FB^{-1},$$

we have that A and D are conjugate to each other. As a result, we can determine all the elements which are conjugate to one particular element by simply evaluating Eq. (14.4.11) for fixed C and allowing the element B to be, in turn, each element of the group. Such a set of conjugate elements is termed a *class*. In the present case we see from the multiplication table that

$$IR_2I = R_2,$$

$$R_1R_2R_1 = R_3R_1 = R_2,$$

$$R_2R_2R_2 = IR_2 \quad = R_2,$$

$$R_3R_2R_3 = R_1R_3 = R_2,$$

so that R_2 forms a class by itself. It may be shown that each of the elements of the present illustration forms a class by itself although classes generally consist of more than a single element. The present case is typical of Abelian groups, for if each element of the group commutes, Eq. (14.4.11) becomes

$$A = BCB^{-1} = CBB^{-1} = C,$$

so that the only elements conjugate to each other are those which are self-conjugate. We note that a class is *not* a group, since it generally lacks the identity.

Consider, now, that the multiplication table, Eq. (14.4.10), may be satisfied by groups other than the set of symmetry operations of Eqs. (10.4.9). For example, the identifications

$$(I_1, R_1, R_2, R_3) \leftrightarrow (+1, -1, +1, -1) \qquad (14.4.12)$$

will evidently satisfy Eq. (14.4.10). Moreover, we can verify that

$$(I_1, R_1, R_2, R_3) \leftrightarrow (+1, +1, +1, +1),$$
$$\leftrightarrow (+1, +1, -1, -1), \qquad (14.4.13)$$
$$\leftrightarrow (+1, -1, -1, +1),$$

also satisfy Eq. (14.4.10). Equations (14.4.12) and (14.4.13) are the only identifications of *scalar* quantities with each of the group elements which

will satisfy the group multiplication table. However, it is easy to verify
that the identification

$$I \leftrightarrow \begin{pmatrix} 1 & 0 \\ 0 & 1 \end{pmatrix}, \qquad R_2 \leftrightarrow \begin{pmatrix} 1 & 0 \\ 0 & 1 \end{pmatrix},$$

$$\text{(14.4.14)}$$

$$R_1 \leftrightarrow \begin{pmatrix} -1 & 0 \\ 0 & -1 \end{pmatrix}, \qquad R_3 \leftrightarrow \begin{pmatrix} -1 & 0 \\ 0 & -1 \end{pmatrix},$$

also will satisfy Eq. (14.4.10). The identification of the elements of a
finite group with a set of square matrices satisfying the group multiplication properties is termed a *group representation*. Each group representation
may be regarded as a function of the elements of the group, which determines the identification made for each element. We have considered
only (1×1) and (2×2) matrix representations, but there are clearly
any number of other representations. However, if we restrict our attention to those representations [as in Eq. (14.4.14)] which are diagonal, it
is evident that there will be considerably fewer representations. For, if
$\Gamma(\mathbf{R}_n)$ is a representation of the group and $\mathbf{S}$ is an arbitrary unitary
transformation of the same degree (i.e., same number of rows, and columns,
as the matrices of the representation), then $\Gamma(\mathbf{SR}_n\mathbf{S}^\dagger)$ evidently will
satisfy the group multiplication properties. Only if the $\Gamma(\mathbf{R}_n)$-representa-
tion is diagonal will there be no additional representation thereby generated. (This requirement, however, cannot be imposed upon representations of non-Abelian groups, for the matrices of such representations
generally may not be diagonalized simultaneously.)

If we restrict our attention (for Abelian groups) only to diagonal representations, then we need consider only those of first degree. [Representa-
tions of higher degree are obtained simply from those of first degree and
an appropriate identity matrix as in Eqs. (14.4.14)]. In such cases, each
representation consists of a set of h numbers, where h is the order of the
group. Because this set is a group it must consist only of certain numbers
and their reciprocals. But then, since every power of an element of the
set also must be an element, the elements of the set may consist only of
numbers of unit magnitude. If these are restricted to real numbers, the
elements are ± 1.

How many different such representations are there? While we shall
not prove it, there are as many different representations as there are
elements of an Abelian group. Moreover, it may be shown then that the
different representations of the first degree are orthogonal. That is, if
$\chi^{(i)}(R_n)$ is the ith representation and $\chi^{(j)}(R_n)$ is the jth representation

of the *first* degree [e.g., Eqs. (14.4.13)] of an Abelian group, one can show that

$$\sum_{n=1}^{h} \chi^{(i)}(R_n)\chi^{(j)}(R_n) = h\,\delta_{ij}. \tag{14.4.15}$$

These relations can be generalized (with certain modifications) to non-Abelian groups: the $\chi^{(i)}$ are then related to the *characters* of certain irreducible representations, while the number of irreducible representations is equal to the number of classes.

For the present purposes, we are concerned with symmetry operations which may be assumed to have operators that satisfy eigenvalue relations. Because the symmetry operations are assumed to commute, it follows that their eigenvalues must satisfy the group multiplication table, Eq. (14.4.10). It is here that the relevance of group theory to quantum mechanics becomes emphasized, for the various *kinds* of eigenfunctions now can be related to the different representations; in fact, for each representation we have a *species* of eigenfunction which is completely characterized by the *characters*, $\chi^{(i)}$, of that representation. In the present illustration, we have four *species* of functions, ϕ_1, ϕ_2, ϕ_3, ϕ_4, such that the characters of each representation are the eigenvalues of the relevant symmetry operation. Thus, we take

$$I\phi_1 = \phi_1, \qquad R_1\phi_1 = \phi_1, \qquad R_2\phi_1 = \phi_1, \qquad R_3\phi_1 = \phi_1,$$

$$I\phi_2 = \phi_2, \qquad R_1\phi_2 = -\phi_2, \qquad R_2\phi_2 = \phi_2, \qquad R_3\phi_2 = -\phi_2, \text{ etc.}$$

This is summarized in a *character table:*

	I	R_1	R_2	R_3
ϕ_1	1	1	1	1
ϕ_2	1	-1	1	-1
ϕ_3	1	-1	-1	1
ϕ_4	1	1	-1	-1

$$(14.4.16)$$

As a result, the determination of matrix elements is simplified, for if we proceed to evaluate the matrix of the Hamiltonian of the system in terms of a basis of eigenfunctions of the symmetry operators, we observe that for any R satisfying Eq. (14.4.5),

$$H_{jk} = \int dx\,\phi_k^* \mathbf{H}\phi_j = \int dx\,\phi_k^* \mathbf{R}\mathbf{H}\mathbf{R}^{-1}\phi_j$$

$$= \int dx (\mathbf{R}^\dagger \phi_k)^* \mathbf{H}(\mathbf{R}^{-1}\phi_j).$$

Now, the symmetry operators illustrated here are *unitary* and correspond to the class of transformations which leave distances unaltered by their application. We shall restrict our considerations only to such symmetry operations. Then

$$\mathbf{R}^\dagger = \mathbf{R}^{-1},$$

by Eq. (14.3.20). Since $\mathbf{R}$ is any symmetry element of the group, it follows that H_{jk} vanishes whenever ϕ_j and ϕ_k belong to different species of eigenfunctions. As a result, the secular equation *factors* into separate secular equations for each species of eigenfunction.

We may illustrate what is involved by a more detailed examination of our modified Mathieu equation. The solutions for $\lambda = 0$ which have the symmetry of the system for $\lambda \neq 0$ are certain linear combinations of the solutions of Eq. (12.8.9). In fact, one can verify that the species of unperturbed functions are

$$\phi_1 \leftrightarrow \frac{1}{\sqrt{2\pi}}, \frac{1}{\sqrt{\pi}} \cos K\theta, \qquad K = 2, 4, \ldots,$$

$$\phi_2 \leftrightarrow \frac{1}{\sqrt{\pi}} \sin K\theta, \qquad K = 1, 3, \ldots,$$

$$\varphi_3 \leftrightarrow \frac{1}{\sqrt{\pi}} \sin K\theta, \qquad K = 2, 4, \ldots,$$

$$\phi_4 \leftrightarrow \frac{1}{\sqrt{\pi}} \cos K\theta, \qquad K = 1, 3, \ldots.$$

(14.4.17)

The functions in Eq. (14.2.30) are seen to be of this form. However, if we were to stop at the second-order perturbation theory, we would have no need to use the functions of Eq. (14.4.17). Nevertheless, the matrix of the Hamiltonian in Eq. (14.2.24) is simplified considerably by their use. Thus, it is immediately evident that the symmetry operators and the unperturbed Hamiltonian commute so that the matrix elements of the latter, determined with the functions of Eq. (14.4.17), are diagonal. The nondiagonal elements of the matrix can thus only arise from the integrals

$$\int_0^{2\pi} d\theta \phi_k \cos 2\theta \phi_j = \int_0^{2\pi} d\theta (\mathbf{R}_n \phi_k)(\mathbf{R}_n \cos 2\theta \, \phi_j)$$

$$= \int_0^{2\pi} d\theta (\mathbf{R}_n \phi_k)(\mathbf{R}_n \cos 2\theta)(\mathbf{R}_n \phi_j).$$

Now, for the symmetry operations of Eq. (14.4.9), $\cos 2\theta$ is left invariant, as noted originally. Hence

$$\mathbf{R}_n \cos 2\theta = \cos 2\theta,$$

and the integral must vanish whenever ϕ_j and ϕ_k correspond to different species.

In general, the integral

$$A_{jk} = \int dx\ \phi_k^* \mathbf{A} \phi_j$$

$$= \int dx (\mathbf{R}_n \phi_k)^* (\mathbf{R}_n \mathbf{A})(\mathbf{R}_n \phi_j)$$

$$= \frac{1}{h} \sum_{n=1}^{h} \int dx (\mathbf{R}_n \phi_k)^* (\mathbf{R}_n \mathbf{A})(\mathbf{R}_n \phi_j)$$

$$= \frac{1}{h} \sum_{n=1}^{h} \chi_n^{(j)} \chi_n^{(k)} \int dx\ \phi_k^* (\mathbf{R}_n \mathbf{A}) \phi_j,$$

where

$$\mathbf{R}_n \phi_j = \chi_n^{(j)} \phi_j.$$

In the case of interest,

$$\mathbf{R}_n \mathbf{A} = \chi_n(A) \mathbf{A},$$

so that

$$A_{jk} = \left[\frac{1}{h} \sum_{n=1}^{h} \chi_n^{(j)} \chi_n^{(k)} \chi_n(A) \right] \int dx\ \phi_k^* \mathbf{A} \phi_j. \qquad (14.4.18)$$

Nonvanishing A_{jk} require the bracketed term to be unity. Hence, to determine the species for which nonvanishing matrix elements may occur, one simply examines the sum of the products of the *characters* of the eigenfunctions and the operators. The nonzero value of the integral is not determined by this procedure.

14.5 Indistinguishability and exchange symmetry. As noted in Chapter 6, a basic discussion of the indistinguishability of identical systems requires the use of quantum mechanics. We are now in a position to consider the feature of indistinguishability from the aspect of its relation to the symmetry of the Hamiltonian of a many-particle system.

The results obtained thus far in our discussion of wave mechanics are, as already noted, capable of generalization to many dimensions and, thereby, to many particles. For our purposes it will suffice to consider a system of only two particles which are regarded as *identical*. The Hamiltonian for such a system will be of the form

$$\mathbf{H}(1, 2) = -\frac{\hbar^2}{2m}\nabla_1^2 - \frac{\hbar^2}{2m}\nabla_2^2 + V(\mathbf{r}_1, \mathbf{r}_2), \qquad (14.5.1)$$

where 1 and 2 refer to the two particles comprising the system, and we are tacitly assuming that the particles are *structureless*. (This means that we are disregarding any specification of the particles other than their configurational coordinates and conjugate momenta. As a consequence, the inclusion of *spin* for particles like electrons and protons is omitted entirely. The following results are easily augmented, when necessary, to include such specification.) Clearly, if the particles are to be regarded as indistinguishable, the labeling indicated in Eq. (14.5.1) is suspect: which particle is to be labeled "1" and which is to be labeled "2"? It seems apparent that no difference should result from an interchange of the labels, for the notation is misleading if otherwise is the case. As a consequence, we require that the Hamiltonian shall remain (physically) invariant when the labels are interchanged, *viz.*,

$$\mathbf{H}(1, 2) \equiv \mathbf{H}(2, 1). \qquad (14.5.2)$$

In this way, superficial differences (such as the order in which the labels appear) are rendered innocuous. Moreover, the *meaning of indistinguishability* is made explicit by Eq. (14.5.2).

As a result, we see that the Hamiltonian of the system is left invariant by the transformation

$$\mathbf{X}:\begin{pmatrix}1 \to 2\\2 \to 1\end{pmatrix}, \qquad (14.5.3)$$

and that

$$\mathbf{X}^2 = \mathbf{I}. \qquad (14.5.4)$$

In terms of the results of the previous section, the simultaneous eigenfunctions of $\mathbf{X}$ and $\mathbf{H}$ are either symmetric or antisymmetric with respect to the interchange of the coordinates of identical particles. (This statement is augmented easily to include spin, if necessary.) That is, we can find eigenfunctions such that

$$\mathbf{H}(1, 2)\psi_n(1, 2) = \epsilon_n\psi_n(1, 2),$$
$$\mathbf{X}\psi_n(1, 2) = \pm\psi_n(1, 2). \qquad (14.5.5)$$

The symmetric $(+)$ eigenfunctions are said to satisfy Bose-Einstein statistics, while the antisymmetric $(-)$ eigenfunctions are said to satisfy Fermi-Dirac statistics.

To relate the symmetry properties of the eigenfunctions to the statistical-mechanical restrictions we encountered in Chapter 6, we consider the situation in which the interaction between particles is negligibly small. That is, we take

$$V(\mathbf{r}_1, \mathbf{r}_2) = V(\mathbf{r}_1) + V(\mathbf{r}_2) + \lambda V'(\mathbf{r}_1, \mathbf{r}_2), \qquad (14.5.6)$$

where λ is an adjustable parameter in the sense of perturbation theory, and

$$\mathbf{X}V'(\mathbf{r}_1, \mathbf{r}_2) = V'(\mathbf{r}_1, \mathbf{r}_2). \qquad (14.5.7)$$

We shall be interested in values of $\lambda \ll 1$. Now, in these terms

$$\mathbf{H}(1, 2) = \mathbf{H}(1) + \mathbf{H}(2) + \lambda V'(\mathbf{r}_1, \mathbf{r}_2), \qquad (14.5.8)$$

with

$$\mathbf{H}(1) = -\frac{\hbar^2}{2m}\nabla_1^2 + V(\mathbf{r}_1), \qquad (14.5.9)$$

and similarly for $\mathbf{H}(2)$. If

$$\mathbf{H}(1)\phi_n(1) = \epsilon_n^0\phi_n(1), \qquad (14.5.10)$$

then the function

$$\Phi_{nm}(1, 2) = \phi_n(1)\phi_m(2),$$

will furnish an approximate eigenfunction for $\mathbf{H}(1, 2)$ when $\lambda \to 0$. However, to satisfy Eq. (14.5.5) we must note that

$$\Phi_{mn}(1, 2) = \phi_m(1)\phi_n(2)$$

also will serve as an approximate eigenfunction, as well as

$$\psi_{mn}(1, 2) = [\phi_n(1)\phi_m(2) \pm \phi_m(1)\phi_n(2)]. \qquad (14.5.11)$$

In contrast to the approximate eigenfunctions given previously, Eq. (14.5.11) is also an eigenfunction of $\mathbf{X}$. Accordingly, only unperturbed eigenfunctions of the form of Eq. (14.5.11) may be used.

The effect of the perturbation ($\lambda \neq 0$) easily may be seen to give rise to secular equations involving either antisymmetric unperturbed states or symmetric unperturbed states, but not both. The perturbation, so to speak, does not eliminate the exchange symmetry. As a result, we may proceed with the assurance that a "better" unperturbed approximation will not subsequently alter our conclusions. (In terms of the succeeding chapter, the symmetry property is a constant of the motion.)

Upon examination of Eq. (14.5.11) we discern a behavior for the symmetric functions which is different from that for the antisymmetric functions. No restrictions whatever are placed upon m and n in the former case. As a consequence, each particle of the identical pair may be said to have allowed occupancy of any (unperturbed) state whatever. This statement is easily extended to more than a pair of identical particles and forms the basis for the counting employed in the Bose-Einstein statistics of Chapter 6.

By contrast, the antisymmetric states of Eq. (14.5.11) may not have m and n the same; otherwise the unperturbed function vanishes identically. As a result, no more than a single particle may be said to occupy a given state, a statement which also may be extended to any number of identical particles. This restriction can be seen to be incorporated in the Fermi-Dirac statistics of Chapter 6.

One may question if any specific kind of particle satisfies the restrictions which have been noted. This can be answered only by experiment, and it is found that basic particles such as electrons, protons, and neutrons satisfy the Fermi-Dirac statistics; photons, however, satisfy Bose-Einstein statistics. Because of the fact that molecular systems of interest to the chemist involve electrons, the effect of the Fermi-Dirac statistics is especially important in the theoretical description of atomic and molecular structure. In this subject the restriction noted (suitably augmented for electron spin) is referred to as the *Pauli exclusion principle*, which has the important practical effect of restricting the unperturbed wave functions for an electronic system to an enormously smaller set of possibilities.

14.6 Summary. The equivalence between the wave mechanics of Schroedinger and the matrix mechanics of Heisenberg for stationary states has been the subject of the present chapter. However, the means for approximating solutions to the eigenvalue problem have been emphasized, rather than a precise demonstration of the equivalence of the two systems of mechanics.

The variational method of estimating eigenvalues and eigenfunctions by minimizing the expectation value of the energy is discussed. The series perturbation theory due to Rayleigh and Schroedinger is considered, the second-order theory being carried out for nondegenerate states. The first-order theory for degenerate states is examined, and the solution for the eigenvalues expressed in terms of the secular equation.

The algebraic formulation of the eigenvalue problem is carried out through the device of associating a matrix representation with each operator. The algebra of matrices is considered briefly. The symmetry properties of the Hamiltonian are discussed in connection with the practical problems of solving secular equations. The rudiments of group theory are considered, particularly as applicable to Abelian groups. The relevance of the symmetry properties to the choice of unperturbed bases in perturbation theory is discussed, and the use of invariance properties to evaluate integrals is described.

The symmetry properties of the Hamiltonian of identical particles is discussed. Thereby, the Bose-Einstein and Fermi-Dirac statistics are obtained corresponding to species of energy eigenfunctions which are symmetric and antisymmetric, respectively, with respect to interchange of identical particles. The Pauli exclusion principle for systems of electrons is related to these properties.

EXERCISES

1. Obtain the "best" eigenvalue for the ground state of the linear harmonic oscillator, using a polynomial of second degree multiplied by an exponential which is linear in the *magnitude* of the displacement from equilibrium. Compare with the exact eigenvalue.

2. Apply the series perturbation theory to second-order to the problem of Exercise 16 of Chapter 12 and obtain the first three energy eigenvalues. Compare with the exact solution. Evaluate the first-order wave functions and compare with the exact solutions.

3. Use various polynomials in the variable and apply the variational method to obtain estimates for the lowest eigenvalue of Legendre's equation:

$$(1 - u^2) \frac{d^2y}{du^2} - 2u \frac{dy}{du} + \lambda y = 0.$$

4. Verify Eq. (14.2.11).

5. Verify Eq. (14.2.14).

6. Show that C_{nm} of Eq. (14.2.13) vanishes for real wave functions. Show that real wave functions may be assumed for distinct eigenvalues.

7. Determine the second-order correction to the wave functions, assuming nondegenerate eigenvalues.

8. Show that the wave functions correct to first order are orthonormal to (but not including) second order.

9. Show that Eq. (14.2.26) results from the secular equation of Eq. (14.2.17), and no other degeneracy need be considered.

10. Verify Eqs. (14.2.29).

11. Diagonalize the matrix

$$\begin{pmatrix} 1 & 2 \\ 2 & -1 \end{pmatrix}$$

and determine the matrix of the orthogonal transformation which will diagonalize it.

12. Diagonalize the matrix

$$\begin{pmatrix} 1 & 2 & 0 \\ 2 & -1 & 3 \\ 0 & 3 & 0 \end{pmatrix}$$

and determine the matrix of the orthogonal transformation which will diagonalize it.

13. Show that the unitary transformation of a three-dimensional vector leaves invariant the sum of the squares of the vector components. Show also that scalar products are left invariant by such a transformation. Extend to multidimensional vectors.

14. Show that the sum of the diagonal elements (the so-called *trace*) of a matrix is invariant to a unitary transformation of the matrix [as in Eq. (14.3.23).]

15. Verify Eq. (14.3.18).

16. Show that Hermitian operators must have Hermitian matrix representations.

17. Verify Eqs. (14.4.4) and (14.4.8).

18. Prove that Hermitian matrices which commute may be diagonalized simultaneously by the same unitary transformation.

19. Obtain the multiplication table Eq. (14.4.10).

20. Determine the symmetry of the linear harmonic oscillator, and establish the *species* of its eigenfunctions. Do this also for the particle in a box.

21. Show that the eigenvalues of the operators of an Abelian group must satisfy the group multiplication properties.

22. Verify Eqs. (14.4.17).

23. Discuss a means for approximating the next-to-the-lowest eigenvalue, using a variational method.

24. Use the variational method to obtain a "best" approximation for the lowest eigenvalue of Eq. (14.2.24).

25. Verify Eqs. (14.2.7).

26. Using matrix multiplication verify that $2 \sin \theta \cos \theta = \sin 2\theta$.

27. Construct the matrix representation for the kinetic energy of the linear harmonic oscillator in that representation which diagonalizes the total energy. Do likewise for the potential energy.

28. Determine the matrix for the momentum of a linear harmonic oscillator in terms of a basis of energy eigenfunctions. Do likewise for the matrix of displacement from the equilibrium position. Hence verify the commutation relation of Heisenberg, Eq. (12.2.3), by direct matrix multiplication.

29. In analogy with the illustration in the text, determine the symmetry operators which leave the Hamiltonian of Eq. (14.2.20) invariant and discuss the (symmetry) species of the eigenfunctions of the latter.

30. Use Eq. (14.4.18) to verify Eq. (14.4.15).

31. Devise a procedure for constructing an appropriate set of unperturbed wave functions for three identical particles which satisfy Fermi-Dirac statistics.

32. Devise a procedure for constructing an appropriate set of unperturbed wave functions for four particles, two of which satisfy Fermi-Dirac statistics and two of which satisfy Bose-Einstein statistics.

33. Show that square matrices operating upon column matrices of the form of Eq. (14.3.9) satisfy the algebra of linear operators discussed in Section 11.6.

CHAPTER 15

NONSTATIONARY STATES

15.1 Schroedinger's time-dependent equation. The previous chapters have emphasized the stationary states and the Schroedinger equation that determines these states. For equilibrium situations nothing more needs to be said to relate the properties of a macroscopic system to those of the constituent microscopic subsystems. However, as we have already noted, the dynamical behavior of systems is of interest in describing phenomena other than those involved in equilibrium situations. We shall indicate in the present chapter how such phenomena may be treated.

We begin with a formal examination of the time-dependent wave function $\Psi(x, t)$. If we imagine that this function can be represented by a power series in t, we would have

$$\Psi(x, t) = \sum_{n=0}^{\infty} \frac{t^n}{n!} f_n(x). \tag{15.1.1}$$

But, now we can obtain that

$$f_n(x) = \lim_{t \to 0} \frac{\partial^n}{\partial t^n} \Psi(x, t). \tag{15.1.2}$$

Making use of Schroedinger's time-dependent equation, Eq. (11.6.10) (and, of course, its generalization to many dimensions) for conditions where the Hamiltonian does not depend explicitly upon the time,

$$\frac{\partial^n}{\partial t^n} \Psi(x, t) = \left(\frac{1}{i\hbar}\right)^n \mathbf{H}^n \Psi(x, t).$$

Hence, Eq. (15.1.2) becomes

$$f_n(x) = \left(\frac{1}{i\hbar}\right)^n \mathbf{H}^n \Psi(x, 0), \tag{15.1.3}$$

and

$$\Psi(x, t) = \sum_{n=0}^{\infty} \frac{t^n}{n!} \left(\frac{1}{i\hbar}\right)^n \mathbf{H}^n \Psi(x, 0). \tag{15.1.4}$$

Clearly, $\Psi(x, 0)$ is the initial value of the wave function, which is arbitrary. (It must be supposed, however, that it satisfies the appropriate boundary conditions.)

275

In formal terms, we may express the series as an exponential operator, so that

$$\Psi(x, t) = (e^{-it\mathbf{H}/\hbar})\Psi(x, 0). \qquad (15.1.5)$$

When $\Psi(x, 0)$ is an eigenfunction of $\mathbf{H}$, Eq. (12.1.7) obtains. The operator $e^{-it\mathbf{H}/\hbar}$ is a unitary operator and, clearly,

$$(e^{-it\mathbf{H}/\hbar})(e^{-it\mathbf{H}/\hbar})^{\dagger} = 1. \qquad (15.1.6)$$

From this we see that the expectation value of a physical observable with the operator $\boldsymbol{\alpha}$ as given by Eq. (11.6.1) becomes

$$E_{\Psi}(\boldsymbol{\alpha}) = \frac{\int dx \Psi^*(x, 0) \{e^{it\mathbf{H}/\hbar}\boldsymbol{\alpha} e^{-it\mathbf{H}/\hbar}\}\Psi(x, 0)}{\int dx \Psi^*(x, 0)\Psi(x, 0)}, \qquad (15.1.7)$$

because of the fact that

$$\int dx \, (e^{-it\mathbf{H}/\hbar}f)^*g = \sum_{n=0}^{\infty} \frac{t^n}{n!} \int dx \left[\left(\frac{1}{i\hbar}\mathbf{H}\right)^n f\right]^* g$$

$$= \sum_{n=0}^{\infty} \frac{t^n}{n!} \left(\frac{i}{\hbar}\right)^n \int dx (\mathbf{H}^n f)^* g$$

$$= \sum_{n=0}^{\infty} \frac{t^n}{n!} \left(\frac{i}{\hbar}\right)^n \int dx \, f^*(\mathbf{H}^n g)$$

$$= \int dx \, f^*(e^{it\mathbf{H}/\hbar}g).$$

The expectation value of Eq. (15.1.7) is now explicitly determined by the initial value of the wave function.

15.2 Heisenberg's equation of motion. The relationship between Schroedinger's wave mechanics and Heisenberg's matrix mechanics acquires an additional tie from the following consideration. In the Heisenberg scheme, we regard the operator in braces in Eq. (15.1.7) as that corresponding to the physical observable; the state functions are assumed to be time-independent. In the Schroedinger scheme, of course, the temporally dependent roles are inverted.

If we identify

$$\mathbf{A}(t) \equiv e^{it\mathbf{H}/\hbar}\boldsymbol{\alpha}(t)e^{-it\mathbf{H}/\hbar}, \qquad (15.2.1)$$

$$\frac{\partial \mathbf{A}(t)}{\partial t} \equiv e^{it\mathbf{H}/\hbar}\frac{\partial \boldsymbol{\alpha}(t)}{\partial t}e^{-it\mathbf{H}/\hbar}, \qquad (15.2.2)$$

then we see that

$$E_{\Psi(x,t)}[\boldsymbol{\alpha}(t)] \equiv E_{\Psi(x,0)}[\mathbf{A}(t)]. \tag{15.2.3}$$

We may easily obtain the time derivative of $\mathbf{A}(t)$ by assuming that the derivative of a product is obtained by the usual rule for differentiation, but that the factors appear in their original order. Thus

$$\frac{d}{dx}\,\mathbf{A}(x)\mathbf{B}(x) = \mathbf{A}(x)\,\frac{d\mathbf{B}(x)}{dx} + \frac{d\mathbf{A}(x)}{dx}\,\mathbf{B}(x), \qquad \text{etc.}$$

Hence, one can show that

$$\frac{d}{dt}\,\mathbf{A}(t) = \left(\frac{i}{\hbar}\right)[\mathbf{H}\mathbf{A}(t) - \mathbf{A}(t)\mathbf{H}] + \frac{\partial\mathbf{A}(t)}{\partial t}, \tag{15.2.4}$$

which is the Heisenberg *equation of motion* for the operator of a physical observable. For operators which do not depend explicitly upon time, we obtain

$$i\hbar\frac{d}{dt}\,\mathbf{A}(t) = \mathbf{A}(t)\mathbf{H} - \mathbf{H}\mathbf{A}(t), \tag{15.2.5}$$

which can be constant in time only if the right side vanishes. But, by Eq. (15.2.1), this implies that $\boldsymbol{\alpha}$ and $\mathbf{H}$ *commute*. Thus observables which are *constants of the motion* commute with the Hamiltonian, and vice versa.

We can obtain some insight into the Heisenberg scheme by examining the equation of motion for position and momentum. We can obtain for a one-dimensional Hamiltonian

$$i\hbar\,\frac{d\mathbf{p}(t)}{dt} = \mathbf{p}(t)\mathbf{H} - \mathbf{H}\mathbf{p}(t).$$

If we make use of Eq. (15.2.1) we obtain ultimately

$$i\hbar\,\frac{d\mathbf{p}(t)}{dt} = e^{it\mathbf{H}/\hbar}(\mathbf{p}V - V\mathbf{p})e^{-it\mathbf{H}/\hbar}$$

$$= \frac{\hbar}{i}\,e^{it\mathbf{H}/\hbar}\,\frac{dV}{dx}\,e^{-it\mathbf{H}/\hbar},$$

using the Schroedinger representation, or

$$\frac{d\mathbf{p}(t)}{dt} = -e^{it\mathbf{H}/\hbar}\,\frac{dV}{dx}\,e^{-it\mathbf{H}/\hbar}$$

$$\equiv -\left(\frac{d\mathbf{V}}{d\mathbf{x}}\right)(t). \tag{15.2.6}$$

Now, we obtain also the *velocity* in the Heisenberg scheme

$$\frac{d\mathbf{x}(t)}{dt} = \frac{1}{m}\,\mathbf{p}(t), \qquad (15.2.7)$$

where again the Schroedinger representation for the operators has been used.

Equations (15.2.6) and (15.2.7) are the operator analogs of the Hamiltonian equations of motion of a classically described system. That is, the behavior of a system in a specified initial state may be said to satisfy the classical equations of motion in the sense of expectation values. This emphasizes a connection between the wave- or quantum-mechanical and the classical-mechanical, but the relation must not be overemphasized. Thus, to illustrate, the expectation value of the potential energy does not depend explicitly upon the expectation value of position. Knowing how the latter changes in time, which is the utility of Eq. (15.2.7), will not yield directly the variation of the expectation value of the potential energy with time. In the classical case, of course, a knowledge of the potential-energy function and the velocity will yield directly the time derivative of the potential energy. (We are assuming here that the latter is an explicit function of position alone. Generalization is easy when such is not the case.)

We may indicate that a convenient starting point for the quantum-mechanics is provided by Eq. (15.2.4) and the quantum conditions of Chapter 12. We need also to define the Hamiltonian. As a result, one may exploit the Heisenberg scheme to construct operators for physical observables. It must be apparent, however, that some basic assumption must be introduced which permits one to deal with more than just the equations mentioned. This generalization due to Dirac is motivated by a comparison between the equation of motion of the operator of a physical observable and its classical counterpart. In the latter instance, a quantity A is regarded as a function of position, conjugate momentum, and time. Thus (for one-dimensional motion)

$$\frac{dA(x, p, t)}{dt} = \frac{\partial A(x, p, t)}{\partial t} + \frac{\partial A(x, p, t)}{\partial x}\frac{dx}{dt} + \frac{\partial A(x, p, t)}{\partial p}\frac{dp}{dt}.$$

With the classical equations of motion, analogous to Eqs. (15.2.6) and (15.2.7)

$$\frac{dx}{dt} = \frac{1}{m}\,p = \frac{\partial H}{\partial p}, \qquad \frac{dp}{dt} = -\frac{\partial V}{\partial x} = -\frac{\partial H}{\partial x},$$

we obtain

$$\frac{dA(x, p, t)}{dt} = \frac{\partial A(x, p, t)}{\partial t} + \left(\frac{\partial A}{\partial x}\frac{\partial H}{\partial p} - \frac{\partial H}{\partial x}\frac{\partial A}{\partial p}\right). \qquad (15.2.8)$$

The quantity in large parentheses is the one-dimensional classical *Poisson bracket* of A and H. It is defined for any two variables as

$$(u, v) = \frac{\partial u}{\partial x} \frac{\partial v}{\partial p} - \frac{\partial v}{\partial x} \frac{\partial u}{\partial p}. \tag{15.2.9}$$

(The extension to more dimensions is carried out simply by summing over all pairs of conjugate variables.) A comparison of Eqs. (15.2.4), (15.2.8), and (15.2.9) prompts the assumption that the classical Poisson bracket may be *identified* with the commutator

$$(u, v) \leftrightarrow \frac{1}{i\hbar} (\mathbf{uv} - \mathbf{vu}) \equiv \frac{1}{i\hbar} [\mathbf{u}, \mathbf{v}], \tag{15.2.10}$$

where **u** and **v** are the quantum-mechanical operators corresponding to the classical quantities u and v respectively. (The commutator is defined by the *square* bracket; the choice of constant factor is only justified by a final comparison with experiment.)

We may note that the classical Poisson bracket

$$(x_j, p_k) = \delta_{jk}, \tag{15.2.11}$$

so that Eq. (15.2.10) yields

$$\mathbf{x}_j\mathbf{p}_k - \mathbf{p}_k\mathbf{x}_j = i\hbar\, \delta_{jk},$$

which is the many-dimensional extension of Eq. (12.2.3). Hence, even the quantum conditions need not be introduced explicitly. In fact, Eq. (15.2.10) may be regarded as the basic equation of quantum mechanics. However, we shall not pursue these matters further.

15.3 Time-dependent perturbation theory of Dirac. As in the case of stationary states, the precise solution of Schroedinger's time-dependent equation is generally limited to simple cases. Clearly, if the eigenfunctions of the relevant Hamiltonian are known (i.e., the stationary states) the time-dependent solutions are readily determined.

For most systems of physical interest, this situation is not achieved. Moreover, there are some physical situations where the stationary states are of no interest. Such cases involve time-dependent Hamiltonians; then, Eq. (15.1.4) does *not* obtain. (We may recognize that Schroedinger's time-dependent equation is not separable under these conditions.) We shall be particularly concerned with an approximation method (due to Dirac) which pertains to time-dependent Hamiltonians.

We consider a Hamiltonian, as in Eq. (14.2.1)

$$\mathbf{H} = \mathbf{H}_0 + \lambda\mathbf{H}_1(t), \tag{15.3.1}$$

but now allow the perturbation to be explicitly dependent on the time; the unperturbed Hamiltonian $\mathbf{H}_0$ is not explicitly dependent on the time. It may be presumed that the eigenfunctions and eigenvalues of $\mathbf{H}_0$ are known,

$$\mathbf{H}_0\psi_n^0(x) = \epsilon_n^0\psi_n(x). \tag{15.3.2}$$

In these terms, the solution of Eq. (11.6.10) may be taken as

$$\Psi(x, t) = \sum_{n=0}^{\infty} C_n(t)\psi_n^0(x)e^{-i\epsilon_n^0 t/\hbar}, \tag{15.3.3}$$

where we have used the superposition principle to express $\Psi(x, t)$ in terms of a basis of orthonormal, time-dependent eigenfunctions of $\mathbf{H}_0$. Clearly,

$$C_m(t) = e^{i\epsilon_m^0 t/\hbar} \int dx \, [\psi_m^0(x)]^*\Psi(x, t). \tag{15.3.4}$$

The substitution of this expression into Eq. (15.3.3) will yield an integral equation for $\Psi(x, t)$. We shall consider only those time-dependent wave functions which are normalized to unity, viz.,

$$\int dx \Psi^*(x, t)\Psi(x, t) = \sum_{n=0}^{\infty} C_n^*(t)C_n(t) = 1, \tag{15.3.5}$$

by Eq. (15.3.3).

However, we shall examine the differential equation for the C's. We obtain

$$i\hbar \frac{dC_m(t)}{dt} = -\epsilon_m^0 C_m(t) + e^{i\epsilon_m^0 t/\hbar} \int dx \, [\psi_m^0(x)] \left[i\hbar \frac{\partial \Psi}{\partial t}(x, t) \right]$$

$$= -\epsilon_m^0 C_m(t) + e^{i\epsilon_m^0 t/\hbar} \int dx \, (\psi_m^0)^*(\mathbf{H}_0 + \lambda\mathbf{H}_1)\Psi(x, t)$$

$$= \lambda e^{i\epsilon_m^0 t/\hbar} \int dx \, (\psi_m^0)^*\mathbf{H}_1\Psi(x, t). \tag{15.3.6}$$

Substitution of Eq. (15.3.3) yields

$$i\hbar\dot{C}_m(t) = \lambda \sum_{n=0}^{\infty} C_n(t)e^{-i(\epsilon_n^0 - \epsilon_m^0)t/\hbar}\mathbf{H}'_{nm}(t), \tag{15.3.7}$$

with

$$H'_{nm}(t) = \int dx \, [\psi_m^0(x)]^*\mathbf{H}_1(x, t)\psi_n^0(x).$$

Equations (15.3.7) comprise a set of coupled, linear, first-order differential equations for the C's. A solution of these equations will entail some approximations. To guide us in obtaining a convenient approximation let us assume a *form* for the C's with regard to the dependence on λ. In fact, let

$$C_n(t) = \sum_{r=0}^{\infty} \lambda^r C_n^{(r)}(t), \tag{15.3.8}$$

and substitute into Eq. (15.3.7). Combining terms with the same power of λ, the coefficients of each power of λ of the resulting series thus vanishing, we obtain

$$i\hbar \dot{C}_m^{(r+1)}(t) - \sum_{n=0}^{\infty} C_n^{(r)}(t) e^{-i(\epsilon_n^0 - \epsilon_m^0)t/\hbar} H'_{nm}(t), \tag{15.3.9}$$

so that integration yields for the $(r + 1)$st-order coefficient

$$i\hbar[C_m^{(r+1)}(t) - C_m^{(r+1)}(0)] = \sum_{n=0}^{\infty} \int_0^t d\tau C_n^{(r)}(\tau) e^{-i(\epsilon_n^0 - \epsilon_m^0)\tau/\hbar} H'_{nm}(\tau). \tag{15.3.10}$$

Equations (15.3.10) comprise the formal solution of Schroedinger's time-dependent equation. It is readily seen that the zeroth-order (i.e., $r = 0$) values of the C's must be specified *a priori;* moreover, by Eq. (15.3.10), they are constant in time since by Eq. (15.3.8) we may take negative-order C's to be null. We shall consider only the case in which all the zeroth-order values except one are null; in that case the remaining value must be a number of magnitude unity, by Eq. (15.3.5).

We take

$$C_n^{(0)} = \delta_{mn}. \tag{15.3.11}$$

Moreover, we simplify matters by taking

$$C_n^{(r)}(0) = 0, \quad \text{all } n, \text{ all } r > 0. \tag{15.3.12}$$

This choice corresponds to the initial condition (which we must specify)

$$\lim_{t \to 0} \Psi(x, t) = \psi_m^{(0)}(x).$$

With these simplifications and no undue loss of generality, we obtain the *first-order* contribution to the C's:

$$C_n^{(1)}(t) = \frac{1}{i\hbar} \int_0^t d\tau e^{-i(\epsilon_m^0 - \epsilon_n^0)\tau/\hbar} H'_{mn}(\tau). \tag{15.3.13}$$

These equations, upon being substituted into Eq. (15.3.10), give the *second-order* contribution to the C's:

$$C_n^{(2)}(t) = -\frac{1}{\hbar^2} \sum_{n=0}^{\infty} \int_0^t d\tau_1 H'_{nm}(\tau_1) e^{-i(\epsilon_n^0 - \epsilon_m^0)\tau_1/\hbar}$$

$$\times \int_0^{\tau_1} d\tau e^{-i(\epsilon_m^0 - \epsilon_n^0)\tau/\hbar} H'_{mn}(\tau). \qquad (15.3.14)$$

Hence, we are in a position to approximate the C's to order λ^2. However, unless $C_n^{(1)}(t)$ vanishes, we shall generally not use the second-order of approximation.

We are interested in an explicit form for $C_n^{(1)}(t)$. Hence we must specify $\mathbf{H}_1(t)$. For many problems of interest the perturbation operator can be restricted to the following form:

$$\mathbf{H}_1(t) = 0, \qquad t < 0,$$

$$= \mathbf{H}_1(x) \cos(2\pi\nu t + \alpha), \qquad t \geq 0, \qquad (15.3.15)$$

where α here is a phase constant. This form includes the case for a discontinuous change in the Hamiltonian, when the frequency ν is set equal to zero. With this form, we obtain from Eq. (15.3.13)

$$C_n^{(1)}(t) = \frac{H'_{mn}(0)}{i\hbar} \int_0^t d\tau e^{-i(\epsilon_m^0 - \epsilon_n^0)\tau/\hbar} \cos(2\pi\nu\tau + \alpha)$$

$$= H'_{mn}(0) \left[e^{-i\alpha} \frac{e^{-i(\epsilon_m^0 - \epsilon_n^0 + h\nu)t/\hbar} - 1}{2(\epsilon_m^0 - \epsilon_n^0 + h\nu)} + e^{i\alpha} \frac{e^{-i(\epsilon_m^0 - \epsilon_n^0 - h\nu)t/\hbar} - 1}{2(\epsilon_m^0 - \epsilon_n^0 - h\nu)} \right].$$

$$(15.3.16)$$

15.4 Transition probabilities. Having indicated how the Schroedinger time-dependent equation may be solved in an iterative manner, we are in a position to discuss the physical significance of the solutions and their approximations.

We begin by inquiring into the physical meaning of the C's. If we recall the probability interpretation of the constant coefficients for non-normalizable wave functions (Sections 12.4 and 13.1), we recognize that the C's assume a similar role. We *interpret* the C's to mean the following: $|C_n(t)|^2$ is the probability of finding the system in the state with the wave function $\psi_n^0(x)e^{-i\epsilon_n^0 t/\hbar}$. This interpretation seems a reasonable one when considered from a measurement viewpoint that involves reducing the Hamiltonian to its original value (i.e., "before" the perturbation was imposed) at the time of measurement. Then the coefficients in Eq. (15.3.3) become constant in time, and the measurement process may be imagined as selecting the appropriate eigenstate with the indicated probability.

Under the circumstances of usual interest which we have introduced already, the initial values of all but one of the coefficients are zero. Then, as time develops, nonzero values are obtained. It is convenient to regard the system as having made a transition from the (unperturbed) state m to the (unperturbed) state n (in the notation of the previous section). For those coefficients with zero initial values the quantity $|C_n(t)|^2$ is termed the *transition probability*. The results of the previous section may be directed toward the evaluation of the transition probabilities. Then, if we consider the result which obtains when the transition probability is averaged over the phase constant (see Chapter 11), we obtain, for $n \neq m$,

$$\overline{|C_n^{(1)}(t)|^2} = |H'_{mn}(0)|^2 \left\{ \frac{1 - \cos\left[(\epsilon_m^0 - \epsilon_n^0 + h\nu)t/\hbar\right]}{2(\epsilon_m^0 - \epsilon_n^0 + h\nu)^2} \right.$$
$$\left. + \frac{1 - \cos\left[(\epsilon_m^0 - \epsilon_n^0 - h\nu)t/\hbar\right]}{2(\epsilon_m^0 - \epsilon_n^0 - h\nu)^2} \right\}. \qquad (15.4.1)$$

[The phase averaging is introduced here in order to eliminate a cross-product term arising from Eq. (15.3.10), thereby simplifying the resulting expression for the transition probability. However, in any comparison with experiment, the transition probability would be averaged over an appropriate ensemble of systems in which some specification of the phases is necessary. In the present context we are exploiting the condition of "random phase" referred to in Chapter 11.]

From the normalization condition, Eq. (15.3.5), we obtain

$$\overline{|C_m^{(1)}(t)|^2} = 1 - \sum_{n \neq m} \overline{|C_n^{(1)}(t)|^2}. \qquad (15.4.2)$$

When Eq. (15.4.1) is used with zero frequency, the result is one-half the result which would be obtained when the function periodic in time is suppressed. This factor arises from the phase average of the square of the function, $\cos^2 \alpha$. Hence for temporally discontinuous perturbations,

$$\mathbf{H}_1(t) = 0, \qquad t < 0,$$
$$= \mathbf{H}_1(x), \qquad t \geq 0, \qquad (15.4.3)$$

we obtain, for $n \neq m$,

$$|C_n^{(1)}(t)|^2 = 2|H'_{mn}(0)|^2 \left\{ \frac{1 - \cos\left[(\epsilon_m^0 - \epsilon_n^0)t/\hbar\right]}{(\epsilon_m^0 - \epsilon_n^0)^2} \right\}. \qquad (15.4.4)$$

Equation (15.4.2) may be used with this approximation for $|C_n^{(1)}(t)|^2$. In either of Eqs. (15.4.1) or (15.4.4) we have to deal with the function

$$\frac{1 - \cos\left[(\epsilon_m^0 - \epsilon_n^0 \pm h\nu)t/\hbar\right]}{(\epsilon_m^0 - \epsilon_n^0 \pm h\nu)^2} = 2\,\frac{\sin^2\left[(\epsilon_m^0 - \epsilon_n^0 \pm h\nu)t/2\hbar\right]}{(\epsilon_m^0 - \epsilon_n^0 \pm h\nu)^2}. \tag{15.4.5}$$

For large values of $|\epsilon_m^0 - \epsilon_n^0 \pm h\nu|$ this function will be very small. For very small values,

$$\lim_{x \to 0} \frac{\sin^2 (xt/2\hbar)}{x^2} = \frac{4t^2}{\hbar^2}, \tag{15.4.6}$$

which can be enormously large for sufficiently large values of t. As a result, we see that transitions will occur with a predominant likelihood, *if they occur at all*, whenever

$$h\nu = \pm(\epsilon_m^0 - \epsilon_n^0) > 0, \tag{15.4.7}$$

which is the celebrated *Bohr frequency condition*. When $(\epsilon_n^0 - \epsilon_m^0) > 0$, the negative sign is used and one refers to the *absorption* of energy by the system; when $(\epsilon_n^0 - \epsilon_m^0) < 0$, the positive sign is used and one refers to the *emission* of energy. These processes refer, of course, to radiation absorbed or emitted, but this is not obvious from our considerations. It is necessary to suppose that Eq. (15.3.15) approximates the interaction of radiation with our system in order to justify the interpretation which has been made.

When the frequency is set equal to zero, corresponding to the perturbation in Eq. (15.4.3), we obtain the condition of conservation of energy in the transition, $\epsilon_n^0 = \epsilon_m^0$. However, when the energy $h\nu$ is taken into account (see, for example, Section 11.5), we have the general condition of energy conservation, but from our discussion we see that this condition is satisfied only in the sense of transitions otherwise being extremely improbable (but not impossible).

In particular cases of interest, we may often encounter the situation that the sum in Eq. (15.4.2) is of interest, or that the perturbation does not consist of a single frequency. Moreover, in the former of these instances, the summation over final energy states is justifiably replaced by an integration. In the latter case we generally have to determine

$$\int_0^\infty d\nu\, g(\nu)\overline{|C_n^{(1)}(t)|^2} = |H'_{mn}(0)|^2 \int_0^\infty d\nu\, g(\nu)\,\frac{\sin^2\left[(\epsilon_m^0 - \epsilon_n^0 + h\nu)t/2\hbar\right]}{(\epsilon_m^0 - \epsilon_n^0 + h\nu)^2}$$

$$+ |H'_{mn}(0)|^2 \int_0^\infty d\nu\, g(\nu)\,\frac{\sin^2\left[(\epsilon_m^0 - \epsilon_n^0 - h\nu)t/2\hbar\right]}{(\epsilon_m^0 - \epsilon_n^0 - h\nu)^2}.$$

Here $g(\nu)$ is the frequency density, similar to that of Chapter 10. Since the trigonometric function in Eq. (15.4.5) is peaked about the value indicated in Eq. (15.4.7), we can obtain a good approximation to the integrals by evaluating $g(\nu)$ at the values indicated by Eq. (15.4.7) and then integrating. In other words, we take

$$\int_0^\infty d\nu\, g(\nu)\, \frac{\sin^2\left[(\epsilon_m^0 - \epsilon_n^0 + h\nu)t/2\hbar\right]}{(\epsilon_m^0 - \epsilon_n^0 + h\nu)} \cong g\left(\frac{\epsilon_n^0 - \epsilon_m^0}{h}\right)$$

$$\times \int_0^\infty d\nu\, \frac{\sin^2\left[(\epsilon_m^0 - \epsilon_n^0 + h\nu)t/2\hbar\right]}{(\epsilon_m^0 - \epsilon_n^0 + h\nu)^2}.$$

Since the integrand is so peaked, no serious error results from taking the limits to be $\pm\infty$. Then, since

$$\int_{-\infty}^{+\infty} dx\, \frac{\sin^2 xt/2\hbar}{x^2} = \frac{\pi^2 t}{h}, \tag{15.4.8}$$

we obtain

$$\int_0^\infty d\nu\, g(\nu)\overline{|C_n^{(1)}(t)|^2} \cong \frac{\pi^2 t}{h^2}\, |H_{mn}'(0)|^2 g\left\{\left|\frac{\epsilon_m^0 - \epsilon_n^0}{h}\right|\right\}. \tag{15.4.9}$$

We emphasize that Eq. (15.4.9) consists of *both* absorption and (stimulated) emission terms: a given unperturbed state can be related to the initial state in only one of these ways.

In an entirely comparable manner, Eq. (15.4.4) can be summed over all final states. If the number of final states per unit of energy is $\rho_f(\epsilon_n^0)$ (and this is a quantity that requires a knowledge of the energy eigenvalues for the system), we wish to consider

$$\sum_{n \neq m} |C_n^{(1)}(t)|^2 \doteq \int d\epsilon_n^0\, \rho_f(\epsilon_n^0)|C_n^{(1)}(t)|^2$$

$$= 4|H_{nm}'(0)|^2 \int d\epsilon_n^0\, \rho_f(\epsilon_n^0)\, \frac{\sin^2\left[(\epsilon_m^0 - \epsilon_n^0)t/2\hbar\right]}{(\epsilon_m^0 - \epsilon_n^0)^2}$$

$$\cong \frac{4\pi^2 t}{h}|H_{nm}'(0)|^2\rho_f(\epsilon_m^0). \tag{15.4.10}$$

In both Eqs. (15.4.9) and (15.4.10) we have managed to contrive an approximation to the transition probability which is proportional to the duration of the perturbation regarded as causing the transition. Clearly this leads ultimately to a value for the probability in excess of unity, which is manifestly impossible. As a result, the approximations which have been obtained must be used with circumspection. In either case, the change in probability with time is constant; this is usually equated or identified with the relative change (per unit time) in the numbers of systems in an ensemble undergoing the transition. Thus if we introduce the *transition probability per unit time* $w(m \rightarrow n)$, we have for the number of quanta of radiation *absorbed* per unit time in the transition from state m to state n,

$$N(m \rightarrow n) = w(m \rightarrow n)N_m \qquad (15.4.11)$$

$$= \frac{\pi^2}{h^2} N_m |H'_{nm}(0)|^2 g \left(\left| \frac{\epsilon_n^0 - \epsilon_m^0}{h} \right| \right), \qquad (15.4.12)$$

where N_m is the number of systems of the ensemble in the state m. The over-all rate of absorption of radiation requires the inclusion of stimulated emission and spontaneous emission. Since the latter is calculated in an intricate manner, we leave such over-all absorption expressions undetermined by the present treatment.

15.5 Selection rules. As we have indicated, the transition probability per unit time is proportional to the square of the magnitude of the matrix element of the perturbation, this matrix element connecting the states involved in the transition. Hence, not all transitions will have nonzero probabilities of occurring. Accordingly, there is manifest a selectivity with regard to which transitions *may* occur, the restrictions being referred to as *selection rules*.

We may illustrate the restrictions imposed upon the radiative transitions (i.e., absorption or emission) of the planar rigid rotor. We need to assume that the rigid rotor has along its axis an electric dipole which interacts with the electric field of the radiation. For simplicity we may take the direction of the field to be the x-axis (see Section 12.8). Then the interaction of the electric dipole and the field can be expressed as

$$\mathbf{H}_1(t) = \mu\mathcal{E} \cos \theta \cos (2\pi\nu t + \alpha), \qquad t \geq 0, \qquad (15.5.1)$$

in accord with Eq. (15.3.15), where μ is the electric dipole, $\mathcal{E}$ is the magnitude of the electric field, and θ is the angle between the axis of the planar rigid rotor and the field.

We have to compute [using the functions of Eq. (12.8.9)]

$$H'_{mn}(0) = \frac{\mu\mathcal{E}}{2\pi} \int_0^{2\pi} d\theta \, e^{-in\theta} \cos \theta e^{im\theta}$$

$$= \frac{\mu\mathcal{E}}{2} (\delta_{n,m+1} + \delta_{n,m-1}), \qquad (15.5.2)$$

according to Eq. (14.2.21). The selection rules are contained within Eq. (15.5.2) and only states of the rigid planar rotor which differ by unity in the quantum number may experience radiative transitions as a result of dipolar interactions. Consequently, the *absorption* frequencies for such a system are

$$\nu_{nm} = \epsilon_n^0 - \epsilon_m^0 = \frac{\hbar^2}{2I}[(|m| + 1)^2 - |m|^2]$$

$$= \frac{\hbar^2}{2I}(2|m| + 1), \qquad |m| = 0, 1, \ldots. \quad (15.5.3)$$

For other perturbations there will be a different frequency spectrum.

It is evident that the absorption frequencies are directly observable, while the energy values are not. Hence, the selection rules are essential to permit an analysis of the measured absorption spectra (or emission spectra) to be made that ultimately can test the correctness of model systems which serve as approximations for real physical systems.

We conclude the present section with a calculation of a transition process which can be related to an analogous stationary description. Specifically, we consider the process of reflection by a potential barrier, as considered in Chapter 13. We imagine that

$$\mathbf{H}_1(t) = 0, \qquad t < 0,$$

$$= V(x), \qquad t \geq 0,$$

where $V(x)$ is defined by Eqs. (13.1.1) through (13.1.3). We imagine the initial state to be that of a free particle moving toward the right. The final state of interest is that of a free particle moving toward the left. Equation (15.4.10) will be used to compute the relevant transition probability.

Now, before proceeding, we note that the formalism which has been presented is suited to normalizable wave functions. Its utility in the present case requires some modification in the unperturbed problem. We can accomplish this modification simply by assuming that the wave functions are those of a free particle but normalized to unity in a very large interval which, subsequently, will be increased without limit. Thus if

$$\psi_1(x) = \frac{1}{\sqrt{2L}} e^{ip_1x/\hbar}, \qquad -L \leq x \leq +L, \quad (15.5.4)$$

$$= 0 \quad \text{otherwise},$$

we obtain

$$\int dx \psi_2^*(x)\psi_1(x) = \frac{1}{2L} \int_{-L}^{+L} dx e^{i(p_1 - p_2)x/\hbar}$$

$$= \frac{\sin(p_1 - p_2)L/\hbar}{[(p_1 - p_2)L]/\hbar}, \quad (15.5.5)$$

which vanishes for $L \to \infty$ when $p_1 \neq p_2$; otherwise it is unity. We need also to determine $\rho_f(\epsilon_n^0)$ for this system. There is an energy eigenvalue for each and every value of the momentum. If we simply estimate their distribution as the limit attained from the particle-in-a-box distribution, as the size of the box is made indefinitely large, we shall have a density in energy which corresponds to the choice of wave functions we have made. For the energy spectrum of a particle in a (linear) box, we have, as a modification of Eq. (12.5.4),

$$dn = \sqrt{\frac{8mL^2}{h^2 \epsilon_n^0}} \, d\epsilon_n^0, \tag{15.5.6}$$

where the box size has been set equal to $2L$, V_0 has been taken equal to zero in Eq. (12.5.4), and n is the number of states of energy less or equal to ϵ_n^0. However, since we are interested only in those final states which are moving *away* from the barrier, we obtain

$$\rho_f(\epsilon_n^0) = \frac{1}{2} \sqrt{\frac{8mL^2}{h^2 \epsilon_n^0}}, \tag{15.5.7}$$

the factor of one-half correcting Eq. (15.5.6) for this feature.

With the wave functions of Eq. (15.5.4), we obtain

$$H'_{nm}(0) = \frac{1}{2L} \int_{-l}^{+l} dx e^{ipx/\hbar} V_0 e^{ipx/\hbar}$$

$$= V_0 \frac{\sin 2pl/\hbar}{2pL/\hbar}. \tag{15.5.8}$$

Hence the transition probability per unit time is

$$w(p \to -p) = \frac{V_0^2 \sin^2 (2l\sqrt{2m\epsilon/\hbar^2})}{2(8m)^{1/2} \epsilon^{3/2} L}, \tag{15.5.9}$$

where we have taken $\epsilon = p^2/2m$, and have omitted the superscripts and subscripts for the sake of simplicity. In terms of Eq. (15.4.11), we can obtain the rate at which particles are reflected by the barrier. To determine the reflection coefficient we must know the rate at which they approach the barrier. This is easily seen to be the product of N_m in Eq. (15.4.11) and the probability current discussed in Chapter 12. With the present wave functions, we obtain [e.g., Eq. (12.4.9)]

$$J_p = \left(\frac{2\epsilon}{m}\right)^{1/2} \cdot \frac{1}{2L}. \tag{15.5.10}$$

The reflection coefficient evidently is, to the present approximation,

$$R_\epsilon = \frac{w(p \rightarrow -p)}{J_p} = \frac{V_0^2}{4\epsilon^2} \sin^2 \left(2l \sqrt{\frac{2m\epsilon}{\hbar^2}} \right). \qquad (15.5.11)$$

This result may be compared with the result which is obtained from Eqs. (13.1.17) and (13.1.19) for $V_0/\epsilon \ll 1$. It is seen that the limiting value so obtained is identical with Eq. (15.5.11). We may emphasize that the successful use of the perturbation theory involves *small* perturbations [i.e., small λ in Eq. (15.3.1)]. In the present case this corresponds to small values of V_0; hence Eq. (13.1.17) is approached as a limit, but not Eq. (13.1.18).

15.6 Summary. We have considered in the present chapter certain nonstationary aspects of wave mechanics. A formal result for the solution of Schroedinger's time-dependent equation was obtained in which the initial value of the function is operated upon by a function of the Hamiltonian. This function is, itself, a unitary operator and enables the (time-dependent) expectation value of any physical observable to be expressed as the expectation value of a time-dependent operator corresponding to the physical observable, the expectation value being determined for the initial wave function.

The temporal evolution of the time-dependent operator is examined, and Heisenberg's equation of motion for the operator is determined. This equation forms the basic equation in the Heisenberg scheme of quantum mechanics. It is shown that operator equations obtain which are entirely analogous to Hamilton's equations of motion for classically describable systems. An extension due to Dirac involves the identification of the classical Poisson bracket of two physical quantities with a multiple of the commutator of the operators. This serves to yield the quantum conditions and Heisenberg's equation of motion in a unified manner. Moreover, this extension affords the opportunity to construct operators from their classical counterparts.

The solution of Schroedinger's time-dependent equation is considered from a perturbation viewpoint. A method due to Dirac permits the solution to be obtained in terms of powers of the magnitude of the perturbation. The application of the first-order theory to simple physical systems shows that time-dependent phenomena may be viewed as making transitions from one unperturbed state to another. In such transitions energy essentially is conserved; however, this conservation is not precise, but rather is statistical. In addition to energy-conservation limitations, transitions may occur (in the order considered) only between certain sets of unperturbed states. The factor featuring these restrictions is the so-called matrix element of the perturbation. The restrictions themselves are referred to as selection rules.

The first-order, time-dependent perturbation theory is applied to the problem of absorption and emission of radiation and to the problem of scattering by a potential barrier.

EXERCISES

1. Verify Eq. (15.1.6).
2. Extend the usual definition of a derivative to obtain the derivative of a product of matrices.
3. Verify Eq. (15.2.4).
4. Verify the following relations satisfied by the classical Poisson bracket:

$$(u, v) = -(v, u),$$

$$(u, c) = 0, \quad c \text{ a constant,}$$

$$(u_1 u_2, v) = (u_1, v)u_2 + u_1(u_2, v),$$

$$(u, (v, w)) + (v, (w, u)) + (w, (u, v)) = 0.$$

Show that these relations also are satisfied by commutators.

5. Determine the equation of motion for the operator corresponding to the fluctuation, or dispersion, in position for a particle constrained to move in a straight line.

6. Using the Poisson-bracket identification, Eq. (15.2.10), evaluate $(\frac{1}{2}x^2, \frac{1}{2}p^2)$, and hence construct the operator for the physical quantity xp.

7. Show that the quantum conditions, Eqs. (15.2.10) and (15.2.11), do not lead to the Schroedinger operator representation as a unique solution.

8. Derive the conditions implied by Eq. (15.3.5) when the substitution of Eq. (15.3.8) is employed. Compare with Eqs. (14.2.9).

9. Verify Eq. (15.4.1).

10. Verify Eq. (15.4.4).

11. Assume that the dipole of a particle in a linear box is proportional to the displacement of the particle from the center of the box. Determine the dipolar selection rules for radiative transitions of the particle in a box.

12. With the dipole of a linear harmonic oscillator proportional to the displacement from the so-called equilibrium position, determine the dipolar selection rules for the linear harmonic oscillator.

13. Obtain the dipolar selection rules for the nonplanar rigid rotor.

14. Obtain the *quadrupolar* selection rules for a planar rigid rotor. The quadrupole moment has an angular dependence given by the Legendre polynomial $P_2 (\cos \theta)$.

15. Verify Eq. (15.5.6).

16. Verify Eq. (15.5.8).

17. Carry out the expansion of Eq. (13.1.17) with Eq. (13.1.9) called for in the text.

18. Formulate the transition-probability problem for the case in which there is no continuous spectrum of energy eigenvalues and the perturbation is given by Eq. (15.4.3). Then determine the variation of the transition probability between two discrete, unperturbed energy eigenstates. Determine the time interval for the transition probability to be a maximum and its value at that time.

19. Determine the second-order transition probability under the assumption that the first-order theory gives a negligible contribution.

20. Determine the first-order transition probability for large t, for the perturbation

$$\mathbf{H}_1(t) = 0, \qquad\qquad t < 0,$$
$$= \mathbf{H}_1(x), \qquad 0 \leq t \leq T,$$
$$= 0, \qquad\qquad T < t.$$

21. Since the dipole of a system changes sign upon inversion through the origin, show how this limits the selection rules for radiative transitions to unperturbed states of different symmetries. Apply the same kind of analysis to quadrupolar transitions.

22. Show that the first-order correction to the wave functions of stationary perturbation theory are obtained as the time average (for large time intervals) of the time-dependent correction in the sense that for the perturbation of Eq. (15.4.3)

$$\lim_{T \to \infty} \frac{1}{T} \int_0^T dt\, C_n^{(1)}(t) = \int dx\, [\psi_n^{(0)}]^* \psi_m^{(1)}$$

of Eqs. (14.2.11) and (14.2.12).

23. Show that the transitions induced by a barrier, as discussed in Section 15.5, are predominantly those for which $p \to -p$.

REFERENCES

REFERENCES

Mathematics and Physics

ERDÉLYI, A., MAGNUS, W., OBERHETTINGER, F. and TRICOMI, F. G., *Higher Transcendental Functions*. 3 vols. New York: McGraw-Hill, 1953, 1955.

GOLDSTEIN, HERBERT, *Classical Mechanics*. Reading, Massachusetts: Addison-Wesley, 1950.

JAHNKE, E. and EMDE, F., *Tables of Functions*. New York: Dover, 1945.

JOOS, GEORG, *Theoretical Physics*. Ira M. Freeman, translator. London: Blackie, 1934.

INCE, E. L., *Ordinary Differential Equations*. New York: Dover, 1944.

MARGENAU, HENRY, and MURPHY, GEORGE MOSELEY, *The Mathematics of Physics and Chemistry*. New York: van Nostrand, 1943.

VON NEUMANN, J. *Mathematical Foundations of Quantum Mechanics*. Robert T. Beyer, translator. Princeton: University Press, 1955.

WILSON, EDWIN BIDWELL, *Advanced Calculus*. Boston: Ginn, 1911.

Thermodynamics and Statistical Mechanics

EPSTEIN, PAUL S., *Textbook of Thermodynamics*. New York: Wiley, 1937.

FOWLER, R. H., and GUGGENHEIM, E. A., *Statistical Thermodynamics*. Cambridge: University Press, 1939.

GIBBS, J. WILLARD, *Collected Works*. 2 vols. New York: Longmans, Green, 1931.

A Commentary on the Scientific Writings of J. Willard Gibbs, Edited by F. G. Donnan and Arthur Haas. New Haven: Yale University Press, 1936.

LANDAU, L. D., and LIFSHITZ, E. M., *Statistical Physics*. Reading, Massachusetts: Addison-Wesley, 1958.

LINDSAY, ROBERT BRUCE, *Introduction to Physical Statistics*. New York: Wiley, 1941.

SCHROEDINGER, *Statistical Thermodynamics*. 2nd ed. Cambridge: University Press, 1952.

TOLMAN, R. C., *The Principles of Statistical Mechanics*. Oxford: University Press, 1938.

WILSON, A. H., *Thermodynamics and Statistical Mechanics*. Cambridge: University Press, 1957.

Quantum Mechanics

BOHM, DAVID, *Quantum Theory*. New York: Prentice-Hall, 1951.

FRENKEL, J., *Wave Mechanics*. Vol. 1., "Elementary Theory." New York: Dover, 1950.

LANDAU, L. D., and LIFSHITZ, E. M., *Quantum Mechanics—Non-Relativistic Theory*. Reading, Massachusetts: Addison-Wesley, 1958.

(*continued*)

MOTT, N. F., and SNEDDON, I. N., *Wave Mechanics and Its Applications.* Oxford: Clarendon Press, 1948.

PAULING, LINUS, and WILSON, E. BRIGHT, JR., *Introduction to Quantum Mechanics.* New York: McGraw-Hill, 1935.

ROJANSKY, VLADIMIR, *Introductory Quantum Mechanics.* New York: Prentice-Hall, 1946.

TEMPLE, G., *The General Principles of Quantum Theory.* London: Methuen, 1951.

INDEX

INDEX